5-23-69

ANTARCTIC
RESEARCH
SERIES

American Geophysical Union

FRONTISPIECE

Habitat group at 23 meters, off Hut Point, Ross Island, Antarctica: The large, simple ascidian, *Cnemidocarpa verrucosa,* has a young individual attached at base. The expanded atrial opening is directed upward; the branchial aperture, not seen in this view, is directed downward and away from the camera from the upper end of the animal. The branching 'coral' above the young ascidian has been tentatively identified as *Alcyonium paessleri;* the grasslike growth in the foreground, as *Clavularia frankliniana.* Nearby, to the right, is a sea anemone, *Isotealia antarcticus;* not yet determined is the thick growth of hydroids on the rest of the *Cnemidocarpa.* The fish is the common nototheniid, *Trematomus bernacchii,* and at the extreme lower left is a starfish, an *Odontaster.* Photographed November 30, 1968, by Paul K. Dayton, University of Washington, Seattle (NSF grant GA-1187).

Volume 13

ANTARCTIC
RESEARCH
SERIES

Antarctic Ascidiacea

Monographic account of the known species
based on specimens collected under
U. S. government auspices, 1947–1965

Patricia Kott

Published with the aid of a grant from the National Science Foundation

PUBLISHER

AMERICAN GEOPHYSICAL UNION

OF THE

National Academy of Sciences—National Research Council

Publication No. 1725

May 29, 1969

Volume 13 | ANTARCTIC
RESEARCH
SERIES

ANTARCTIC ASCIDIACEA

PATRICIA KOTT

Library of Congress Catalogue Card No. 77-601086
Worldwide Book No. 87590113

List Price, $16.50

Printed by
THE HORN-SHAFER COMPANY
DIVISION OF
Geo. W. King Printing Co.
Baltimore, Maryland

THE ANTARCTIC RESEARCH SERIES

THE ANTARCTIC RESEARCH SERIES is designed to provide a medium for presenting authoritative reports on the extensive and detailed scientific research work being carried out in Antarctica. The series has been successful in eliciting contributions from leading research scientists engaged in antarctic investigations; it seeks to maintain high scientific and publication standards. The scientific editor for each volume is chosen from among recognized authorities in the discipline or theme it represents, as are the reviewers on whom the editor relies for advice.

Beginning with the scientific investigations carried out during the International Geophysical Year, reports of research results appearing in this series represent original contributions too lengthy or otherwise inappropriate for publication in the standard journals. In some cases an entire volume is devoted to a monograph. The material published is directed not only to specialists actively engaged in the work but to graduate students, to scientists in closely related fields, and to interested laymen versed in the biological and the physical sciences. Many of the earlier volumes are cohesive collections of papers grouped around a central theme. Future volumes may concern themselves with regional as well as disciplinary aspects, or with a comparison of antarctic phenomena with those of other regions of the globe. But the central theme of Antarctica will dominate.

In a sense, the series continues the tradition dating from the earliest days of geographic exploration and scientific expeditions—the tradition of the expeditionary volumes which set forth in detail everything that was seen and studied. This tradition is not necessarily outmoded, but in much of the present scientific work one expedition blends into the next, and it is no longer scientifically meaningful to separate them arbitrarily. Antarctic research has a large degree of coherence; it deserves the modern counterpart of the expeditionary volumes of past decades and centuries which the Antarctic Research Series provides.

With the aid of a grant from the National Science Foundation in 1962, the American Geophysical Union initiated the Antarctic Research Series and appointed a Board of Associate Editors to implement it. A supplemental grant received in 1966, the income from the sale of volumes in the series, and income from reprints and other sources have enabled the AGU to continue this series. The response of the scientific community and the favorable comments of reviewers cause the Board to look forward with optimism to the continued success of this endeavor.

To represent the broad scientific nature of the series, the members of the Board were chosen from all fields of antarctic research. At the present time they include: Eugene L. Boudette, representing geology and solid Earth geophysics; A. P. Crary, seismology and glaciology; George A. Llano, botany and zoology; Martin A. Pomerantz, aeronomy and geomagnetism; Morton J. Rubin, meteorology; Waldo L. Schmitt, marine biology and oceanography; and Laurence M. Gould, honorary chairman. Fred G. Alberts, secretary to the U. S. Advisory Committee on Antarctic Names, gives valuable assistance in verifying place names, locations, and maps. AGU staff members responsible for the series are: Judith S. McCombs, managing editor, and Marie L. Webner, chief of editorial services.

MORTON J. RUBIN
Chairman, Board of Associate Editors
Antarctic Research Series

PREFACE

BASIC TO ANY DISCUSSION of the lives and behavior—the biology in the broadest sense of the term—of the animal and plant life of any region, continental, insular, or oceanic, is the authoritative identification of each of their kinds and the determination of their distribution, horizontal as well as vertical.

With this thought in mind, Dr. Patricia Kott (Mrs. Wharton B. Mather), Research Fellow, University of Queensland, Brisbane, Australia, undertook this monographic account of the antarctic Ascidiacea at the request of the Smithsonian Institution.

Dr. Kott began work on the Australian ascidian fauna some twenty years ago under the guidance of the late Dr. Harold Thompson, chief of the C.S.I.R.O. (Commonwealth Scientific and Industrial Research Organization) Division of Fisheries. Since then she has had considerable experience with the group, both at home and abroad, and is an acknowledged leading authority on these tunicates.

The present work is the first Antarctic Research Series monograph about a particular widespread major group of antarctic marine organisms that is complete in one volume. Within its covers is a detailed review of all previously recorded antarctic species of ascidians and a host of new records that are based on the author's identification of several thousand specimens collected over the years by the United States antarctic expeditions, Deep Freeze expeditions and others dating from 1947–1948 through eleven cruises of the USNS *Eltanin*, which span the period from June 1962 to April 1965. Two new genera and eleven new species were discovered in that abundant material.

The author has personally examined most of the 126 different ascidians known from, or occurring in, the antarctic and subantarctic areas. For each of the 122 specifically determined forms she gives a complete synonymy, lists new and previous records, and summarizes the distribution. So far as possible, she fully describes the species and adds notes and observations on the biology and larvae (where known), which more often than not are of taxonomic significance. Finally, the discussion of each species is concluded by a section of pertinent remarks, taxonomic or otherwise.

For the purpose of illustrating their salient characters, Dr. Kott has drawn or, where specimens were not available, has adapted from published sources all but 18 of the forms dealt with, has supplied a diagrammatic representation of the terms used in ascidian descriptions, and has prepared a chart of the areas covered and referred to in the concluding zoogeographic discussion.

The extensive collections that have passed through Dr. Kott's hands and the wide range of literature that necessarily had to be consulted in the course of their identification quite naturally led to a review of current schemes of ascidian classification and phylogeny and the relations of the antarctic ascidian fauna to its physical and biologic environment, its ecology, so to speak, as well as the distribution of its species throughout the Southern Ocean and its abysses.

Dr. Kott's *Antarctic Ascidiacea* exemplifies to a very high degree the type of systematic-taxonomic studies that are actively being sought for publication by the Board of Editors of the Antarctic Research Series. One ventures the hope that other students and specialists interested in the study of any part of the antarctic fauna or flora will be impressed by what this author has accomplished and will follow her lead in first producing comparable monographic accounts of the antarctic organisms with which they may concern themselves before embarking upon the ever tempting ecologic, zoogeographic, and related discussions of those forms of life.

vii

It is not inappropriate here to acknowledge the keen interest of Navy and Coast Guard personnel and the indispensable services that they have rendered and continue to render biologists who have been so fortunate as to travel with them to Antarctica and its surrounding seas. Nor to be overlooked is the helpful assistance rendered by the officers and crew of the USNS *Eltanin*. It is the wholehearted cooperation of all ships' personnel that makes possible the rewarding accomplishment of definitive monographs as complete in coverage and as scientifically valuable as the present one.

WALDO L. SCHMITT

CONTENTS

1. INTRODUCTION

FROM THE PIONEERING EFFORTS of the mid-nineteenth century to the intensive work resulting from activities associated with the International Geophysical Year and facilitated by the establishment of numerous permanent bases, faunal collections have been made in Antarctica by various national expeditions (see below). These collections have generally included representatives of the class Ascidiacea. The present work correlates information from earlier reports with the more recent circumpolar material, which was taken mainly from the USNS *Eltanin* cruises (1962–1965), the U. S. Navy Antarctic Expedition (1947–1948), the Deep Freeze Expeditions I, II, III, and IV, and a collection made by Dr. Waldo L. Schmitt from the South Shetland Islands, the Antarctic Peninsula, and the adjacent islands.

The areas under consideration are

1. *The Antarctic:* the area between the antarctic continent and the antarctic convergence, where cold, dense, less saline (ice diluted) water of the Antarctic meets the more saline and lighter water of the subantarctic zone.

2. *The Subantarctic:* the area extending from the antarctic convergence to the subtropical convergence, where, at about latitude 40°S, the subantarctic water meets and sinks beneath the warmer subtropical water.

The following antarctic and subantarctic quadrants of Markham [1912] and Waite [1916] are referred to only for the purposes of indicating positions and have no greater significance. The corresponding quadrant designation used by the American Geographical Society (map of *Antarctica*, New York, August 1968; scale 1:3 million; 4 sheets) are given here for references purposes only.

ANTARCTIC AND SUBANTARCTIC QUADRANTS

	American Geographical Society (Antarctic)	Markham (Antarctic)	Waite (Subantarctic)
90°E to 180°	Australian	Victoria	Australian Zonal
180° to 90°W	Pacific	Ross	Pacific Zonal
90°W to 0°	American	Weddell	American Zonal
0° to 90°E	African	Enderby	African Zonal

The abundant new material gathered from the expeditions indicated above was supplemented by a large part of the ascidian collections of the British-Australian-New Zealand Antarctic Research Expedition, which at present are held in the Australian Museum, Sydney. Thus, it was possible to examine extensive material representative of the whole area under discussion. One hundred twenty-two species are fully described and discussed. Where specimens were not immediately accessible, text figures have been copied, as noted, from previous works of various authors. Otherwise, text figures are from camera-lucida or freehand scale drawings and are semi-diagrammatic.

Not included in the foregoing enumeration is a representative of the genus *Podoclavella* (p. 25), which is a new record generically for the Antarctic, but of which the material is too fragmentary to warrant specific designation. Of the species discussed, only 31 have not actually been examined in relation to the present work. Of these 31 species, 15 are known only from inadequate descriptions and may not be valid; 5 are rare abyssal species; 11 others are well characterized, but, being less common species of limited range, were not present in the collections. Eleven new species are established, of which 6 are abyssal. Thus, although further collecting may indicate an even greater range for certain species, it seems probable that the more conspicuous components of the shelf and slope antarctic ascidian fauna and their distribution are now known, the abyssal fauna is still relatively unknown.

As is true for other groups in polar seas, the nature of the rigorous but constant environment (both vertical and horizontal) favors large populations of comparatively few species. However, species diversity is also comparatively high. The fauna is well characterized and is, in some respects, archaic. The degree of specific and generic endemism is high. The antarctic continent was probably colonized by ascidians from the north in some more clement age. Species thus established were later isolated in the Antarctic and spread into the Subantarctic along the submarine or land bridges. Subsequent glaciation further isolated the fauna and drove species from the antarctic con-

1

tinental shelf into deeper waters. Owing to their sessile habit and the short duration of free-swimming
larvae, the distribution of Ascidiacea into and around
Antarctica along submarine or land bridges is thought
to be more likely than a distribution effected by ocean
currents or the West Wind Drift. Longitudinal biogeographical boundaries, especially south of the antarctic convergence, are not generally defined, and the
vertical and circumpolar range of most species is
great. North of the antarctic convergence there is no
continuous land mass and the continental shelf regions
of isolated islands are separated by abyssal basins
which prevent the contemporary spread of the shallow
water species. Consequently, there is a clearer definition of zoogeographical boundaries in the Subantarctic
than in the Antarctic.

Consideration has been given to the phylogeny of
the Ascidiacea with respect to adult and larval relationships (see chapter 3, Classification, and chapter
8, Phylogeny). Accordingly, modifications in the accepted classification are proposed. The Cionidae and
Diazonidae are considered members of the Aplousobranchia, together with Polycitoridae, Clavelinidae,
Polyclinidae, and Didemnidae. The subfamily Euherdmaniinae in the Polyclinidae is considered of poly-
phetic origin and includes the genera *Tylobranchion*
and *Protopolyclinum*. The family Hypobythiidae (genera *Hypobythius, Megalodicopia, Dicopia,* and *Benthascidia*) is considered a family of the Phlebobranchia.

2. PREVIOUS EXPEDITIONS

THE ASCIDIANS COLLECTED by these expeditions are credited to the authors of expeditionary reports here and in the Previous Records accompanying each species in chapter 6, Systematic Discussion.

The areas from which species were taken by the USNS *Eltanin* and other American expeditions are listed under New Records (accompanying each species in chapter 6) and are identified by their coordinates in the Station List, chapter 5.

For a more detailed historical synopsis of exploration in the Antarctic, see 'Introductory Remarks,' by J. Schell, pp. ix–xv, *Biogeography and Ecology in Antarctica*, edited by J. van Mieghem and P. van Oye, The Hague, 1965 and 'List of Expeditions,' by K. J. Bertrand and F. G. Alberts, pp. 9–36, *Geographic Names of Antarctica* (revised edition), *Gazetteer 14*, United States Board on Geographic Names, 1956.

WEDDELL QUADRANT

Expedition	Report	Area
Astrolabe, 1826–1829 (French)	Quoy and Gaimard, 1834–1835	Cape Horn
Eugenie, 1852 (Swedish)		Patagonia Magellanic area
Gazelle, 1876 (German)	Pfeffer, 1889; 1890	South Georgia
Romanche, 1883 (French)		Cape Horn Antarctic Peninsula
Michaelsen et al., 1892 (German)	Michaelsen, 1898; 1900; 1907	Magellanic area Falkland Is. South Georgia
Active, 1893 Dundee Whaling Co. (Scottish)	Calman, 1894	South Atlantic Ocean Erebus and Terror Gulf
Antarctic, 1904 (Swedish)	Ärnbäck, 1938; 1950	Falkland Is. South Georgia Antarctic Peninsula
Scotia, 1902–1904 (Scottish)	Herdman, 1912	Falkland Is. South Orkney Is. Weddell Sea area
Français, 1903–1905 (French)	Sluiter, 1905b; 1906; 1906a	Antarctic Peninsula
Pourquoi Pas?, 1908–1910 (French)	Sluiter, 1912; 1914	Antarctic Peninsula
Norvegia, 1927–1931 (Norwegian)	Sluiter, 1932	South Georgia
Discovery, 1925–1927 (British)	Millar, 1960	South Georgia Scotia Ridge Antarctic Peninsula

ROSS QUADRANT

Expedition	Report	Area
Erebus and *Terror*, 1843 (English)		Victoria Land
Belgica, 1899 (Belgian)	Van Beneden and Selys Longchamps, 1913	Bellingshausen Sea
Discovery, 1901–1904 (British)	Herdman, 1910	Ross Sea
Terra Nova, 1910–1913 (British)		Ross Sea McMurdo Sound

VICTORIA QUADRANT

Expedition	Report	Area
Wilkes, 1840 (American)		Wilkes Land
Eugenie, 1852 (Swedish)		Kerguelen Is.
Gazelle, 1876 (German)	Studer, 1879; 1889 Pfeffer, 1890	Kerguelen Is.
Challenger, 1876 (British)	Herdman, 1882; 1886; 1888	Kerguelen Is. Queen Mary Coast
Southern Cross, 1900 (English)	Herdman, 1902	Victoria Land
Gauss, 1901 (German)	Hartmeyer, 1911	Wilhelm II Coast
Aurora, 1911–1914 (Australasian)	Herdman, 1923 Harant and Vernières, 1938	Commonwealth Bay, Adélie Coast
British-Australian-New Zealand Antarctic Research Expedition, 1929–1931	Kott, 1954	Kerguelen Is. Heard I. Antarctic Continent
Russian Antarctic Expedition, 1955–1958	Vinogradova, 1962	Indian Ocean sector of Antarctica
A.N.A.R.E., 1947–1954 (Australian National Antarctic Research Expedition)	Kott, 1957a	Macquarie I. Heard I.

ENDERBY QUADRANT

Challenger, 1876 (British)	Herdman, 1882; 1886; 1888	Bouvet I.
Valdivia 1898–1900 (German)	Michaelsen, 1904	Kerguelen Is.
	Hartmeyer, 1912	Bouvet I. Enderby Land
British-Australian- New Zealand Antarctic Re- search Expedi- tion 1929–1931	Kott, 1954	Kerguelen Is. Heard I. Enderby Land Wilkes Land

ABYSSAL ZONE

Valdivia, 1898–1900 (German)	Hartmeyer, 1912 Michaelsen, 1904	Enderby Land

3. CLASSIFICATION

A SATISFACTORY CLASSIFICATION of the class Ascidiacea was first achieved by Lahille [1887 and 1890], who established the groups *Aplousobranchia, Phlebobranchia,* and *Stolidobranchia,* based on the structure of the branchial sac. Perrier [1898] proposed an alternative system based on the reproductive organs to establish the groups *Hemi-* or *Enterogona, Hypogona,* and *Pleurogona.* Garstang [1895 and 1928] revised Lahille's and Perrier's classifications and combined the two, adding evidence from the development of stigmata and epicardial cavities and from the processes and organs involved in vegetative reproduction, in support of the groupings established by Lahille and Perrier. This classification was adopted by Huus [1937].

Berrill [1936] proposed a classification based on the condition of the epicardium and heart, in which Diazonidae were united with other aplousobranch families as Epicardiocoela, while phlebobranchiate Corellidae and Ascidiidae were linked with stolidobranch families to form the Nephrocoela. Cionidae and Perophoridae each stood alone as Diplocoela and Acoela, respectively. This classification denied, however, other relationships indicated by the branchial sac, larvae, budding, colonial system, and position of gonads. The heart is also an unsatisfactory character because the two limbs of the V tend to straighten out according to the condition of the stolon.

Webb [1939], working on constituents of the blood in Ascidiacea, confirmed the presence of two main ascidian stocks, represented by Perrier's orders Enterogona and Pleurogona. This conclusion was confirmed by the vanadium content. Thus Berrill [1950, p. 56], indicating the importance of recognizing 'two main ascidian stocks, or at least that the group . . . (Stolidobranchia) is a natural one derived at one time from the other,' withdrew his earlier classification based on the epicardium and modified Huus' [1937] groupings within the Phlebobranchia by maintaining (after Garstang) Perophoridae and Diazonidae as families rather than subfamilies of Ascidiidae and Cionidae, respectively. This classification recognized to some extent the relationships resulting from the derivation of the Stolidobranchia (Pleurogona) and the Aplousobranchia (Enterogona), the most highly evolved of the two main stocks, from Phlebobranchia (Enterogona). The Stolidobranchia develop from Cionidae via Ascidiidae; the Aplousobranchia, from the Diazonidae. The grouping into Enterogona and Pleurogona serves no practical taxonomic purpose, however, and Van Name [1945] dispensed with Perrier's groups and gave equal status to Lahille's three groups as orders of the class Ascidiacea.

In the present work the existence of two main lines of evolution is accepted, but the definition of both Lahille's and Perrier's suborders and orders have been modified to reconcile relationships indicated by the epicardium, the mechanism of budding, and the larval form with the relationships based on the branchial sac and reproductive organs. The classification proposed below thus combines that of Garstang (and its modifications by various authors) with some of the concepts presented by Berrill [1936]. The development of renal vesicles is considered characteristic of Stolidobranchia and Phlebobranchia, and Cionidae and Diazonidae are removed to the Aplousobranchia, where there is a gradual involvement of the unspecialized epicardium in the mechanism of vegetative reproduction leading to highly developed colonial systems. Thus, the primitive Aplousobranchia are considered to be the ancestral stock from which the Phlebobranchia and Stolidobranchia are derived by the involvement of the epicardium with excretion rather than budding. Nevertheless, the grouping of Phlebobranchia and Aplousobranchia as Enterogona is maintained to indicate the extent to which primitive aplousobranch characters persist in the phlebobranch ascidians. The highly specialized Stolidobranchia remain separated from their immediate ancestors, the Phlebobranchia, and comprise the Pleurogona.

The inclusion of the family Diazonidae in the Aplousobranchia has also alleviated the problems in adhering to Lahille's suborders that are created by the genera *Tylobranchion* and *Protopolyclinum,* which are now accommodated in the polyphyletic subfamily Euherdmaniinae.

The genus *Hexacrobylus* Sluiter, 1905, is shown to be a synonym of *Oligotrema* Bourne, 1903, a genus of Molgulidae, and does not represent a distinct evolutionary trend justifying the suborder Aspiriculata Seeliger 1893–1907.

Order ENTEROGONA Perrier, 1898

Atrial opening from fusion of 2 separate peribranchial invaginations. Budding epiblastic and mesoblastic or endoblastic but never from the mantle wall. Gonads unpaired in thorax, abdomen, or posterior abdomen; body may or may not be divided into thorax, abdomen, or posterior abdomen. Test gelatinous or delicate, rarely leathery. Branchial sac not folded. Epicardium present as renal vesicles or perivisceral sac.

Suborder APLOUSOBRANCHIA Lahille, 1887

Body divided into thorax, abdomen, and sometimes posterior abdomen. Epicardium present as perivisceral sac. Heart V-shaped or straight in abdomen or posterior abdomen.

Family CIONIDAE Lahille, 1890

Solitary. Gut loop posterior to branchial sac, a horizontal loop. Heart V-shaped between stomach and base of endostyle. Gonads in gut loop. Branchial sac with many rows of stigmata and inner longitudinal vessels with secondary papillae. Epicardia form 2 large sacs enveloping viscera and communicating with peribranchial cavity. Oviparous. Simple larval papillae.

Genus: *Ciona* Fleming, 1822.

Family DIAZONIDAE Garstang, 1891a

Usually colonial. Zooids with independent openings to the exterior. Body divided into thorax and abdomen. Gut loop in abdomen, a vertical loop. Heart V-shaped at base of abdomen. Gonads in gut loop. Branchial sac with numerous rows of stigmata with either inner longitudinal vessels or primary papillae but no secondary papillae. Epicardia fused to form a single vertical sac lying between digestive tube and heart. Buds produced by abdominal constriction. Oviparous. Simple larval papillae.

Genera: *Diazona* Savigny, 1816, *Rhopalaea* Philippi, 1843 (> *Rhopalopsis* Herdman, 1891), *Syndiazona* Oka, 1926.

Family CLAVELINIDAE Forbes and Hanley 1848

Body divided into thorax and abdomen. Gut loop vertical in abdomen. Heart straight, ventral and parallel to loop of gut. Gonads in gut loop. Branchial sac without longitudinal vessels or papillae. Epicardia fused to form single tube lying between gut and heart. Stolonic vessel well developed with mesenchymatous septum. Budding from stolonic vessel. Viviparous. Larval papillae usually with accessory epidermal suckers. Papillae triradiate arrangement.

Subfamily CLAVELININAE Seeliger, 1893–1907

Zooids open separately to the exterior. Branchial sac with variable number of rows of stigmata. Budding from isolated terminals of stolonic vessel involving mesenchyme and epidermis only. Fertilization in atrial cavity. Large number of ova. Eggs develop in atrial cavity.

Genera: *Clavelina* Savigny, 1816 (> *Chondrostachys* Macdonald, 1858), *Oxycorynia* von Drasche, 1882 (>*Nephtheis* Gould, 1852–1856, *Colella* Herdman, 1886 [part]), *Podoclavella* Herdman, 1891 (> *Stereoclavella* Herdman, 1891), *Archiascidia* Julin, 1904.

Subfamily HOLOZOINAE Berrill, 1950

Zooids usually open into cloacal system. Branchial sac with reduced number of rows of stigmata. Budding from vascular stolon into which epicardium projects, involving epicardium (endodermal) and epidermis. Fertilization in brood pouch or base of oviduct. Eggs develop in brood pouch formed by diverticulum of oviduct at base of thorax. Ova reduced in number.

Genera: *Atapozoa* Brewin, 1956 (> *Hypodistoma* Tokioka, 1967), *Distaplia* Della Valle, 1881 (> *Holozoa* Lesson 1830, *Julinia* Calman, 1894, *Colella* Herdman, 1886 [part]), *Sycozoa* Lesson, 1830 (> *Colella* Herdman, 1886 [part]), *Hypsistozoa* Brewin, 1953, *Protoholozoa* new genus, *Cyathocormus* Oka 1913.

Family POLYCITORIDAE Michaelsen, 1904a
(> DISTOMIDAE Giard, 1872)

Zooids with separate openings to the exterior; small. Body divided into thorax and abdomen. Gut loop vertical in abdomen. Heart more or less V-shaped, or curved, at base of abdomen. Gonads in gut loop. Branchial sac with reduced number of rows of stigmata; with neither longitudinal vessels nor papillae. Epicardia fuse to form a single sac lying between gut and heart. Buds produced by abdominal constriction. Viviparous; fertilization at base of oviducts. Ova reduced in number. Larval papillae in median vertical line with accessory epidermal cups.

Genera: *Archidistoma* Garstang, 1891, *Polycitor* Renier, 1804, *Sigillina* Savigny, 1816 (> *Paessleria* Michaelsen, 1907, *Eudistoma* Caullery, 1909, *Hyperiodistoma* Michaelsen, 1930), *Pycnoclavella* Garstang, 1891a, *Cystodytes* von Drasche, 1883, *Polycitorella* Michaelsen, 1924, ? *Tetrazona* Michaelsen, 1930.

Family POLYCLINIDAE Verrill, 1871
(> SYNOICIDAE Hartmeyer, 1908)

Zooids divided into thorax, abdomen, and posterior abdomen. Gut loop vertical in the abdomen. Heart V-shaped behind gonads in posterior abdomen. Gonads in posterior abdomen. Branchial sac with or without longitudinal vessels and papillae. Epicardia usually fused, forming tube extending into posterior abdomen. Budding by strobilation of abdomen and/or posterior abdomen. Viviparous. Fertilization at base of oviduct.

Subfamily EUHERDMANIINAE Seeliger, 1893–1907

Zooids open separately to the exterior, not always embedded in common test. Larval papillae triradiate or in a median vertical line.

Genera: *Tylobranchion* Herdman, 1886, *Euherdmania* Ritter, 1904, *Placentela* Redikorzev, 1913, *Pseudodistoma* Michaelsen, 1924, *Ritterella* Harant, 1931, *Protopolyclinum* Millar, 1960, *Dumus* Brewin, 1952, *Pharyngodictyon* Herdman, 1886.

Subfamily POLYCLININAE Adams and Adams 1858

Atrial openings into common cloaca. Zooids always embedded in common test. Larval papillae in median vertical line with ectodermal cups.

Genera: *Polyclinum* Savigny, 1816 (> *Glossophorum* Lahille, 1886), *Aplidiopsis* Lahille, 1890, *Aplidium* Savigny, 1816 (> *Amaroucium* Milne Edwards, 1841), *Synoicium* Phipps, 1774 (> *Macroclinum* Verrill, 1871, *Lissamaroucium* Sluiter, 1906), *Sidnyum* Savigny, 1816 (> *Parascidia* Milne Edwards, 1841), *Morchellium* Giard, 1872, *Sidneioides* Kesteven, 1909.

Family DIDEMNIDAE Giard, 1872

Zooids very small, open into cloacal systems. Body divided into thorax and abdomen. Heart straight, alongside gut loop. Gonads in loop of gut. Branchial sac reduced to 3 or 4 rows of stigmata without longitudinal vessels or papillae. Epicardium vestigial, reduced to two small sacs in esophageal region. Budding from esophageal region involving epicardium. No oviduct. Eggs liberated from ovary and develop in common test. Larval papillae in median vertical line with ectodermal cups. Test usually has spicules.

Genera: *Trididemnum* Della Valle, 1881, *Didemnum* Savigny, 1816, *Polysyncraton* Nott, 1892, *Leptoclinides* Bjerkan, 1905, *Lissoclinum* Verrill, 1871 (> *Diplosomoides* Herdman, 1886), *Diplosoma* Macdonald, 1859 (> *Leptoclinum* Hartmeyer, 1909), *Echinoclinum* Van Name, 1902, *Coelocormus* Herdman, 1886, *Sinecloaca* Carlisle and Carlisle, 1954, *Askonides* Kott, 1962.

Suborder PHLEBOBRANCHIA Lahille, 1887

Body not divided. Epicardium when present eventually forms renal vesicles. Gut loop on left or right of branchial sac. Gonads, unpaired, in gut loop. Heart a curved tube on the right side of the branchial sac. Species often laterally flattened with strong transverse muscles around the dorsal and ventral aspect of the body.

Family PEROPHORIDAE Giard, 1872

Colonial, zooids free, connected by stolons. Internal longitudinal vessels occasionally reduced. Dorsal lamina with languets. Budding from stolon involving epidermis and mesenchyme.

Genera: *Ecteinascidia* Herdman, 1880, *Perophora* Wiegmann, 1835.

Family CORELLIDAE Lahille, 1890
(> RHODOSOMATIDAE Hartmeyer, 1908)

Solitary. Gut on right side of branchial sac. Internal longitudinal vessels without secondary papillae. Dorsal lamina with languets.

Subfamily RHODOSOMATINAE Seeliger, 1893–1907
Stigmata straight.
Genera: *Rhodosoma* Ehrenberg, 1828, *Abyssascidia* Herdman, 1880.

Subfamily CORELLINAE Herdman, 1882

Stigmata spiral.

Genera: *Corella* Alder and Hancock, 1870, *Corynascidia* Herdman, 1882, *Corellopsis* Hartmeyer, 1903, *Chelyosoma* Broderip and Sowerby, 1830, *Xenobranchion* Ärnbäck, 1950.

Family HYPOBYTHIIDAE Sluiter, 1895

Solitary. Gut on right, dorsal to or behind branchial sac. Branchial sac without internal longitudinal vessels, stigmata short and irregular.

Genera: *Hypobythius* Moseley, 1876, *Benthascidia* Ritter, 1907, *Dicopia* Oka, 1913a, *Megalodicopia* Oka, 1918.

Family ASCIDIIDAE Herdman, 1880

Solitary. Gut on left of branchial sac. Stigmata straight. Internal longitudinal vessels usually with secondary papillae. Dorsal lamina continuous membrane. Muscles on right and left sides of the body never independent.

Genera: *Phallusia* Savigny, 1816 (> *Phallusiopsis* Hartmeyer, 1908), *Ascidia* Linnaeus, 1767 (> *Bathyascidia* Hartmeyer, 1901), *Ascidiella* Roule, 1884.

Family AGNESIIDAE Huntsman, 1912

Solitary. Gut on left of branchial sac. Internal longitudinal vessels without secondary papillae, and often reduced. Dorsal lamina with languets or continuous membrane. Muscles on right and left sides of the body often independent.

Subfamily CIALLUSIINAE Huus, 1937

Stigmata straight.
Genera: *Ciallusia* Van Name, 1918, *Pterygascidia*, Sluiter, 1904.

Subfamily AGNESIINAE Huus, 1937

Stigmata spiral.
Genera: *Caenagnesia* Ärnbäck, 1938, *Agnesia* Michaelson, 1898, *Adagnesia* Kott, 1963a.

Family OCTACNEMIDAE Herdman, 1888

A rare aberrant family [see Millar, 1956 and 1959]. Genera: *Octacnemus* Moseley 1876, *Polyoctacnemus* Ihle, 1935.

Order PLEUROGONA Perrier, 1898

Atrial opening from single median dorsal invagination bifurcating ventrally to form atrial cavity; budding only epiblastic from mantle wall. Gonads usually paired, in body wall both sides of branchial sac. Body never divided. Test usually leathery. Epicardium present as renal vesicles.

Suborder STOLIDOBRANCHIA Lahille, 1887

Branchial sac folded. Solitary or colonial. Apertures 4- to 6-lobed or not lobed.

Family STYELIDAE Sluiter, 1895
(> TETHYIDAE Hartmeyer, 1908)

Colonial or solitary. Apertures not lobed or with 4 lobes each. Tentacles simple. Branchial sac with a maximum of 4 folds per side. Stigmata straight. Dorsal lamina smooth edged. No lobed liver.

Subfamily POLYZOINAE Hartmeyer, 1903

Colonial. Zooids united by stolons or embedded in common test. Atrial openings separate. More than 3 internal longitudinal vessels per side. Folds when present less than 4 per side. Gonads on one side or on both sides.
Genera: *Berrillia* Brewin, 1952, *Protostyela* Millar, 1954a, *Polyzoa* Lesson, 1830 (> *Goodsiria* Cunningham, 1871), *Metandrocarpa* Michaelsen, 1904a, *Alloeocarpa* Michaelsen, 1900, *Theodorella* Michaelsen, 1922, *Chorizocarpa* Michaelsen, 1904a, *Kukenthalia* Hartmeyer, 1903, *Symplegma* Herdman, 1886 (> *Di-*

androcarpa Van Name, 1902), *Botryllocarpa* Hartmeyer, 1909–1911, *Dictyostyela* Oka, 1926a, *Psilostyela* Sluiter, 1923, *Dextrocarpa* Millar, 1955, *Monobotryllus* Oka, 1915, *Amphicarpa* Michaelsen, 1922, *Polyandrocarpa* Michaelsen, 1904a (> *Eusynstyela* Michaelsen, 1904a), *Oculinaria* Gray, 1886 (> *Gynandrocarpa* Michaelsen, 1900, *Syncarpa* Redikorzev, 1913), *Stolonica* Lacaze-Duthiers and Delage, 1892, *Oligocarpa* Hartmeyer, 1911, *Distomus* Gaertner, 1774, *Arnbackia* Brewin, 1950b.

Subfamily BOTRYLLINAE Adams and Adams, 1858

Colonial, zooids embedded in test. Atrial openings into common cloaca. Apertures smooth rimmed. Branchial sac with 3 internal longitudinal vessels per side, no folds present.
Genera: *Botryllus* Gaertner, 1774 (> *Leptobotrylloides* Oka, 1927a, *Polycyclus* Oka, 1927a, *Myxobotrus* Oka, 1931, *Psammobotrus*, Oka, 1932), *Botrylloides* Milne Edwards, 1841 (> *Metrocarpa* Ärnbäck, 1923, *Sarcobotrylloides* Oka, 1927a).

Subfamily STYELINAE Herdman, 1881

Solitary. Apertures 4-lobed. Usually 4 branchial folds per side. Gonads on one side or on both sides.
Genera: *Polycarpa* Heller, 1878 (> *Pandocia* Fleming, 1822, *Paratona* Huntsman, 1913), *Cnemidocarpa* Huntsman, 1912 (> *Ypsilocarpa* Ärnbäck 1922). *Styela* Fleming, 1822 (> *Tethyum* Hartmeyer, 1908, *Goniocarpa* Huntsman, 1912, *Katatropa* Huntsman, 1912, *Botryorchis* Huntsman, 1913, *Vannamea* Oka, 1932a), *Asterocarpa* Brewin, 1946, *Dendrodoa* Mac-Leay, 1825, *Styelopsis* Traustedt, 1883, *Pelonaia* Goodsir and Forbes, 1841, *Dicarpa* Millar, 1955a, *Minostyela* new genus, *Skaiostyela* Sluiter, 1904, *Podostyela* Harant and Vernières, 1933, *Azygocarpa* Oka 1932b, *Bathyoncus* Herdman, 1882 (> *Bathystyeloides* Seeliger, 1893–1907), *Hemistyela* Millar, 1955a.

Family PYURIDAE Hartmeyer, 1908
(>TETHYIDAE Huntsman, 1912a)

Solitary. Branchial sac with more than 4 folds per side. Stigmata straight. Openings with 4 lobes. Tentacles compound. Lobed liver. No single large renal vesicles.
Genera: *Pyura* Molina, 1782 (> *Cynthia* Savigny, 1816 [part], *Pyuropsis* Michaelsen, 1912, *Podocynthia* Oka, 1929, *Hyalocynthia* Oka, 1930, *Paracynthia* Ärnbäck, 1938), *Halocynthia* Verrill and Rathbun, 1879 (> *Tethyum* Huntsman, 1912), *Herdmania* Lahille, 1888, *Microcosmus* Heller, 1878 (> *Rhabdocynthia* Herdman, 1891a), *Boltenia* Savigny, 1816, *Bathypera*

Michaelsen, 1904 (> *Halomolgula* Ritter, 1907), *Ctenyura* Van Name, 1918, *Culeolus* Herdman, 1881.

Family MOLGULIDAE Lacaze-Duthiers, 1877
(> CAESIRIDAE Hartmeyer, 1908)

Solitary. Branchial sac with or without folds. Stigmata spiral. Branchial aperture with 6 lobes. Atrial aperture with 4 lobes. Tentacles compound. Lobed liver. Usually a single large renal vesicle on right side of the body.

Genera: *Molgula* Forbes, 1848 (> *Caesira* Fleming, 1822, *Lithonephyra* Giard, 1872, *Ctenicella* Lacaze-Duthiers, 1877, *Ascopera* Herdman, 1881, *Eugyriopsis*

Roule, 1886, *Astropera* Pizon, 1898[1]), *Molguloides* Huntsman, 1922, *Eugyra* Alder and Hancock, 1870 (> *Gamaster* Pizon, 1896, *Eugyrioides* Seeliger, 1893–1907), *Pareugyrioides* Hartmeyer, 1914, *Paramolgula* Traustedt, 1885 (> *Stomatropa* Pizon, 1898), *Bostrichobranchus* Traustedt, 1883, *Anomopera* Hartmeyer, 1923, *Rhizomolgula* Ritter, 1901, *Fungulus*

---

[1] *Hartmeyeria* Ritter, 1913, was thought to be related to *Microcosmus* in the family Pyuridae [Van Name, 1945]. Tokioka has demonstrated, however, that a kidney is present in the two Pacific species [Tokioka, 1967]; the genus is therefore a member of the Molgulidae. It is not known by what character *Hartmeyeria* may be distinguished from *Molgula*.

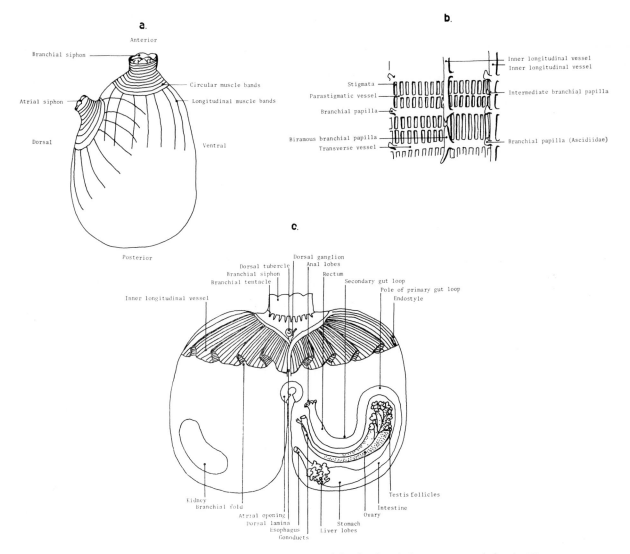

Diagram illustrating the morphological characters commonly used in the descriptive taxonomy of the Ascidiacea.

(*a*) Body removed from test to show musculature of body wall.

(*b*) Portion of branchial sac showing variations in condition of inner longitudinal and transverse vessels.

(*c*) Body opened around ventral and posterior border; major part of branchial sac removed to expose atrial cavity and organs on inner surface of the body wall.

Herdman, 1882, *Oligotrema* Bourne, 1903 (> *Hexacrobylus* Sluiter, 1905).

Family ?

Stolidobranchia (Pyuridae but tentacles simple).
Genera: *Heterostigma* Ärnbäck, 1924, *Eupera* Michaelsen, 1904, *Boltenopsis* Harant, 1927.

WORKING KEY TO ASCIDIACEA

This key to the orders, suborders, families, and subfamilies is based on characters present and conspicuous in adult specimens. Entries marked with an asterisk, in conformity with the practice followed in the generic keys, are represented in the Antarctic by one or more species.

Couplet numbers immediately following family names in five instances lead to the characters by means of which their subfamilies may be distinguished. For reference in the text to non-antarctic taxa consult the index.

1. Gonads always unpaired; test never leathery; branchial sac always unfolded (ENTEROGONA) 2
   Gonads usually paired; test generally leathery; branchial sac usually folded (PLEUROGONA: STOLIDOBRANCHIA) 16
2. Body divided (APLOUSOBRANCHIA) 3
   Body not divided (PHLEBOBRANCHIA) 10
3. Solitary ....*CIONIDAE p. 23
   Colonial 4
4. Branchial sac with internal longitudinal vessels ....
   ....DIAZONIDAE
   Branchial sac without internal longitudinal vessels 5
5. Posterior abdomen absent 6
   Posterior abdomen present ....*POLYCLINIDAE—9
6. Both apertures 6-lobed ....*POLYCITORIDAE p. 36
   Both apertures not 6-lobed 7

7. Colony not usually an investing-sheet; no spicules present ....*CLAVELINIDAE—8
   Colony usually an investing sheet; spicules present....
   ....*DIDEMNIDAE p. 74
8. Usually with atrial lip; colonial systems usually present
   ....*HOLOZOINAE p. 25
   Always with atrial siphon; colonial systems never present
   ....*CLAVELININAE p. 25
9. Zooids open separately to exterior ....
   ....*EUHERDMANIINAE p. 40
   Zooids open into common cloaca ....
   ....*POLYCLININAE p. 45
10. Colonial, zooids connected by stolons ....
    ...................................PEROPHORIDAE
    Solitary individuals 11
11. Gut not on left side of branchial sac 12
    Gut on left side of branchial sac 14
12. Internal longitudinal vessels present ....*CORELLIDAE—13
    Internal longitudinal vessels absent ....
    ....*HYPOBYTHIIDAE p. 88
13. Stigmata straight ....*RHODOSOMATINAE p. 83
    Stigmata spiral ....*CORELLINAE p. 84
14. Inner longitudinal vessels usually with secondary papillae
    ....*ASCIDIIDAE p. 89
    Secondary branchial papillae absent; longitudinal vessels often reduced ....*AGNESIIDAE—15
15. Stigmata straight .. ..CIALLUSIINAE
    Stigmata spiral ....*AGNESIINAE p. 94
16. Branchial tentacles simple; no lobed liver ....
    ....*STYELIDAE—17
    Branchial tentacles compound; lobed liver present 19
17. Atrial openings into common cloaca ....BOTRYLLINAE
    Atrial openings separately to exterior 18
18. Colonial zooids united by stolons or embedded in common test ....*POLYZOINAE p. 99
    Solitary individuals ....*STYELINAE p. 106
19. Stigmata straight; no renal vesicle .....*PYURIDAE p. 127
    Stigmata spiral; single renal vesicle present on right side of body ....*MOLGULIDAE p. 145

4. SPECIES LIST

ALL SPECIES RECORDED from Antarctica are listed below. Abyssal species are indicated. The number of previous records for species not available for examination are given. Where identification is doubtful or the specimens examined were from the B.A.N.Z.A.R.E. collection but not from the currently available United States collections, these facts are also indicated.

+   Not present in new collections.
B   Reexamined from British-Australian-New Zealand Antarctic Research Expedition Collection.
A   Abyssal species.
?   Identification doubtful.

The figure in parentheses represents the number of previous records.

Order ENTEROGONA
Suborder APLOUSOBRANCHIA
Family CIONIDAE

Ciona intestinalis (Linnaeus)   + ? (1)

Family CLAVELINIDAE
Subfamily CLAVELININAE

? *Podoclavella* sp.

Subfamily HOLOZOINAE

Sycozoa sigillinoides Lesson
Sycozoa georgiana (Michaelsen)
Sycozoa gaimardi (Herdman)   + (4)
Distaplia cylindrica (Lesson)
Distaplia colligans Sluiter
Hypsistozoa fasmeriana (Michaelsen)   + B
Hypsistozoa obscura new species   A
Protoholozoa pedunculata new genus, new species   A

Family POLYCITORIDAE

Cystodytes antarcticus Sluiter
Polycitor glareosus Sluiter   + ? (1)
? *Polycitor clava* Harant and Vernières   + ? (1)
Sigillina (Paessleria) magalhaensis Michaelsen
                                      + ? (1)
Sigillina (Hyperiodistoma) moebiusi (Hartmeyer)

Family POLYCLINIDAE
Subfamily EUHERDMANIINAE

Tylobranchion speciosum Herdman
Placentela translucida, new species

Pharyngodictyon mirabile Herdman   A
Pharyngodictyon reductum Sluiter   + ? (1)

Subfamily POLYCLININAE

Aplidium abyssum, new species   A
Aplidium fuegiense Cunningham
Aplidium irregulare (Herdman)
Aplidium vastum (Sluiter)
Aplidium variabile (Herdman)
Aplidium loricatum (Harant and Vernières)
Aplidium radiatum (Sluiter)
Aplidium globosum (Herdman)   + B
Aplidium fuscum (Herdman)   + B
Aplidium circumvolutum (Sluiter)
Aplidium stanleyi Millar   + (1)
Aplidium vanhoeffeni Hartmeyer   + ? (1)
Aplidium stewartense (Michaelsen)
Aplidium recumbens (Herdman)
Aplidium caeruleum (Sluiter)
Synoicium adareanum (Herdman)
Synoicium ramulosum new species
Synoicium kuranui Brewin
Synoicium giardi (Herdman)   + B
Synoicium tentaculatum new species   A
Synoicium kerguelenense (Hartmeyer)   + ? (1)
Synoicium triplex (Sluiter)   + ? (1)
Synoicium perreratum (Sluiter)
Aplidiopsis pyriformis (Herdman)   + B
Aplidiopsis georgianum (Sluiter)
Aplidiopsis discoveryi Millar

Family DIDEMNIDAE

Didemnum biglans (Sluiter)
Didemnum studeri Hartmeyer
Didemnum trivolutum Millar   + (1)
Didemnum tenue (Herdman)   + (2)
Polysyncraton chondrilla (Michaelsen)
Trididemnum auriculatum Michaelsen   + (3)
Trididemnum propinquum (Herdman)   + ? (1)
Leptoclinides kerguelensis Kott   + B
Diplosoma (Diplosoma) longinquum (Sluiter)
Diplosoma (Diplosoma) antarcticum new species

Suborder PHLEBOBRANCHIA
Family CORELLIDAE
Subfamily RHODOSOMATINAE

Abyssascidia wyvillii Herdman   + A (2)

11

Subfamily CORELLINAE

Corella eumyota Traustedt
Corynascidia suhmi Herdman
Xenobranchion insigne Ärnbäck   + (1)

Family HYPOBYTHIIDAE

Megalodicopia hians Oka   A

Family ASCIDIIDAE

Ascidia challengeri Herdman
Ascidia meridionalis Herdman
Ascidia translucida Herdman   + B
Ascidia sp. ?

Family AGNESIIDAE
Subfamily AGNESIINAE

Caenagnesia schmitti new species
Caenagnesia bocki Ärnbäck
Agnesia glaciata Michaelsen
Adagnesia antarctica new species

Order PLEUROGONA
Suborder STOLIDOBRANCHIA
Family STYELIDAE
Subfamily POLYZOINAE

Polyzoa opuntia Lesson
Polyzoa reticulata (Herdman)
Alloeocarpa incrustans (Herdman)   + (8)
Alloeocarpa bridgesi Michaelsen   + ? (2)
Alloeocarpa bacca Ärnbäck   + (1)
? *Polyandrocarpa placenta* (Herdman)   + ? (1)
Oligocarpa megalorchis Hartmeyer   —

Subfamily STYELINAE

Polycarpa minuta Herdman   + ? (1)
Cnemidocarpa verrucosa (Lesson)
Cnemidocarpa zenkevitchi Vinogradova   + (1)
Styela schmitti Van Name
Styela nordenskjoldi Michaelsen   A
Styela wandeli (Sluiter)
Styela grahami Sluiter   + (2)
Styela insinuosa (Sluiter)
Styela serpentina Sluiter   + (2)
Styela pfefferi Michaelsen
Styela paessleri Michaelsen   + (3)

Styela ohlini Michaelsen   + (1)
Styela sericata Herdman   A
Styela sp. ?
Styelopsis tricostata (Millar)   + (1)
Minostyela clavata new genus, new species   A
Bathyoncus enderbyanus Michaelsen   + A (4)
Bathyoncus herdmani Michaelsen   + A (1)
Bathyoncus mirabilis Herdman   + A (1)

Family PYURIDAE

Pyura setosa (Sluiter)
Pyura paessleri (Michaelsen)
Pyura georgiana (Michaelsen)
Pyura legumen (Lesson)
Pyura squamata Hartmeyer   A
Pyura discoveryi (Herdman)
Pyura tunica new species
Pyura obesa Sluiter
Pyura vittata (Stimpson)
Bathypera splendens Michaelsen   A
Bathypera hastaefera Vinogradova   + (2)
Culeolus murrayi Herdman   A

Family MOLGULIDAE

Molgula pedunculata Herdman
Molgula setigera Ärnbäck
Molgula pyriformis Herdman
Molgula malvinensis Ärnbäck
Molgula pulchra Michaelsen
Molgula confluxa (Sluiter)
Molgula sluiteri (Michaelsen)
Molgula euplicata Herdman
Molgula kerguelenensis Kott   + B
Molgula gigantea Herdman
Molguloides immunda (Hartmeyer)   A
Molguloides vitrea (Sluiter)   + A (5)
Eugyra kerguelenensis Herdman
Pareugyrioides galatheae (Millar)   A
Pareugyrioides arnbackae Millar
Pareugyrioides filholi Herdman
Paramolgula gregaria (Lesson)
Fungulus cinereus Herdman   A
Oligotrema psammites Bourne   A
Oligotrema sp.

5. STATION LIST

Stations from which specimens have been collected are listed alphabetically by ship. The expeditions are given in chronological order. Early records are incomplete. Place names adopted by the United States Board on Geographic Names [*Antarctica* (second edition), *Official Name Decisions, Gazetteer 14*, 1966] are used throughout.

USS *Atka*

Deep Freeze III, January 1958, collected by L. W. Wilson.

Sta. 21, Ross Sea, Moubray Bay; 72°14′S, 171° 09′E; January 8, 1958; 390 meters.
   Distaplia cylindrica, 1 colony
   Aplidium caeruleum, 1 colony
Sta. 23, Ross Sea, Moubray Bay, off Cape Hallett; 72°06′S, 172°14.2′E; January 12, 1958; 392 meters.
   Aplidium radiatum, numerous colonies
   Didemnum biglans, small particle
Sta. 29, Knox Coast, Vincennes Bay, Wilkes Land; 66°17′35″S, 110°18′40″E; January 27, 1958; 135 meters.
   Distaplia cylindrica, 1 colony
   Tylobranchion speciosum, few small colonies
   Aplidium radiatum, 3 colonies
   Synoicium adareanum, 1 head
   Diplosoma antarcticum, 1 colony (new species)
   Ascidia challengeri, 1 specimen

USS *Burton Island*

Deep Freeze III, January 1958, collected by R. B. Starr.

Sta. 3, Ross Sea, east of Cape Hallett: 72°08′S, 172°10′E; January 13, 1958; 434 meters.
   Tylobranchion speciosum, 1 particle
   Didemnum biglans, particles of
   Ascidia challengeri, 1 small specimen
   Styela nordenskjoldi, 1 specimen
Sta. 5, Davis Sea, near Mirnyy, Queen Mary Coast; 66°33′S, 92°54′E; January 29, 1958; 80 meters.
   Sycozoa georgiana, numerous colonies
   Distaplia cylindrica, 1 colony
   Aplidium radiatum, 2 colonies

USS *Edisto*

United States Navy Antarctic Expedition (Operation Windmill) 1947–1948; collection made by Cmdr.

David C. Nutt, USNR, assisted by various members of the ship's personnel.

Sta. 12, Davis Sea; 66°35′S, 90°40′E; December 30, 1947; 274 meters; Bottom Dredge.
   Synoicium adareanum, 1 colony
Sta. 33, Off Bigelow Rock; 66°15′S, 95°20′E; January 3, 1948; Wilhelm II Coast; 79 meters; brought up on anchor.
   Cnemidocarpa verrucosa, 1 specimen
Sta. 44, Knox Coast; 65°25′S, 100°13′E; January 14, 1948; 184 meters; Bottom Dredge.
   Synoicium ramulosum, numerous colonies (new species)
   Caenagnesia bocki, 7 specimens
   Pyura tunica, 28 specimens (new species)
   Molguloides immunda, 2 specimens
Sta. 45, Knox Coast; 65°25′S, 101°13′E; January 13, 1948; 184 meters; Bottom Dredge.
   Synoicium adareanum, 1 colony
   Synoicium ramulosum, numerous colonies (new species)
   Agnesia glaciata, 4 small specimens
Sta. 104, Ross Island, off Cape Royds, Ross Sea; off ship's anchorage; January 29, 1948; 107 meters; Bottom Dredge.
   Ascidia challengeri, 1 specimen
   Cnemidocarpa verrucosa, 1 specimen
Sta. 115, Off Point #13 Island, Knox Coast; 66° 31′S, 110°26′E; January 19, 1948; 184 meters; Vertical Tow-Net Haul.
   Distaplia colligans, 4 colonies
   Synoicium adareanum, 1 colony
Sta. 146, Peter I Island, Bellingshausen Sea; 68°47′S, 90°35′W; February 15, 1948; 56 meters; Bottom Dredge Haul 'A.'
   Sycozoa georgiana, 100+ specimens
   Caenagnesia bocki, 24 specimens
   Eugyra kerguelenensis, 2 specimens
   Pareugyrioides arnbackae, 36 specimens

14   ANTARCTIC ASCIDIACEA

STA. 147, Peter I Island, Bellingshausen Sea;
68°47'S, 90°35'W; February 15, 1948; 56 meters;
Bottom Dredge.
  Cnemidocarpa verrucosa, 1 specimen
STA. 148, Peter I Island, Bellingshausen Sea;
68°47'S, 90°35'W; February 15, 1948; 56 meters;
Bottom Dredge Haul 'A.'
  Sycozoa georgiana, 2 colonies
  Pareugyrioides arnbackae, 1 specimen
STA. 152, Peter I Island, Bellingshausen Sea;
68°47'S, 90°35'W; February 15, 1948; 56 meters;
Bottom Dredge.
  Sycozoa georgiana, 2 colonies
STA. 161, Peter I Island, Bellingshausen Sea;
68°47'S, 90°35'W; February 15, 1948; 56 meters;
Bottom Dredge Haul 'B.'
  Pareugyrioides arnbackae, 1 specimen
STA. 162, Peter I Island, Bellingshausen Sea;
68°47'S, 90°35'W; February 15, 1948; 56 meters;
Bottom Dredge Haul 'B.'
  Sycozoa georgiana, 61 specimens
  Styela wandeli, 1 specimen
STA. 180, Marguerite Bay, Antarctic Peninsula;
68°30'S, 68°30'W; February 20, 1948; 156–193
meters; Bottom Dredge.
  Styela insinuosa, 2 specimens
  Styela pfefferi, 2 specimens
STA. 189, Marguerite Bay, Antarctic Peninsula;
68°30'S, 68°30'W; February 20, 1948; 64 meters;
Bottom Dredge.
  Tylobranchion speciosum, 1 colony
  Aplidium radiatum, 1 colony
  Styela wandeli, 3 specimens
  Pyura setosa, 8 specimens
  Pyura discoveryi, 1 specimen
  Molgula confluxa, 1 specimen
STA. 190, Marguerite Bay, Antarctic Peninsula;
68°30'S, 68°30'W; February 20, 1948; 64 meters;
Bottom Dredge.
  Cnemidocarpa verrucosa, 2 small specimens
STA. 193, Marguerite Bay, Antarctic Peninsula;
68°30'S, 68°30'W; February 20, 1948; 64 meters;
Bottom Dredge.
  Cnemidocarpa verrucosa, 1 specimen
  Styela wandeli, 2 specimens
  Bathypera splendens, 1 specimen
STA. 194, Marguerite Bay, Antarctic Peninsula;
68°30'S, 68°30'W; February 20, 1948; 64 meters;
Bottom Dredge.
  Ascidia challengeri, 1 specimen
STA. 225, Marguerite Bay, Antarctic Peninsula;

68°30'S, 68°30'W; February 22, 1948; 74 meters;
Bottom Dredge.
  Cnemidocarpa verrucosa, 17 specimens
STA. 226, Marguerite Bay, Antarctic Peninsula;
68°30'S, 68°30'W; February 22, 1948; 74 meters;
Bottom Dredge (on shell fragments).
  Polysyncraton chondrilla, 1 colony
  Cnemidocarpa verrucosa, 4 specimens
  Styela wandeli, 8 specimens
  Molgula confluxa, 1 specimen
STA. 230, Marguerite Bay, Antarctic Peninsula;
68°30'S, 68°30'W; February 22, 1948; 74 meters;
Bottom Dredge.
  Pyura setosa, 1 specimen
STA. 232, Marguerite Bay, Antarctic Peninsula;
68°30'S, 68°30'W; February 22, 1948; 74 meters;
Bottom Dredge.
  Cystodytes antarcticus, 1 colony
  Synoicium pererratum, 1 colony
  Styela wandeli, 2 specimens
STA. 234, Marguerite Bay, Antarctic Peninsula;
68°30'S, 68°30'W; February 22, 1948; 73 meters;
Bottom Dredge.
  Ascidia challengeri, 1 specimen (juvenile)
  Cnemidocarpa verrucosa, 1 specimen
  Styela wandeli, 1 specimen
  Molgula confluxa, 1 specimen

USS *Edisto*

Deep Freeze I, January–February 1956, collected by
L. W. Wilson, W. H. Littlewood, and J. Q. Tierney.
  (STA. ?), Ross Sea, Kainan Bay, Ross Ice Shelf;
78°14'S, 161°55'W; January 27, 1956; depth ?.
  Distaplia cylindrica, 2 colonies
  Pyura georgiana, 2 specimens
  Pyura discoveryi, 2 specimens
STA. 3, Ross Sea area, Robertson Bay; 71°32'S,
170°18'E; February 6, 1956; 27 meters; Orange
Peel Grab.
  Aplidium loricatum, 6 heads
STA. 4, Ross Sea area, Relay Bay, S.W. Robertson
Bay; 71°30'S, 169°32'E; February 7, 1956; 400
meters; Orange Peel Grab.
  Tylobranchion speciosum, many colonies
  Caenagnesia schmitti, 1 specimen (new species)
STA. 5, Ross Sea area, Robertson Bay; 71°31'S,
169°20'E; February 9, 1956; 400 meters.
  Sycozoa georgiana, numerous heads
  Distaplia cylindrica, 1 colony
  Tylobranchion speciosum, few colonies
  Synoicium adareanum, 1 head
  Pareugyrioides arnbackae, 1 specimen

Deep Freeze IV, January–April 1959, collected by John Tyler.

STA. 15, TD 3, Weddell Sea, west of Cape Norvegia; 71°55′S, 15°35′W; January 23, 1959; 1280 meters; Triangular Bottom Dredge.

Ascidia sp., 1 specimen (too immature for identification)

STA. 17, TR 3, Weddell Sea, west of Cape Norvegia; 71°40′S, 15°35′W; January 24, 1959; 1454 meters; Bottom Trawl.

Pyura georgiana, 1 specimen

STA. 18, TR 4, Weddell Sea, west of Cape Norvegia; 71°40′S, 15°35′W; January 25, 1959; 1555 meters; Bottom Trawl.

Megalodicopia hians, 1 specimen
Pyura georgiana, 1 specimen

STA. 20, TR 5, Weddell Sea, off Vahsel Bay (Duke Ernst Bay); 77°40′S, 35°30′W; January 28, 1959; 384 meters; Bottom Trawl.

Tylobranchion speciosum, 1 particle
Polysyncraton chondrilla, 3 colonies
Corella eumyota, 1 specimen
Pyura discoveryi, 1 specimen
Molgula pedunculata, 1 specimen

STA. 20, TR 6, Weddell Sea, off Vahsel Bay; 77°40′S, 35°30′W; January 28, 1959; 394 meters; Bottom Trawl.

Tylobranchion speciosum, 1 specimen
Aplidium radiatum, 1 colony
Aplidium caeruleum, 1 colony
Polysyncraton chondrilla, 1 colony
Caenagnesia bocki, 2 specimens
Pyura discoveryi, 8 specimens
Pareugyrioides arnbackae, 1 specimen

STA. 21, TR 7, Weddell Sea, off Vahsel Bay; 77°40′S, 35°30′W; January 30, 1959; 412 meters; Bottom Trawl.

Aplidium radiatum, numerous colonies
Polysyncraton chondrilla, 1 colony
Styela insinuosa, 1 specimen
Pyura discoveryi, 1 specimen
Bathypera splendens, 1 specimen

STA. 21, TR 8, Weddell Sea, off Vahsel Bay; 77°40′S, 35°30′W; January 30, 1959; 413 meters; Bottom Trawl.

Pyura discoveryi, 2 specimens
Molgula malvinensis, 1 specimen

STA. 23, TR 10, Weddell Sea, off Ellsworth, I.G.Y. station; 77°40′S, 40°50′W; February 1, 1959; 810 meters; Bottom Trawl.

Megalodicopia hians, 1 specimen

STA. 28, TD 4, Antarctic Peninsula, off Hugo Island; 65°08′S, 66°04′W; March 22, 1959; 135 meters; Triangular Dredge.

Synoicium adareanum, 1 large colony
Bathypera splendens, 1 small specimen

STA. 28, TR 14, West coast Antarctic Peninsula, Hugo Island; 65°08′S, 66°04′W; March 22, 1959; 129 meters; Bottom Trawl.

Tylobranchion speciosum, 6 small colonies
Aplidium radiatum, 3 specimens
Corella eumyota, 1 specimen
Molgula gigantea, 1 specimen

STA. 31, TD 6, West coast Antarctic Peninsula, off Lavoisier Island (Nansen Island); 66°20′S, 67°47′W; March 25, 1959; 325 meters; Triangular Dredge.

Cnemidocarpa verrucosa, 1 specimen

STA. 34, TR 17, Antarctic Peninsula, off Lavoisier Island; 66°09′S, 67°53′W; April 1, 1959; 409 meters; Bottom Trawl.

Cnemidocarpa verrucosa, 1 specimen

STA. 35, TR 18, Antarctic Peninsula, off Lavoisier Island; 65°58′S, 66°51′W; April 4, 1959; 154 meters; Bottom Trawl.

Tylobranchion speciosum, few colonies
Aplidium radiatum, 2 colonies
Pyura setosa, 1 specimen
Pyura discoveryi, 1 specimen

STA. 36, TR 19, Antarctic Peninsula, off Lavoisier Island; 65°39′S, 66°17′W; April 5, 1959; 307 meters; Bottom Trawl.

Pyura georgiana, 1 specimen

STA. 38, OP 17, Antarctic Peninsula, off southwest coast of Wiencke Island; 64°50′S, 63°33′W; April 7, 1959; 129 meters; Orange Peel Bottom Grab.

Synoicium adareanum, 1 head
Aplidiopsis georgianum, 1 head

USNS *Eltanin*[1]

Cruise 3, June 1962.

STA. 37, Peru-Chile Trench, floor and west wall; 08°10′05″S, 81°08′01″W; June 8, 1962; 6006 meters; 10′ Beam Trawl.

Hypsistozoa obscura, 1 colony (new species)
Aplidium abyssum, 1 slightly battered colony (new species)
Oligotrema sp., 1 empty test

STA. 43, Peru-Chile Trench; 13°15′S, 78°06′W; June 12, 1962; 5234–5314 meters; Menzies Trawl.

[1] *Eltanin* station numbers in this list are those of the University of Southern California except the stations of Cruise 17, which was undertaken by the Smithsonian Institution Sorting Center (SOSC).

Megalodicopia hians, 4 specimens (identification doubtful)

Styela nordenskjoldi, 3 specimens

Cruise 4, July–August 1962.

STA. 87, 80 miles west of Valparaiso; 32°03′S, 72°40′W; July 6, 1962; 5929 meters; muddy bottom; Menzies Trawl.

Molguloides immunda, 3 specimens

STA. 135, South Shetland Islands, 62°39′36″S, 64°02′W; August 6, 1962; 3752 meters; Menzies Trawl.

Culeolus murrayi, 1 specimen

Cruise 5, September–November 1962.

STA. 217, Drake Passage; 54°22′S, 64°42′W; September 23, 1962; 110 meters; 40′ Otter Trawl.

Sycozoa sigillinoides, numerous colonies

Distaplia cylindrica, 1 specimen (♂ mature)

Aplidium variabile, 7 heads

Polyzoa reticulata, numerous specimens

STA. 219, Drake Passage, about 20 miles east of Islas Barnevelt; 55°47′S, 66°16.5′W; September 23, 1962; 115 meters; Peterson Grab.

Aplidium fuegiense, 2 heads

Aplidium stewartense, numerous colonies

Didemnum studeri, numerous colonies

Polyzoa reticulata, few specimens

Styela schmitti, 3 specimens

Pyura paessleri, 10 specimens

Molgula setigera, 18 specimens

Molgula pyriformis, 5 specimens

Molgula malvinensis, 9 specimens

Molgula pulchra, 10 specimens

Pareugyrioides filholi, 1 juvenile (identification doubtful)

STA. 222, Tierra del Fuego; 53°14′07″S, 66°51′03″W; September 27, 1962; 79 meters; 40′ Otter Trawl.

Aplidium fuegiense, 1 colony

STA. 268, West of Antarctic Peninsula; 64°01′02″S, 67°44′07″W; October 20, 1962; 2818 meters; 10′ Blake Trawl.

Protoholozoa pedunculata, 1 colony with larvae (new species)

Culeolus murrayi, 1 specimen

Fungulus cinereus, 1 specimen

STA. 291, West of Antarctic Peninsula; 65°58′S, 70°05′W; October 26–27, 1962; 370 meters; 40′ Otter Trawl.

Placentela translucida, 3 colonies (new species)

Pyura georgiana, 5 specimens

STA. 317, West end Drake Passage; 57°04.8′S,

70°59.3′W; November 4, 1962; 3790 meters; Rock Dredge.

Protoholozoa pedunculata, 1 colony, active budding (new species)

Cruise 6, December 1962 to January 1963.

STA. 337, Tierra del Fuego; 52°44.8′S, 66°33.6′W; December 2, 1962; 92 meters; 40′ Otter Trawl.

Sycozoa sigillinoides, 1 colony

STA. 339, Falkland Islands–Burdwood Bank, 53°05′04″S, 59°31′00″W; 586 meters, 40′ Otter Trawl.

Sycozoa sigillinoides, about 10 young colonies and stalks

Aplidium fuegiense, 1 colony

Corella eumyota, 1 specimen

STA. 344, South of Falkland Islands; 54°04′03″S, 58°46′02″W; December 4, 1962; 119 meters; Menzies Trawl.

Sycozoa sigillinoides, 1 branched colony

Styela nordenskjoldi, 3 specimens

STA. 365, South Shetland Islands; 58°06′S, 59°27′05″W; December 9, 1962; 4385 meters; Rock Dredge.

Fungulus cinereus, 1 specimen

STA. 369, Drake Passage; 57°03′05″S, 63°35′04″W; December 12, 1962; 293 meters; rocky bottom; Rock Dredge.

Aplidium variabile, numerous colonies

Aplidium circumvolutum, 3 colonies

Synoicium kuranui, several colonies

Molgula setigera, 2 specimens

Molgula pulchra, 1 specimen

STA. 370, Scotia Sea, Burdwood Bank; 53°54′S, 64°35′05″W; December 12, 1962; 104–115 meters; 40′ Otter Trawl.

Tylobranchion speciosum, 1 colony

Aplidium fuegiense, 1 colony

Didemnum studeri, numerous colonies

Styela nordenskjoldi, 30 specimens

Pyura paessleri, 3 specimens

Pyura legumen, 1 specimen

Molgula pulchra, 1 specimen

Paramolgula gregaria, 5 large specimens

STA. 406, South Shetland Islands; 61°12.1′S, 56°17.5′W; December 31, 1962; 287 meters; Peterson Grab.

Pyura georgiana, 1 specimen

STA. 410, South Shetland Islands; 61°18′S, 56°08′05″W; December 31, 1962; 240 meters; 5′ Blake Trawl.

Sigillina moebiusi, 1 specimen

Aplidium recumbens, 4 colonies

Synoicium adareanum, 100 heads
Aplidiopsis georgianum, 3 specimens
Polysyncraton chondrilla, 2 colonies
Ascidia challengeri, 1 large specimen
Styela schmitti, 1 specimen
Pyura setosa, 2 specimens
Pyura georgiana, many specimens
Molgula gigantea, 2 specimens
Pareugyrioides arnbackae, 1 specimen

STA. 416, South Shetland Islands; 62°39.8′S, 56°12.7′W; January 2, 1963; 507 meters; Menzies Trawl.

Didemnum biglans, numerous colonies

STA. 418, South Shetland Islands; 62°38.9′S, 56°10.2′W; January 2, 1963; 426 meters; 5′ Blake Trawl.

Aplidiopsis georgianum, numerous colonies
Corella eumyota, 1 large specimen

STA. 419, South Shetland Islands; 62°14.2′S, 58°17.2′W; January 3, 1963; 552 meters; Rock Dredge.

Aplidiopsis georgianum, 1 head

STA. 426, South Shetland Islands; 62°26′05″S, 57°57′06″W; January 5, 1963; 809–1116 meters; 5′ Blake Trawl.

Pyura georgiana, 2 specimens

STA. 428, South Shetland Islands; 63°40′07″S, 57°50′07″W; January 5, 1963; 662–1120 meters; 5′ Blake Trawl.

Aplidium circumvolutum, 1 colony
Aplidium caeruleum, 1 colony
Didemnum biglans, 1 colony
Polysyncraton chondrilla, 8 colonies
Caenagnesia schmitti, 1 specimen (new species)
Pyura georgiana, 2 specimens

STA. 430, South Shetland Islands; 62°38.4′S, 59°36.5′W; January 7, 1963; 681–1409 meters; 5′ Blake Trawl.

Pyura georgiana, 2 specimens

STA. 432, South Shetland Islands; 62°52′03″S, 59°27′02″W; January 7, 1962; 935 meters; 5′ Blake Trawl.

Aplidium circumvolutum, 40 colonies
Polysyncraton chondrilla, 5 colonies
Pyura georgiana, 4 specimens

STA. 434, South Shetland Islands; 63°14.8′S, 58°43.3′W; January 8, 1963; 77 meters; Peterson Grab.

Distaplia cylindrica, 1 colony
Ascidia challengeri, 3 specimens
Cnemidocarpa verrucosa, 10 large specimens

STA. 435, South Shetland Islands; 63°14′S, 58°40′01″W; January 8, 1963; 73 meters; 40′ Otter Trawl.

Distaplia cylindrica, 2 large specimens
Aplidium radiatum, numerous colonies
Aplidium circumvolutum, 2 colonies
Synoicium adareanum, 2 heads
Cnemidocarpa verrucosa, 13 large specimens
Molgula gigantea, 5 specimens

STA. 436, South Shetland Islands; 63°14′S, 58°45′W; January 8, 1963; 73 meters; 40′ Otter Trawl.

Distaplia cylindrica, 1 large specimen (♀ mature)
Tylobranchion speciosum, 2 specimens
Ascidia challengeri, 10 specimens
Cnemidocarpa verrucosa, 100 specimens
Pyura setosa, 2 specimens
Molgula gigantea, 5 large and small specimens

STA. 437, South Shetland Islands; 62°49′06″S, 60°40′W; January 9, 1963; 311 meters; 5′ Blake Trawl.

Aplidium radiatum, numerous heads
Aplidium circumvolutum, 10 colonies
Aplidium caeruleum, 1 colony
Caenagnesia bocki, 6 specimens
Pyura georgiana, 2 specimens

STA. 439, South Shetland Islands; 63°51′02″S, 62°37′06″W; January 9, 1963; 123–165 meters; 5′ Blake Trawl.

Aplidium circumvolutum, 6 colonies
Synoicium adareanum, 2 colonies
Styela nordenskjoldi, 1 specimen
Molguloides immunda, 1 specimen

STA. 441, South Shetland Islands; 63°26′06″S, 62°37′02″W; January 10, 1963; 253 meters; 5′ Blake Trawl.

Pyura georgiana, 1 specimen

STA. 445, South Shetland Islands; 62°01′07″S, 59°04′07″W; January 12–13, 1963; 101 meters; 40′ Otter Trawl.

Aplidium radiatum, numerous heads
Synoicium adareanum, 30 heads
Cnemidocarpa verrucosa, 1 specimen

STA. 451, Drake Passage, south of Tierra del Fuego; 55°54′01″S, 58°59′06″W; January 18, 1963; 4026 meters; 5′ Blake Trawl.

Protoholozoa pedunculata, 1 colony (new species)
Culeolus murrayi, 10 specimens
Fungulus cinereus, 5 specimens

STA. 453, Drake Passage; 54°27′S, 66°12′W; January 21, 1963; 31 meters; Peterson Grab.

Aplidium irregulare, 1 head

Cruise 7, February 1963.

STA. 469, Scotia Sea, west of Shag Rocks; 55°01.5′S,

44°20.5′W; February 12, 1963; 3714 meters; 5′ Blake Trawl (modified).

    Culeolus murrayi, 2 specimens

STA. 480, South Orkney Islands; 58°06′S, 44°55.5′W; February 15, 1963; 2800 meters; Menzies Trawl.

    Podoclavella sp.?, 1 specimen
    Synoicium tentaculatum, 2 colonies (new species)

STA. 494, South Orkney Islands; 60°42′S, 42°50′W; February 19, 1963; 1226 meters; Rock Dredge.

    Pharyngodictyon mirabile, 1 colony
    Styela nordenskjoldi, 4 specimens
    Pyura squamata, 2 specimens
    Bathypera splendens, 1 specimen

STA. 496, South Orkney Islands; 61°10′S, 45°09.5′W; February 20, 1963; 234 meters; Rock Dredge.

    Tylobranchion speciosum, traces attached to test stalks of *Pyura georgiana*
    Aplidium circumvolutum, 6 colonies
    Pyura georgiana, 30 specimens
    Molgula pedunculata, 1 specimen

STA. 499, South of South Orkney Islands; 62°05.5′S, 45°08′W; February 20, 1963; 485 meters; Rock Dredge.

    Aplidium recumbens, 1 colony
    Pyura georgiana, 2 specimens

Cruise 8, April 1963.

STA. 564, South Sandwich Islands; 54°17′S, 27°25′W; April 12, 1963; 5188 meters; Menzies Trawl.

    Corynascidia suhmi, 1 specimen

STA. 596, Northeast of South Sandwich Islands; 55°52′S, 24°49′W; April 30 to May 1, 1963; 5673–5918 meters; 5′ Blake Trawl.

    Fungulus cinereus, 1 specimen

Cruise 9, August–September 1963.

STA. 690, Scotia Sea, south of South Georgia; 56°18′S, 37°04.3′W; August 27, 1963; 3446 meters; 5′ Blake Trawl.

    Protoholozoa pedunculata, 1 colony (new species)

STA. 732, Scotia Sea area, north of South Georgia; 53°35.7′S, 36°50.8′W; September 12, 1963; 265 meters; 10′ Blake Trawl.

    Tylobranchion speciosum, 1 colony
    Polysyncraton chondrilla, 2 colonies
    Ascidia meridionalis, 24 specimens
    Molgula gigantea, 1 specimen

Cruise 11, February 1964.

STA. 969, Off Tierra del Fuego; 54°56′S, 65°03′W; February 10–11, 1964; 229–265 meters; 5′ Blake Trawl.

    Aplidium variabile, 5 colonies

STA. 981, Off Tierra del Fuego; 52°44′S, 67°42′W; February 14, 1964; 40–49 meters; 10′ Blake Trawl.

    Sycozoa sigillinoides, 15 colonies (disintegrating heads and headless stalks)
    Aplidium fuegiense, 2 colonies
    Aplidium irregulare, 4 colonies
    Aplidiopsis discoveryi, 1 colony
    Didemnum studeri, 22 colonies
    Polyzoa opuntia, 1 colony
    Styela nordenskjoldi, 1 specimen
    Pyura legumen, 1 specimen
    Molgula setigera, 2 specimens
    Paramolgula gregaria, 3 specimens

Cruise 12, March–April 1964.

STA. 991, North of South Shetland Islands; 60°57′S, 56°52′W; March 13, 1964; 2672–3020 meters; 5′ Blake Trawl.

    Molguloides immunda ?, empty test only
    Oligotrema psammites, 2 specimens

STA. 997, North of South Shetland Islands; 61°44′S, 55°56′W; March 14, 1964; 769 meters; 10′ Blake Trawl.

    Sycozoa sigillinoides ?, 2 headless stalks only
    Eugyra kerguelenensis, 1 specimen

STA. 1003, Between South Shetland Islands and South Orkney Islands; 62°41′S, 54°43′W; March 15, 1964; 210–220 meters; 10′ Blake Trawl.

    Pyura obesa, 2 specimens

STA. 1081, South Orkney Islands; 60°35′S, 40°44′W; April 13, 1964; 631–641 meters; 5′ Blake Trawl.

    Molgula gigantea ?, torn test only

STA. 1082, South Orkney Islands; 60°50′S, 42°55′W; April 14, 1964; 298–302 meters; 5′ Blake Trawl.

    Distaplia cylindrica, 20+ colonies
    Aplidium fuegiense, 1 colony
    Aplidium circumvolutum, several colonies
    Didemnum studeri, several colonies
    Ascidia challengeri, 3 specimens
    Pyura setosa, 1 specimen
    Pyura georgiana, 1 specimen
    Pyura discoveryi, 12 specimens
    Molgula pedunculata, 5 specimens

STA. 1083, South Orkney Islands; 60°51′S, 42°57′W; April 14, 1964; 284 meters; 10′ Blake Trawl.

    Pyura georgiana, 2 specimens
    Pyura discoveryi, 10 specimens

STA. 1084, West of South Orkney Islands; 60°22′S,

46°50′W; April 15, 1964; 298–403 meters; 5′ Blake Trawl.

   Tylobranchion speciosum, 1 colony
   Aplidium recumbens, 1 colony
   Pyura georgiana, 1 specimen
   Pyura discoveryi, 6 specimens
   Molgula pedunculata, 1 specimen

Cruise 13, June 1964.
  STA. 1140, Pacific Antarctic Basin; 66°11′S, 102°28′W; June 1, 1964; 4731 meters; 5′ Blake Trawl.
   Culeolus murrayi, 4 specimens
   Pareugyrioides galatheae, 2 specimens
  STA. 1150, Southeast Pacific Basin (Pacific Antarctic Basin); 65°37′S, 121°06′W; June 17, 1964; 4758–4804 meters; 5′ Blake Trawl.
   Culeolus murrayi, 2 specimens
  STA. 1154, Southeast Pacific Basin; 65°37′S, 123°55′W; June 18, 1964; 4709 meters; 5′ Blake Trawl.
   Protoholozoa pedunculata, 1 colony
   Culeolus murrayi, 1 specimen
  STA. 1161, Southeast Pacific Basin; 62°03′S, 129°38′W; June 23–24, 1964; 4447–4502 meters; 5′ Blake Trawl.
   Culeolus murrayi, 1 specimen

Cruise 14, August–September 1964.
  STA. 1209, Southwest Pacific Basin; 58°18′S, 160°03′W; August 11, 1964; 3587–3817 meters; Menzies Trawl.
   Minostyela clavata, 2 specimens (new species)
  STA. 1248, Southeast Pacific Basin; 59°57′S, 136°37′W; August 25, 1964; 3386–3477 meters; Menzies Trawl.
   Styela sp. ?, juvenile
  STA. 1283, Southeast Pacific Basin; 43°13′S, 97°43′W; September 13, 1964; 146–174 meters; 10′ Blake Trawl.
   ? *Corynascidia suhmi*, 1 specimen (test only)

Cruise 15, November 1964.
  STA. 1400, Chatham Islands; 44°03′S, 178°09′W; November 29, 1964; 436–430 meters; 40′ Otter Trawl.
   Aplidium irregulare, 1 colony

Cruise 16, February 1965.
  STA. 1417, West of Macquarie Island; 54°24′S, 159°01′E; February 10, 1965; 79–93 meters; 5′ Blake Trawl.
   Aplidium circumvolutum, 1 colony
   Didemnum studeri, numerous colonies
   Corella eumyota, 100+ specimens
   Polyzoa reticulata, 2 specimens

   Pyura vittata, 10 specimens
   Molgula setigera, 2 specimens
  STA. 1418, West of Macquarie Island; 54°32′S, 159°02′E; February 10, 1965; 86–101 meters; 10′ Blake Trawl.
   Aplidium recumbens, several colonies
   Didemnum studeri, 5 colonies
   Corella eumyota, 100+ specimens
   Adagnesia antarctica, 3 specimens (new species)
   Polyzoa reticulata, numerous specimens
   Oligocarpa megalorchis, 5 specimens
   Pyura vittata, 6 specimens
   Molgula setigera, 1 specimen
   Molgula malvinensis, 1 specimen
   Molgula pulchra, 17 specimens
   Molgula sluiteri, 3 specimens
  STA. 1419, West of Macquarie Island; 54°32′S, 159°02′E; February 10, 1965; 494–714 meters; 10′ Blake Trawl.
   Didemnum studeri, several colonies
  STA. 1422, South of Macquarie Island; 56°19′S, 158°29′E; February 12, 1965; 833–842 meters; 10′ Blake Trawl.
   Didemnum studeri, several colonies
   Corella eumyota, 5 specimens
   Polyzoa reticulata, numerous specimens
  STA. 1423, South of Macquarie Island; 56°21′S, 158°28′E; February 12, 1965; 1574–1693 meters; 10′ Blake Trawl.
   Didemnum studeri, numerous colonies
   Corynascidia suhmi, 6 specimens (3 damaged)
  STA. 1425, Auckland Island; 50°52′S, 166°42′E; February 19, 1965; 135–139 meters; 10′ Blake Trawl.
   Aplidium fuegiense, 2 colonies
   Didemnum studeri, numerous colonies
   Corella eumyota, 20 specimens

Cruise 17, March–May 1965.
  SHIP STA. 14, SOSC sample 42. Southeast Pacific Basin; 68°03′S, 130°46′W; April 7, 1965; 4192–4197 meters; 5′ Blake Trawl.
   Styela sericata, 2 specimens

USS *Glacier*

Deep Freeze I, March 1956, collected by J. Q. Tierney and T. J. Hillman.
  STA. 1, Knox Coast, Vincennes Bay, Wilkes Land; 66°55.5′S, 110°58.5′E; March 18, 1956; 120 meters.
   Corella eumyota, 1 specimen
   Molgula gigantea, 1 small specimen

Deep Freeze II, November 1956 to February 1957, collected by W. L. Tressler and L. W. Wilson.

OCEAN STA. 1, Ross Sea, 1½ mile west of Inaccessible Island, McMurdo Sound; 77°40'S, 166°14'E; November 4, 1956; 386 meters.

Synoicium adareanum, 1 head

(STA. ?), Knox Coast, Vincennes Bay, Wilkes Land; 66°15'51"S, 110°33'11"E; February 14, 1957; on ship's anchor.

Distaplia cylindrica, 1 colony
Molgula pulchra, 1 specimen

Deep Freeze III, February 1958, collected by W. H. Littlewood and W. L. Tressler.

STA. BL-13, Ross Sea, 1½ mile off Hut Point, Cape Armitage, Ross Island, McMurdo Sound; 77°50.8'S, 166°34'E; February 5, 1958; 125 meters.

Synoicium adareanum, 1 colony
Polysyncraton chondrilla, 3 colonies

STA. BL-16, Ross Sea, 2 miles northeast of Marble Point, near Cape Bernacchi; 77°26'S, 163°50'E; February 9, 1958, 142 meters.

Distaplia colligans, 3 small colonies

USCGC *Northwind*

Deep Freeze II, January–March 1957, collected by J. Q. Tierney.

STA. 2 (Sample 3), Ross Sea, Moubray Bay, off Cape Hallett; 72°12'S, 170°20'E; January 1, 1957; 203 meters; Orange Peel Grab.

Pyura setosa, 1 specimen

STA. 5, Ross Sea, McMurdo Sound; 77°51'S, 166°37'E; March 11, 1957; depth ?.

Cnemidocarpa verrucosa, 1 large specimen

Deep Freeze IV, January 1959, collected by L. W. Wilson.

STA. 8, Ross Sea, Moubray Bay, off Cape Hallett; 72°16'40"S, 170°18'E; January 12, 1959; 135 meters.

Distaplia colligans, 2 colonies
Aplidium vastum, 1 colony
Synoicium adareanum, 8 heads
Polysyncraton chondrilla, 3 colonies

USS *Staten Island*

Deep Freeze II, December 1956 to February 1957, collected by W. H. Littlewood.

STA. 17, B 10-3, Weddell Sea; 71°18'S, 13°32'W; December 27, 1956; 239 meters; Orange Peel Grab.

Synoicium adareanum, 7 heads

STA. 1, Weddell Sea; 77°32'S, 44°45'W; January 12, 1957; 284 meters; Bottom Trawl 3.

Distaplia cylindrica, 4 large colonies with larvae (STA. ?), Weddell Sea; 75°27'S, 57°12'W; January 17, 1957; 552 meters; Bottom Trawl.

Pyura georgiana, 2 specimens

STA. 24, Weddell Sea; 77°21'S, 44°30'W; January 20, 1957; 300 meters; Orange Peel Grab.

Distaplia cylindrica, 1 colony with larvae

STA. 25, OP 10, Weddell Sea; 75°12'S, 26°54'W; February 13, 1957; 331 meters.

Pyura discoveryi, 2 specimens

Deep Freeze IV, January 1959, collected by R. G. Miller and R. B. Starr.

OCEAN STA. 10-1, Ross Sea area, Robertson Bay; 71°27.5'S, 169°55.5'E; January 23, 1959; 439 meters.

Distaplia cylindrica, 1 colony
Tylobranchion speciosum, numerous small specimens

OCEAN STA. 10-2, Ross Sea area, Robertson Bay; 71°21.5'S, 170°05'E; January 23, 1959; 128 meters.

Tylobranchion speciosum, numerous colonies
Synoicium adareanum, 27 heads

USS *Staten Island*

Oceanographic Cruise 1962–1963; biological investigations; Antarctic Peninsula, January–March 1963; collection made by Waldo L. Schmitt with the assistance of ship's personnel and survey team.

STA. 5/63, Antarctic Peninsula, Janus Island, off Arthur Harbor; 64°46'S, 64°04'W; January 23, 1963; 48 meters; Fish Trap.

Molgula gigantea, 1 specimen

STA. 6/63, Antarctic Peninsula, Anvers Island, Arthur Harbor; January 24, 1963; 7 meters. From fish trap crushed by small iceberg near Bonaparte Point, very rocky, large rocks.

Ascidia challengeri, single large specimen
Cnemidocarpa verrucosa, 3 specimens
Molgula gigantea, 1 specimen

STA. 7/63, Antarctic Peninsula, Anvers Island, Arthur Harbor; 64°46'S, 64°04'W; January 25, 1963; 21–31 meters; dredged, stiff blue mud, clams, worm tubes, and amphipods.

Corella eumyota, 1 large specimen

STA. 9/63, Antarctic Peninsula, Port Lockroy, Wiencke Island; 64°48'S, 63°30'W; January 26, 1963; 57 meters.

Aplidium radiatum, numerous colonies
Caenagnesia bocki, 1 specimen

STA. 14/63; Antarctic Peninsula, off Argentine

Islands; 65°12'09"S, 64°13'08"W; January 30, 1963; 45–76 meters; dredged, rock, sand, and gravel.

Tylobranchion speciosum, 1 small specimen
Synoicium adareanum, 2 heads
Pyura georgiana, 2 specimens brought up on anchor from 45 meters

STA. 24/63, Antarctic Peninsula, Paradise Harbor, off Danco Coast; 64°51'S, 62°54'W; February 4, 1963; 75 meters; dredged, a very large rock and many smaller ones and pebbles; on large rock size of half an oil drum; gelatinous compound ascidian, large globular one.

Aplidium caeruleum, 1 colony

STA. 27/63, Antarctic Peninsula, Danco Island, off Base O; 64°43'30"S, 63°36'W; February 5, 1963; 75 meters.

Agnesia glaciata, 1 specimen

STA. 32/63, Antarctic Peninsula, Melchior Harbor, off Gamma Island; 64°19'24"S, 62°59'18"W, February 6, 1963; 46 meters; dredged, mud and sand bottom.

Aplidium radiatum, 1 colony
Ascidia challengeri, 16 specimens
Cnemidocarpa verrucosa, 2 specimens
Pyura setosa, 2 specimens
Pyura discoveryi, 2 specimens
Molgula pedunculata, 2 specimens
Molgula euplicata, 1 specimen
Molgula gigantea, 8 specimens

STA. 35/63; Antarctic Peninsula, Melchior Islands; 64°19'24"S, 65°59'18"W; February 7, 1963; 46 meters; from a 20-foot piece of old 4-strand, 3-inch hemp line brought up with anchor.

Didemnum biglans, investing colonies
Ascidia challengeri, 1 specimen
Cnemidocarpa verrucosa, 3 small specimens
Molgula malvinensis, 1 small specimen

STA. 37/63, Antarctic Peninsula, Danco Coast, Wilhelmina Bay, Foyn Harbor; 64°34'00"S, 62°00'00"W; February 8, 1963; 49 meters; dredged, gravel and sand.

Synoicium adareanum, 2 heads
Cnemidocarpa verrucosa, 1 specimen
Pyura setosa, 1 specimen
Molgula euplicata, 2 specimens

STA. 44/63, South Shetland Islands, Yankee Harbor, Greenwich Island; 62°32'15"S, 59°47'00"W; February 13, 1963; 55 meters.

Distaplia cylindrica, 4 colonies
Didemnum biglans, about 12 colonies

Corella eumyota, 1 large specimen
Ascidia challengeri, 10 specimens

STA. 45/63, South Shetland Islands, off Yankee Harbor, Greenwich Island; 62°31'S, 59°47'W; February 13, 1963; 55 meters; dredged, stiff mud bottom.

Synoicium adareanum, 3 heads
Polysyncraton chondrilla, numerous colonies
Ascidia challengeri, 61 specimens
Bathypera splendens, 1 large specimen

STA. 48/63, Antarctic Peninsula, off Seymour Island; 64°15'00"S, 56°25'00"W; February 15, 1963; 70 meters; dredged, sandy mud, small rock fragments, gravel, and sand bottom.

Pareugyrioides arnbackae, 3 specimens

STA. 53/63, Weddell Sea, Dundee Island; 63°39'S, 56°16'18"W; February 20, 1963; 55 meters; dredged at anchorage north of Welchness, mud bottom.

Sycozoa georgiana, immature colonies and stalks
Distaplia cylindrica, 1 colony
Tylobranchion speciosum, 1 particle

STA. 61/63, South Shetland Islands, Livingston Island, False Bay; 62°43'S, 60°22'W; February 25, 1963; 31 meters; dredged at anchorage, mud, muddy coarse sand, rocks, and gravel bottom.

Tylobranchion speciosum, small bits

STA. 62/63, South Shetland Islands, anchorage, Discovery Bay, off Greenwich Island; 62°28'S, 59°37'W; February 26, 1963; 57 meters.

Sycozoa georgiana, 1 colony
Distaplia cylindrica, 8 colonies
Cystodytes antarcticus, 1 colony
Tylobranchion speciosum, 2 colonies
Aplidium radiatum, 2 colonies
Styela wandeli, 2 specimens

STA. 64/63, South Shetland Islands, Collins Harbor, King George Island; 62°12'S, 58°56'W; February 28, 1963; 86 meters; dredge.

Aplidium circumvolutum, numerous colonies
Didemnum biglans, 8 colonies
Polysyncraton chondrilla, 8 colonies
Ascidia challengeri, 12 specimens
Agnesia glaciata, 2 specimens
Pyura setosa, 7 specimens
Pyura georgiana, 1 specimen
Pyura discoveryi, 25 specimens

STA. 66/63, Antarctic Peninsula, Port Lockroy, Wiencke Island; 64°49'05"S, 63°30'05"W; March 1, 1963; 62 meters.

Cystodytes antarcticus, 1 colony
Tylobranchion speciosum, 4 colonies

Synoicium adareanum, 3 colonies
Diplosoma longinquum, 1 colony
Caenagnesia schmitti, 1 specimen (new species)
Agnesia glaciata, 1 damaged specimen

STA. 67/63, Antarctic Peninsula, Anvers Island, Arthur Harbor area; 64°45′01″S, 64°39′W, March 1, 1963; 38 meters.

Synoicium adareanum, 1 colony
Cnemidocarpa verrucosa, 1 specimen
Styela wandeli, 1 specimen
Molgula confluxa, 1 specimen
Molgula gigantea, 2 specimens
Eugyra kerguelenensis, 1 specimen

STA. 75/63, South Shetland Islands, Admiralty Bay, King George Island; 62°04′06″S, 58°20′00″W; March 4, 1963; 40 meters; dredged, mud bottom.

Pyura setosa, 1 specimen

USCGC *Westwind*

Deep Freeze III, January 1958, collected by J. Q. Tierney.

STA. 3, Weddell Sea, off McDonald Ice Rumples, Coats Land; 75°31′S, 26°43′W; January 8, 1958; 210 meters; Triangle Dredge.

Synoicium adareanum, 2 colonies
Pyura georgiana, 1 specimen
Pyura discoveryi, 1 specimen

STA. 4, Weddell Sea, along ice shelf, Ellsworth Station; 77°42′S, 41°04′W; January 11, 1958; 796 meters.

Synoicium adareanum, 3 heads
Caenagnesia bocki, 4 specimens (identification doubtful)

6. SYSTEMATIC DISCUSSION

Order ENTEROGONA

Suborder APLOUSOBRANCHIA Lahille

Family CIONIDAE Lahille

Genus *Ciona* Fleming, 1882

Type species: *Ascidia intestinalis* Linnaeus, 1767

In addition to the ubiquitous *Ciona intestinalis*, two other species have been described, possibly synonyms of the foregoing: *C. mollis* Ritter, 1907 [Van Name, 1945] and *C. flemingi* Herdman, 1882. Several other records represent distinct forms of *C. intestinalis* [Hartmeyer, 1924]. Only the typical cosmopolitan form of *Ciona intestinalis* has been taken in the Antarctic.

Ciona intestinalis (Linnaeus)

Text fig. 1

Ascidia intestinalis Linnaeus, 1767, p. 1087.
Ciona intestinalis Fleming, 1822, p. 512.—Traustedt, 1885, p. 10.
Ciona antarctica Hartmeyer, 1911, p. 471; 1924, p. 90 [has further synonymy].

New Records. None.

Previous Records.
  Antarctic: Wilhelm II Coast [? Hartmeyer, 1911, see Remarks].
  Subantarctic: Strait of Magellan [? Traustedt, 1885, see Remarks].
  Elsewhere: See Distribution following.

Distribution. Circumterrestrial, in arctic, subarctic, northern and southern temperate, tropical, and subtropical seas.

This species has been taken in a wide range of depths from the intertidal zone to 460 meters. Off the east coast of America it has been recorded from Greenland to southern Massachusetts, and off the west coast, from Alaska to southern California [Van Name, 1945]. It has also been taken from Iceland, along the west coasts of Norway and Sweden, the east coast of the British Isles, and the western coast of Europe bordering on the North Sea and extending into the Mediterranean [Millar, 1966a]. South of this wide boreal distribution the range of the species is extended by its occurrence in the harbors of the world (e.g., Plymouth, Suez, Cape of Good Hope, Singapore, Yokohama, Fremantle, Adelaide, Melbourne, Sydney, Rockhampton, and Christchurch [Van Name, 1945; Brewin, 1950a; Kott, 1952; Millar, 1962]).

Description. The body is cylindrical. Atrial and branchial siphons are short. The atrial siphon is one-third the body length from terminal branchial siphon. Test is soft, thin, and semitransparent. From 5 to 7 longitudinal muscle bands extend the whole length of body. External to these bands is a layer of circular muscle fibers. Dorsal tubercle has a C-shaped slit with horns rolled in or out. The dorsal lamina is represented by a row of numerous pointed languets. Internal longitudinal vessels and transverse and intermediate transverse vessels with spatulate papillae at junctions are present in the branchial sac. There are 4 to 10 stigmata per mesh. The gut loop is horizontal and posterior to the branchial sac. Gonads are present in the gut loop. Pyriform testis follicles extend over the surface of the stomach or intestine. The anus opens halfway up the branchial sac.

Biology. The eggs of *Ciona intestinalis* are especially buoyant. The tadpole larva is formed 25 hours after fertilization, and the tadpole is free-swimming for 6 to 36 hours [Berrill, 1950]. Consequently, there is an unusually long interval after the egg is liberated and before the adult metamorphoses and becomes sessile. Therefore, although the species is prolific and breeds throughout the year [Berrill, 1950], in turbulent environments, where eggs and embryos become too widely dispersed, the minimum population density necessary to ensure the fertilization of eggs would not be achieved. This may explain the unusual distribution characteristics. Berrill [1950] has suggested that the gas bubble that is secreted in metamorphosing forms, causing the animal to float, may account for its tendency to attach to ships' bottoms and harbor installations.

Remarks. Ciona intestinalis, as noted, has a completely cosmopolitan distribution outside the Antarctic and could be expected to occur there. It tolerates a

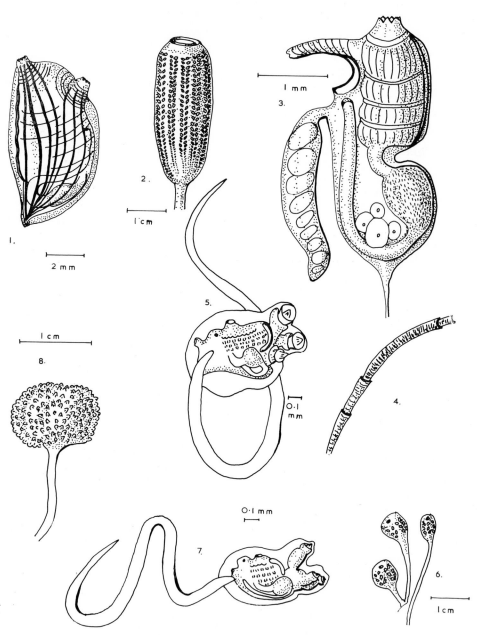

Ciona intestinalis
1. Zooids without test, showing musculature and gut [after Hartmeyer, 1911].

Sycozoa sigillinoides
2. Head of colony with cloacal aperture open.
3. Zooid (♀) with larvae in brood pouch.
4. Basal portion of hardened stalk.
5. Larva.

Sycozoa georgiana
6. Colonies.
7. Larva.

Sycozoa gaimardi
8. Colony [after Sluiter, 1914].

wide range of conditions and colonizes with ease in areas considerably removed from its natural geographic range, especially establishing itself in protected situations in harbors, aquarium tanks, and powerhouse conduits (unpublished data from Bunnerong Power House, Botany Bay, Sydney). Its natural distribution does not extend markedly beyond the normal geographic limits of the boreal region, and new populations in harbors throughout the world remain in the generally confined areas in which they have become established. It is commonly found growing on the hulls of ships [Berrill, 1950], and the suggestion that its distribution has been extended by ships is very probably accurate.

The only antarctic and subantarctic records for the species are those of Traustedt [1885] and Hartmeyer [1911]. Although shipping had passed through the Strait of Magellan prior to Traustedt's expedition, only Wilkes [1840] and the *Challenger* [1874] came into the general area of the *Gauss* station. It is unlikely that Hartmeyer's records can be accounted for by the possibility that those expeditions transported the species to Antarctica.

Hartmeyer described the here synonymized *C. antarctica* from 2 specimens taken in successive years (1902, 1903), one with a very damaged test and another in which the test is missing altogether. It is possible that this record represents specimens that were scraped from the hull of the *Gauss*, although antarctic Bryozoa were taken in the same hauls. If this is not the explanation of these two records of *C. intestinalis* from the Antarctic, it is rather remarkable that there have not been other records from south of Australia and from the Strait of Magellan.

Family CLAVELINIDAE Forbes and Hanley
Subfamily CLAVELININAE Seeliger

Except for the single small specimen described below, this subfamily is not represented in Antarctica, although numerous species have been taken from southern Australia, South Africa, and New Zealand [Kott, 1957; Millar, 1960; 1962; Michaelsen, 1924].

Stereoclavella antarctica Herdman, 1910, and *Oxycorinia mawsoni* Harant and Vernières, 1938, originally described in this subfamily, are probably synonyms of species in the Polyclinidae: *Tylobranchion speciosum* Herdman (Euherdmaniinae) and *Synoicium adareanum* (Herdman) (Polyclininae), respectively.

Genus *Podoclavella* Herdman, 1891

Type species: *Clavelina borealis* Savigny, 1816
Zooids separate, stomach smooth.

? *Podoclavella* sp.

New Records. South Orkney Is.: *Eltanin* Sta. 480 (2800 meters).

Description. A single, fingerlike, solitary zooid 12 mm long. The test is firm and transparent. Posterior rootlike processes with sand particles indicate attachment to the substrate. Apertures are sessile, anterior, and antero-dorsal. The zooid is blue in preservative. There appear to be 8 rows of stigmata, but the number in each row could not be determined because the branchial sac is strongly contracted. The stomach is smooth and rounded.

Remarks. This record represents the only species of the subfamily taken from the antarctic region. Unfortunately, the details of its morphology could not be determined because, despite the good condition of the test, the zooid itself was very contracted and quickly disintegrated. The color is typical of that often shown in preserved specimens of species of this family, e.g. *Clavelina claviformis* (Herdman) and *Podoclavella meridionalis* Herdman. It is possible that the present species has been overlooked in previous collecting, as it is quite inconspicuous and much smaller than other known species of *Podoclavella*.

Subfamily HOLOZOINAE Berrill

This group is well represented in the Antarctic by prolific *Sycozoa sigillinoides* and *Distaplia cylindrica*. A deep-sea representative of the subfamily, *Protoholozoa* new genus, is also included in the present collection. Only three less common species are confined to the antarctic region.

KEY TO GENERA OF HOLOZOINAE

1. Atrial aperture with a well developed anterior lip; 4 rows of stigmata 3
   Atrial aperture with a simple or modified siphon; not with 4 rows of stigmata 2
2. 3 rows of stigmata present . . . . *Atapozoa*
   Stigmata absent . . . . *Protoholozoa*, p. 35
3. Cloacal canals present 4
   No cloacal canals present . . . . *Cyathocormus*
4. Pedunculate colonies; zooids in double rows; extensive common cloacal cavity at apex of head . . . .
   . . . . *Sycozoa*, p. 26
   Pedunculate or sessile; zooids in double rows or circular systems; one or more cloacal apertures 5
5. Gonads project posterior to gut loop . *Hypsistozoa*, p. 32
   Gonads in gut loop . . . . *Distaplia*, p. 29

---

* These genera are reported from Antarctica.

Genus *Sycozoa* Lesson, 1830

Type species: *Sycozoa sigillinoides* Lesson, 1830

Zooids are in double rows radiating from a single terminal common cloacal opening. There are 4 rows of stigmata without parastigmatic vessels. This is a very uniform genus and distinctions between species are not very satisfactory.

Species of *Sycozoa* from adjacent areas are *S. anomala* Millar, 1960, from North Island, New Zealand, *S. murrayi* (Herdman) from southeastern Australia, *S. tenuicaulis* (Herdman) from southern Australia [Kott, 1957], and *S. cerebriformis* (Quoy and Gaimard) from South Australia and South Africa [Brewin, 1953; Kott, 1957; Millar, 1962]. Of these species *S. tenuicaulis* is clearly distinguished by the cone-shaped colony, by a reduced number of embryos, and by the larval form with precocious buds and shorter tail. *S. anomala*, *S. murrayi*, and *S. cerebriformis* have distinctive colonies but larvae similar to those of *S. sigillinoides* and *S. georgiana*. Thus, with the exception of *S. tenuicaulis*, the species of *Sycozoa* from the area adjacent to the Antarctic are closely related to the antarctic species. The genus is confined to the southern hemisphere.

KEY TO ANTARCTIC SPECIES OF *Sycozoa*

1. Colonies mushroom shaped............***gaimardi***, p. 28
   (Magellanic area)
   Colonies cylindrical 2
2. Maximum 3 to 4 zooids per row in mature colony.......
   ....***georgiana***, p. 28
   (circum-antarctic to South Georgia)
   More than 3 to 4 zooids per row in mature colonies.....
   ....***sigillinoides***, p. 26
   (circum-antarctic, Magellanic area, Kerguelen Is.
   to New Zealand and south Australia)

Sycozoa sigillinoides Lesson

Text figs. 2–5

Sycozoa sigillinoides Lesson, 1830, p. 436.—Hartmeyer, 1911, p. 534.—Michaelsen, 1924, p. 288; 1930, p. 505.—Salfi, 1925, p. 2.—Van Name, 1945, p. 151.—Ärnbäck, 1950, p. 29.—Brewin, 1953, p. 56.—Kott, 1954, p. 155; 1957, p. 99.—Millar, 1960, p. 71.
Aplidium pedunculatum Quoy and Gaimard, 1834 (1835), p. 626.—Cunningham, 1871a, p. 490.
Colella pedunculata; Herdman, 1886, p. 74.—Pfeffer, 1889, p. 4 (40); 1890, p. 499.—Sluiter, 1900, p. 5; 1906, p. 6.—Caullery, 1909, pp. 30, 39.
? *Colella quoyi* Herdman, 1886, p. 113.

Colella ramulosa Herdman, 1886, p. 120.—Michaelsen, 1907, p. 53.
Colella umbellata Michaelsen, 1898, p. 371.—Caullery, 1909, p. 53.
Colella sigillionoides; Michaelsen, 1907, p. 43.
Colella umbellata f. *typica* Michaelsen, 1907, p. 54.
Colella umbellata f. *kophameli* Michaelsen, 1907, p. 59.
Colella perrieri Caullery, 1909, p. 33.
Sycozoa perrieri; Hartmeyer, 1909–1911, p. 1439.
Sycozoa aff. *sigillinoides* Hartmeyer, 1911, p. 489.
Sycozoa (*Colella*) *sigillinoides*; Hartmeyer, 1912, p. 315.
Sycozoa (*Colella*) *umbellata*; Sluiter, 1919, p. 12.
? *Sycozoa quoyi*; Harant and Vernières, 1938, p. 6.—Kott, 1954, p. 157; 1957a, p. 1.

New Records. Falkland Islands–Burdwood Bank: *Eltanin* Sta. 339 (586 meters), Sta. 344 (119 meters). South Shetland Islands: *Eltanin* Sta. 997? (769 meters). Drake Passage: *Eltanin* Sta. 217 (110 meters). Tierra del Fuego: *Eltanin* Sta. 337 (92 meters), Sta. 981 (40–49 meters).

Previous Records.

Antarctic: Antarctic Peninsula, South Georgia [Pfeffer, 1889; Sluiter, 1906; Millar, 1960]; Enderby Land, Mac. Robertson Land, Wilhelm II Coast, Queen Mary Coast, Adélie Coast [Hartmeyer 1911; Kott, 1954].

Subantarctic: Kerguelen Is. [Herdman, 1886; Hartmeyer, 1912; Kott, 1954]; Heard I., Macquarie I. [Herdman, 1886; Kott, 1957a]; Chatham Is. [Sluiter, 1900]; Magellanic area, Falkland Is. [Lesson, 1830; Herdman, 1886; Sluiter, 1919; Michaelsen, 1907; Millar, 1960].

Elsewhere: Fremantle to Albany, Western Australia [Quoy and Gaimard, 1834; Michaelsen, 1930; Kott, 1957]; Victoria, Bass Strait, Tasmania [Quoy and Gaimard, 1834; Michaelsen, 1924; Kott, 1954, 1957]; New Zealand [Michaelsen, 1924]; Patagonian Shelf, South Atlantic Ocean [Michaelsen, 1907; Millar, 1960]; tropical Atlantic Ocean [Michaelsen, 1907]; tropical Pacific Ocean [Michaelsen, 1924].

Distribution. The distribution is completely circumpolar from the southern part of the Australian continent, New Zealand, and South America to the antarctic continent. The two records of tropical occurrence in the Atlantic and Pacific are of isolated heads in the plankton. No stalked sessile specimens have been taken farther north than Perth on the West Australian coast.

Depth range is from 18 to 548 meters. That the

deepest locations have been from Adélie Coast, Wilhelm II Coast, Queen Mary Coast, and Enderby Land [Kott, 1954; Hartmeyer, 1911] in the eastern Antarctic is not necessarily significant, since the species has also been taken at shallower stations in the same general areas.

Description. Colonies are stalked. The stalk varies greatly in length; it is usually hard and leathery, marked with annular ridges, becoming harder and narrower basally. In some specimens in the present collection the stalk appears to be jointed, but this is only apparent as there is no flexibility in the joints. Stalks may be branched or unbranched. Zooid-bearing heads, up to 2.5 cm long and 1.0 cm wide, are more or less cylindrical, tapered toward the base. When the terminal common cloacal opening is closed, the free end of the head is also tapered, but, when it is wide open, the central test core is exposed, forming a flat 'platform' in the opening. The free end of the head under these circumstances appears quite flat. Between the sides of the central test platform and the rim of the relaxed cloacal opening surrounding it there is free access to the exterior from the ring canal at the base of the platform. Brewin's [1953] interpretation of the independent opening of cloacal canals to the exterior has arisen from observations on specimens with cloacal opening extended to expose the ring canal. The test is soft and semitransparent, and zooids are clearly seen in double rows on either side of the common cloacal canals, extending along the length of the head and emptying into the ring canal around the free end of the central test core.

Zooids are typical of the genus. The branchial aperture is 6-lobed. The atrial aperture is a wide opening with an enlarged upper lip. Millar [1960] has observed that this lip is pointed and triangular in all zooids except the terminal ones in each row, where the cloacal canal opens into the terminal chamber; here the lip is wide and fringed with short teeth. There are 4 rows of stigmata with about 20 in each row. There are no parastigmatic vessels. The stomach tapers to the intestine and is smooth-walled. There is a narrow duodenal area and sometimes a midintestinal enlargement [Millar, 1960]. The structure of the gastric gland in the loop of the gut varies and the reservoir, cylindrical to spherical, may or may not be present. The zooids of any one colony are all of the one sex. Preserved mature male colonies are brownish-pink, because of the great development of testis follicles (up to 18) in the loop of the gut. Female colonies are greyish-yellow. A long curved brood pouch ex-

tends from the thorax and may contain up to 14 embryos not necessarily in a single row.

Larvae. Small with 3 triradiate papillae on broad stalks and an ectodermal cup surrounding the cone of adhesive cells. When not extended the papillae may be depressed back into the stalk, which forms a 'tirelike' expansion around the base of the sucker. There is a small spherical otolith. The tail is very long and winds around the larval body almost 1½ times. There are 4 rows of definitive stigmata.

Biology. The species has been taken from almost all types of substrate (sand, gravel, mud, and a mixture). Millar [1960] had collections from all months except August and September. His figures may indicate that sexual reproduction does not occur in July and that it is at its peak in March. Most headless stalks occur in his collections in May, June, and July and may indicate a disintegration of the old head after sexual reproduction. Headless stalks then re-form the head: Buds formed from probuds of the vascular stolon after distintegration of the parent zooid repopulate the new head. This process may continue over the winter period; however, regenerating heads were taken [Millar, 1960] in December, March, and May, and mostly in June and July, so that it is more likely a continuous process and this species does not show a very distinct seasonal reproductive pattern. The significance of free heads taken in plankton is not at present known [Millar, 1960].

Remarks. This species is closely related to *Sycozoa quoyi*, which Millar [1960] believes is a synonym. The fleshy short stalk, characteristic of *S. quoyi*, is also present in specimens from South Georgia in the *Discovery* collection. The larvae of these specimens are similar to, and fall within the length range of, larvae of *S. sigillinoides*. Records of larval length range from 0.40 to 0.76 mm for larvae of *S. sigillinoides* with the majority falling between 0.5 and 0.6 mm. Therefore, larvae of *S. sigillinoides*; Kott, 1954 are at the bottom of this range, and *S. quoyi*; Kott, 1954 are at the top of the range. Thus, the synonymy is probably justified, and a short fleshy stalk must also fall within the range of variation of *S. sigillinoides*. Ärnbäck [1950] believes *S. ramulosa* (Herdman) to be a distinct species. The distinction of the number of larvae in the brood pouch is, however, unsatisfactory [Millar, 1960; Kott, 1954; Van Name, 1945], and the species must be regarded as synonymous with *S. sigillinoides*.

Sycozoa georgiana (Michaelsen)

Text figs. 6, 7

Colella concreta; Pfeffer, 1889, p. 4 (40) [not Herdman, 1886].
Colella georgiana Michaelsen, 1907, p. 62.
Sycozoa georgiana profusa Sluiter, 1932, p. 3.
Sycozoa georgiana; Van Name, 1945, p. 154.—Millar, 1960, p. 74.

New Records. Davis Sea: *Burton Island* Sta. 5 (80 meters). Ross Sea: *Edisto* Sta. 5 (400 meters). Weddell Sea; *Staten Island* Sta. 53/63 (55 meters). South Shetland Is.: *Staten Island* Sta. 62/63 (57 meters). Bellingshausen Sea: *Edisto* Sta. 146[1] (56 meters), Sta. 148[1] (56 meters), Sta. 152[1] (56 meters), Sta. 162[1] (56 meters).

Previous Records.

Antarctic: South Georgia [Michaelsen, 1907; Pfeffer, 1889; Sluiter, 1932; Millar, 1960]; South Sandwich Is. [Millar, 1960].

Distribution. The species is known from 55 to 400 meters around the antarctic continent, extending north to South Georgia. Previously the distribution of this species was thought to be confined to the South Georgia–South Sandwich Is. (Weddell quadrant) area. However, new records from the Davis Sea and Victoria quadrant indicate a circumpolar distribution in the Antarctic. The species has not been taken in the Subantarctic.

Description. Stalked colonies; test of the stalk and head semitransparent, although stalk has thin but tough outer cuticle. The head, without the cuticle, is very soft. Maximum length of stalk 4.7 cm; of head 0.7 cm. Many stalked heads may branch from a common basal stalk. The usual common cloacal system with longitudinal canals and terminal common cloaca present, but only 2 or 3 zooids per row. The colonial organization is identical with that of *S. sigillinoides,* and colonies differ from those of *S. sigillinoides* only in the limited number of zooids per row and the corresponding small size of the colony.

Zooids are indistinguishable from those of *S. sigillinoides.* There are 4 rows of stigmata without parastigmatic vessels and from 10 to 20 stigmata in each half row. A long esophagus, a spherical smooth stomach, and a midintestinal enlargement are present. Gonads are present in loop of gut. Colonies are unisexual. Brood pouches are present with 1 or 2 larvae, although Millar [1960] found 10 to 28 in each brood pouch.

_____
[1] U.S. Navy Antarctic Expedition, 1947–1948.

Larvae. Similar to those of *S. sigillinoides* with otolith but no ocellus. The gut forms quite a long loop behind the branchial sac. The tail is long but no longer than in *S. sigillinoides.*

Biology. Specimens collected from the Davis Sea in January have brood pouches and 1 or 2 larvae. Specimens from South Shetland Islands and Robertson Bay collected in February are actively budding with separated vascular stolon and developing probuds. Specimens from the Antarctic Peninsula are immature colonies and headless stalks. This information does not negate the suspected pattern in *S. sigillinoides* in which embryos are liberated from a disintegrating head. The stalk then re-forms a new head from probuds in the stalk. The colony then proceeds to reproduce vegetatively until sexual maturity leads to sexual reproduction. The present colonies, which are in all stages of the life cycle and which were all collected in the antarctic summer, do not add any evidence for a seasonal reproductive pattern.

Remarks. Although this species can be separated from *S. sigillinoides* only by the size of the colony and texture and length of the stalk, these characters appear to be constant. Sexual maturity in the species is reached in colonies with a very small number of zooids, whereas in *S. sigillinoides,* although the stalk is variable, the mature zooid-bearing head has long double rows of zooids.

Sycozoa gaimardi (Herdman)

Text fig. 8

Colella gaimardi Herdman, 1886, p. 103.—Michaelsen, 1907, p. 49.—Caullery, 1909, p. 35, 38.
Sycozoa gaimardi; Hartmeyer, 1909–1911, p. 1438; 1911, p. 488, 499.—Van Name, 1945, p. 150.
Colella racovitzai Van Beneden and Selys Longchamps, 1913, p. 50.

New Records. None.

Previous Records.
Antarctic: None.
Subantarctic: Falkland Is. [Herdman, 1886]; Tierra del Fuego, Strait of Magellan [Michaelsen, 1907; Van Beneden and Selys Longchamps, 1913].

Distribution. The known distribution of this species is limited to a small region of the subantarctic region, where it is found growing on the giant kelp, *Macrocystis,* or on red algae from the shore down to 20 meters.

Description. Colonies are small, slender-stemmed mushrooms with dome-shaped head convex above, flattened below, usually not more than 12 mm in diameter but may extend up to 20 mm. Stalk thickest, up to 3 mm in diameter, where it joins head; usually 25 mm long but may extend up to 40 mm. The test is transparent. Double row arrangement of zooids obscured by their numbers. Single terminal common cloaca present. Zooids are about 3 mm long; often with a dark pigment spot over the dorsal ganglion. Branchial tentacles number 16, larger and smaller ones alternating. There are 20 or 21 stigmata present in each of 4 rows. The stomach is pear-shaped, smooth-walled. Colonies unisexual. The broodpouch sausage-shaped with up to 30 to 40 embryos. In the proximal part of the brood pouch the embryos arranged in double or single rows.

Larvae. Not known.

Biology. Van Beneden and Selys Longchamps [1913] studied the budding of this species from specimens collected in the Magellanic area.

Remarks. The species is distinguished from other species by the shape of the colony.

Genus *Distaplia* Della Valle, 1881, nomen conservandum

Type species: *Distaplia magnilarva* Della Valle, 1881
Zooids in systems; one or more common cloacal openings. Atrial opening with modified anterior lip. Four rows of stigmata with parastigmatic vessels. Embryos in brood pouch in a single series. Colony may be stalked. Gonads present in gut loop.

The genus is represented in the Antarctic by the prolific and conspicuous *Distaplia cylindrica* and by the less common *D. colligans.*

KEY TO ANTARCTIC SPECIES OF *Distaplia*

Colony sessile, cushion-like...............*colligans,* p. 32
(Ross Sea, Knox Coast, Antarctic Peninsula to South Georgia)
Colony stalked, cylindrical, very long......*cylindrica,* p. 29
(circum-antarctic, Magellanic area)

Distaplia cylindrica (Lesson)

Text figs. 9–12, Plate I

Holozoa cylindrica Lesson, 1830, p. 439.—Hartmeyer, 1911, p. 474.—Herdman, 1912, p. 315; 1915, p. 97. —Sluiter, 1914, p. 28.—Van Name, 1945, p. 143.— Kott, 1954, p. 158 [part].—Ärnbäck, 1950, p. 33.
Julinia australis Calman, 1894, p. 14.
Distaplia ignota Herdman, 1902, p. 197.
Julinia ignota Sluiter, 1906, p. 8.—Michaelsen, 1907, p. 40.
Distaplia cylindrica; Millar, 1960, p. 79.

? *Sigillina* (*Hyperiodistoma*) *caerulea;* Harant and Vernières, 1938, p. 8.

New Records. Ross Sea: *Edisto* Sta. ?, Deep Freeze I (depth?); Sta. 5 (400 meters); *Atka* Sta. 21 (390 meters); *Staten Island* Ocean Sta. 10–1 (439 meters). Adélie Coast?[2] Knox Coast, Vincennes Bay: *Glacier* Sta. ?, Deep Freeze II (on ship's anchor, depth ?); *Atka* Sta. 29 (135 meters). Davis Sea: *Burton Island* Sta. 5 (80 meters). Weddell Sea: *Staten Island* Sta. 1 (284 meters), Sta. 24 (300 meters), Sta. 53/63 (55 meters). Wilkes Station: A.N.A.R.E. (Planktonic ?). South Orkney Is.: *Eltanin* Sta. 1082 (298–302 meters). South Shetland Is.: *Staten Island* Sta. 44/63 (55 meters), Sta. 62/63 (57 meters). *Eltanin* Sta. 434 (77 meters), Sta. 435 (73 meters), Sta. 436 (73 meters). Drake Passage: *Eltanin* Sta. 217 (110 meters).

Previous Records.

Antarctic: South Georgia [Michaelsen, 1907; Millar, 1960]; Antarctic Peninsula, South Shetland Is., Palmer Archipelago [Sluiter, 1906; Ärnbäck, 1950; Millar, 1960]; South Sandwich Is. [Millar, 1960]; Erebus and Terror Gulf [Calman, 1894]; Mac. Robertson Land [Kott, 1954]; Wilhelm II Coast [Hartmeyer, 1911]; Cape Adare [Herdman, 1902].

Subantarctic: Strait of Magellan, Tierra del Fuego, Patagonian Shelf [Lesson, 1830; Herdman, 1886; Michaelsen, 1907; Van Beneden and Selys Longchamps, 1913; Millar, 1960].

Distribution. This species is found in both the eastern and the western Antarctic. It has therefore a completely circumpolar distribution, extending into the subantarctic area and along the Patagonian Shelf in the Magellanic area. Depth range is from 25 to 439 meters.

Description. Stalked with cylindrical or tapering head up to 700 cm long [Sluiter, 1914; Ärnbäck, 1950; Millar, 1960] and up to 8 cm in diameter at the widest end, near the stalk. Stalk of a colony 8 cm in diameter at its widest is 6 cm in diameter and 6 to 7 cm long [Ärnbäck, 1950]. Youngest colonies are usually of simple clavate form. Preserved specimens are milky-white to yellowish-white. Youngest specimens have a

---

[2] Colonel Ernest F. Dukes, Jr., USAF, aboard the USCGC *Eastwind* in February 1967, reports (in conversation) that shortly after leaving the Dumont d'Urville antarctic station early in the month the ship passed some hundreds of what were apparently these rope-like colonial ascidians, *Distaplia cylindrica,* floating on the surface of the sea.

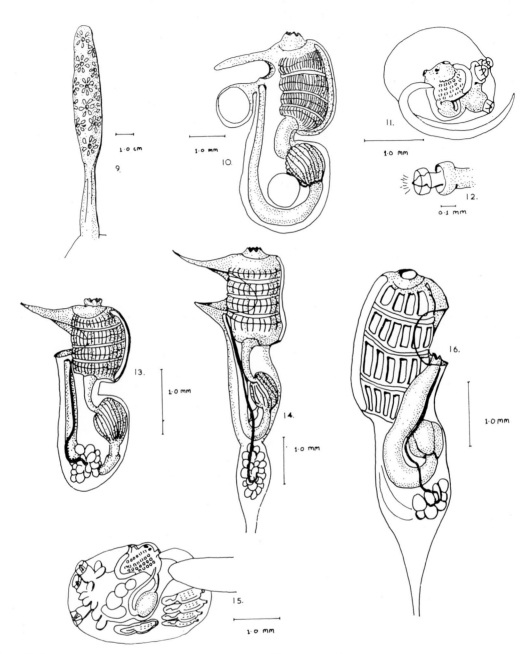

Distaplia cylindrica
9. Young colony [after Hartmeyer, 1911].
10. Zooid (♀).
11. Larva.
12. Larval papillary stalk with adhesive cells activated.

Distaplia colligans
13. Zooid [after Millar, 1960].

Hypsistozoa fasmeriana
14. Zooid [after Millar, 1960].
15. Larva [after Brewin, 1959].

Hypsistozoa obscura new species
16. Zooid.

single terminal cloacal opening, but later zooids are arranged in oval-circular systems all around the head; 6 to 12 zooids around central cloacal openings. As the colony develops these systems may develop into double rows of zooids, but often the crowding of zooids obscures the arrangement of systems. Hartmeyer [1911] had a series of young colonies and those with 5 to 9 zooids formed a single system around a terminal cloacal opening. One specimen with about 50 zooids (head 9 mm long) had a system similar to *Sycozoa* sp. in which the zooids were arranged in double rows from a terminal common cloaca. In specimens that have a head length of 2.4 cm or more, however, the zooids are arranged in circular systems all over the head. In the present collection: one colony from Vincennes Bay, Knox Coast (Deep Freeze II, *Glacier* Sta. ?) has 16 zooids arranged in two concentric circles around the upper surface of the colony; from Robertson Bay (*Edisto* Deep Freeze I) a specimen with numerous lobes 2 cm tall, from a common base, with 5 or 6 zooids per lobe around terminal cloacal opening.

The test is very soft throughout, and the numerous well developed stolonic vessels extending through the central test material and into the stalk are quite characteristic of the species and help to distinguish it when the colony is atypical.

Zooids are up to 5 mm long. The branchial aperture is 6-lobed. The atrial aperture has a long upper lip. There are 12 tentacles, large and small alternating. About 10 longitudinal thoracic muscles. A maximum of 30 stigmata are arranged in 4 rows with parastigmatic vessels across each row. Very young zooids do not always have parastigmatic vessels. The gut loop is simple; the stomach is large, with 18 to 20 fine longitudinal striations or folds internally. Gonads present in the gut loop and only male or female gonads are mature at one time in one colony. The zooids are, however, hermaphrodite, and in immature zooids the group of ova may be seen in the center of the rosette of male lobes. The testis follicles proliferate enormously, and a mature testis has a mulberry-like rather than rosette appearance. There is often an incipient brood pouch at the postero-dorsal corner of the thorax. There is a distinct gastric gland duct but no reservoir has been observed. From 1 to 3 embryos develop in the brood pouch.

Larvae. Nearly 2 mm long and almost as deep. Three triradiate papillae with ectodermal cups and broad stalks from a frontal plate are present anteriorly. When the central cone of cells secretes adhesive, the stalk immediately behind the ectodermal cup is narrowed and appears to rise out of the basal, still wider part of the stalk. There are 4 rows of definitive stigmata, an ocellus, and an otolith.

Biology. Millar [1960] suggests a summer breeding period and larval settlement in April. The present collection also has large specimens, in both male and female phase, with mature gonads taken in January from the South Shetland Islands. Fully developed larvae in a specimen from the Weddell Sea in January indicate, however, that the breeding season may not be as restricted as Millar suggests. Similarly, mature testes in a large specimen (20 cm) from Tierra del Fuego in September indicate that gonads may be maturing over the winter months. As Millar [1960] has observed, there is gradual maturation of zooids along the length of the colony.

This species demonstrates the most prolific process of budding yet observed in Ascidiacea. The process, particularly well developed in Holozoinae [Berrill, 1948], is implemented by the stolonic vessels that are so characteristic of *D. cylindrica*. The vegetative reproduction of holozoinid zooids does not necessarily produce zooids with definitive gonads. After repeated generations sufficient gonadial tissue is accumulated to enable sexual maturation. However, testes may be developed first, resulting in colonies in the male phase. Later generations of zooids have both male and female gonads. Testes mature first [Ärnbäck, 1950] and, once emptied of their contents, form a flat sheet protecting the eggs on the mesial side of the colony, which proceeds to maturity as a colony in the female phase. Millar [1960] has described female colonies in which zooids become moribund once the eggs have passed into the brood pouches. It is likely that embryos are liberated from the test, but the length of colonies is such that it is hard to imagine the dissolution of a great part of the test at any stage in the life of the colony. Probably the test from which embryos are liberated is repopulated by zooids from vegetative reproduction in the remnant stolonial stalks or from other zooids in the colony.

Remarks. Ärnbäck [1950] has established f. *glebulenta* for specimens of this species without a stalk of flattened 'lump-like' colonial form from the Antarctic Peninsula. It is possible that these specimens, together with similar colonies from Cape Adare [Herdman, 1902], represent colonies of *Distaplia colligans*.

Sigillina (*Hyperiodistoma*) *caerulea;* Harant and Vernières, 1938, from Queen Mary Coast (201 meters) is described as 'une colonie comparable à la figure donnée par Herdman pour son *Colella caerulea*'

(Herdman, 1899 pl. Pcl. IV, fig. 1). It seems unlikely that this specimen could be identical with Herdman's species [< *Eudistoma cyanea;* Kott, 1957] from Indonesia and north Australia. However, the colony figured by Herdman resembles a juvenile of *Distaplia cylindrica,* and *Sigillina caerulea;* Harant and Vernières is recorded here as a doubtful synonym of *D. cylindrica.*

Distaplia colligans Sluiter

Text fig. 13

Distaplia colligans Sluiter, 1932, p. 7.—Van Name, 1945, p. 149.—Millar, 1960, p. 77.

Distaplia cylindrica Kott, 1954, p. 158 [part].

? *Distaplia cylindrica* Ärnbäck, 1950, p. 36 (f. *glebulenta*).

? *Distaplia ignota* Herdman, 1902, p. 197 [part].

New Records. Knox Coast: *Edisto* sta. 115³ (184 meters). Ross Sea: *Glacier* Sta. BL–16 (142 meters); *Northwind* Sta. 8 (135 meters).

Previous Records.

Antarctic: ? Antarctic Peninsula [Ärnbäck 1950]; South Georgia [Sluiter, 1932; Millar, 1960]; South Orkney Is. [Millar, 1960]; Bransfield Strait [Millar, 1960]; Mac. Robertson Land [Kott, 1954]; ? Cape Adare [Herdman, 1902].

Distribution. The rare records of this species previously were confined to the Antarctic, in the Weddell quadrant. The present records confirm Millar's [1960] suggestion that the distribution in the Antarctic may be wider than is now known. Depth ranges from 22 to 275 meters.

Description. Color in preservative dull purple-brown. Colonies low, flattened, or pillow-shaped, not subdivided or lobed, up to 3 cm long, 1.5 cm thick, and fixed by whole basal surface. Zooids arranged in circular, oval, or longitudinal systems around large cloacal openings. Zooids are perpendicular to the surface and closely packed and the systems are not always apparent. Test soft, pliable, semitransparent. The thorax and abdomen of zooids in the upper half and the lower half of the test is occupied by the posterior abdominal stolons, which are folded and curved into the basal layer. Pale cells, especially in surface layer, give cloudy appearance to whole colony. Zooids up to 8 mm long. Oral siphon short, with 6 more or less distinct lobes. Atrial opening

with triangular upper lip. Strong thoracic muscles. Tentacles 12 or more. Branchial sac with 4 rows of up to 20 rectangular stigmata each crossed by a parastigmatic vessel, and sometimes very delicate accessory or secondary parastigmatic vessels cross the stigmatic between the transverse vessels and parastigmatic vessels. Esophagus narrow; stomach smooth or with fine oblique ridges externally. Gonads on right of gut loop. Mature testis with about 12 lobes. Ovaries and testes often present together although not mature at the same time, sometimes gonads of only one sex are present. Incipient brood pouch from postero-dorsal corner of thorax.

Remarks. The color of the colonies and at times the arrangement of zooids in double rows resemble *Hypsistozoa fasmeriana* (below). However, there is no sign of gonads shifting posterior to the gut and the low cushion-like colonies are characteristic. Where stomach ridges are present, they are external, unlike *H. fasmeriana.*

Genus Hypsistozoa Brewin, 1953

Type species: *Distaplia fasmeriana* Michaelsen, 1924

Zooids form systems; one or more cloacal openings present; atrial opening modified with anterior lip. Four rows of stigmata; with or without parastigmatic vessels. Gonads extend into posterior abdominal vascular appendage.

The type species of this genus, closely related to *Distaplia,* has been recorded mainly from New Zealand. However, records from Heard Island and the Kerguelen Islands indicate it extends into the eastern Subantarctic. A new species from 6000 meters in the Peru-Chile Trench is described.

KEY TO ANTARCTIC SPECIES OF **Hypsistozoa**

Parastigmatic vessels present............*fasmeriana,* p. 32
                     (Kerguelen Is., Heard I. to New Zealand)
No parastigmatic vessels present............*obscura,* p. 33
                                          (Peru-Chile Trench)

Hypsistozoa fasmeriana (Michaelsen),
nomen conservandum

Text figs. 14, 15

Colella concreta Herdman, 1886, p. 123.

Distaplia fasmeriana Michaelsen, 1924, p. 297.—Brewin, 1946, p. 103; 1950a, p. 344.—Kott, 1954, p. 158.

Hypsistozoa fasmeriana; Brewin, 1953, p. 56; 1956b, p. 435; 1959, p. 575.—Millar, 1960, p. 80.

New Records. None.

---

³ U.S. Navy Antarctic Expedition, 1947–1948.

Previous Records.

Subantarctic: Kerguelen Islands [Herdman, 1886]; Heard Island [Kott, 1954].

Elsewhere: South and North Islands of New Zealand [Brewin, 1946; Millar, 1960]; South Island of New Zealand and Stewart Island [Michaelsen, 1924].

Distribution. Occurs in masses on rocks near the intertidal area, down to 84 meters. This species is common around the North and South Islands of New Zealand and has been taken only twice out of this area.

Description. Colony with or without a stalk. Head about 1.3 cm long, 1.1 cm wide. The color is yellowish- or grayish-brown to purple. More or less cylindrical, rounded anteriorly, tapering posteriorly to the stalk. Stalk up to 1.6 cm long, 0.7 cm wide; dull, pale orange or brown. Usually head and stalk smooth without encrustation of sand.

The test is semitransparent, containing pigment cells. Zooids arranged in double rows, forming branching or long narrow elliptical systems with common cloacal apertures scattered on the surface, mostly near the distal end of the colony. Zooids up to 2 mm long, excluding the vascular appendage. The branchial aperture is 6-lobed. The atrial aperture has a wide upper lip, which may be pointed or broken up into numerous lobes. Widely separated longitudinal muscle bands present on the thorax and transverse bands between the rows of stigmata. Sixteen branchial tentacles present, of three orders, regularly arranged. There are 4 rows of 10 to 12 stigmata each crossed by a parastigmatic vessel. The stomach is large, with 15 to 20 fine longitudinal folds internally. A spherical gastric gland vesicle present in the loop of the gut. Gonads posterior to gut loop extending into proximal distended part of long vascular appendage.

Stalked brood pouch present from postero-dorsal corner of thorax contains single developing embryo.

Larvae. 3.0 mm long. Three anterior papillae, with ectodermal suckers, arranged in a triangle. The mature larva with ectodermal ampullae from the base of broad papillary stalks. Prolific larval budding from a stolon extending from the esophageal region. Both otolith and ocellus are present.

Biology. Brewin [1956a] discusses the life cycle of this interesting species. In specimens from South Island, New Zealand, testes are discernible from early May until July. Single ovum reaches maturity in May.

Remarks. Herdman's record for his species (under the name of *Colella concreta*) from the Kerguelen Islands and Kott's record (under the name of *Distaplia jasmeriana*) from Heard Island represent rather isolated occurrences in view of the numerous records from New Zealand waters. Herdman's specimens resemble *H. jasmeriana* in colony form, parastigmatic vessels, and gonads in proximal part of vascular extension. The stomach of Herdman's specimens is also finely pleated, although Herdman counted 20 to 40 of these stomach plications. The higher number may be associated with larger zooids or may be due to some artefact. The species are probably synonymous. Millar [1960] points out the great temperature range tolerated in a species distributed over the whole extent of New Zealand. It is possible therefore that the distribution may be wider than at present indicated, and further collections may indicate a continuous distribution from New Zealand to the Kerguelen Islands and Heard Island.

Hypsistozoa obscura new species

Text fig. 16

Type Locality. Peru-Chile Trench, *Eltanin* Sta. 37 (6006 meters). Holotype, colony, USNM 11975.

Description. Colony conical, 2 cm high and 2 cm in diameter across the base, which is expanded into a basal plate by which the colony is fixed to the substrate. Zooid-bearing outer layer of test is separated from inner test core by extensive, although shallow, cloacal spaces. Common cloacal openings are not apparent, but this may be due to the damaged condition of the surface of the colony. It seems most likely from the shape of the colony that there is a single terminal cloacal opening. The test is rather soft, gelatinous, and semitransparent. Zooids are numerous in the surface layer of test and are not arranged in any obvious systems. The central test core is more dense than the outer layer and has what appears to be feces balls embedded. Zooids are 5 mm long; the thorax is twice the length of the abdomen. The oral siphon is smooth rimmed. The atrial opening is wide with a broad anterior lip. Thorax is very delicate; body wall is transparent and thin; no muscles were detected. Dorsal languets are biramous. There are 4 rows of 5 or 6 delicate rectangular stigmata. There are no parastigmatic vessels. The gut loop is twisted so that the esophagus crosses the stomach, which is spherical with 4 not very distinct folds. The esophagus is short and the rectum broad, extending halfway up the branchial sac to

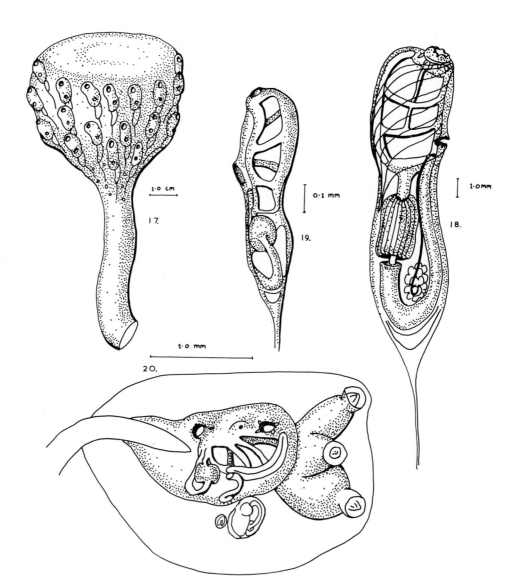

Protoholozoa pedunculata new species

17. Colony.
18. Zooid.
19. Definitive zooid associated with adult vascular stolon.
20. Larva with stolon, single bud, and probud.

open at the base of the atrial opening. The gonads are behind the gut loop, in the proximal part of the vascular appendage, thus forming a posterior abdomen. This is not constricted off from the abdomen proper and varies from 'tear drop' shape to more elongate. There are up to 10 testis follicles arranged in a rosette with a few small ova in the center. The vas deferens curves up past the loop of the gut on the left; however, if the twisted gut were straightened, the vas deferens would pass the gut on the right, as is usual.

The heart is a curved tube in the postero-ventral part of the abdomen. Two embryos, in separate brood pouches, were found in the test.

The structure of the zooid was determined from two undamaged zooids that had remained in the test; the other zooids were very torn.

Larvae. Unfortunately they are not in good condition and little can be made of their structure. They are 1.15 mm long, have 3 anterior papillae, with ectodermal cups, and have a single minute pigmented sense organ.

Biology. The presence of mature testis lobes and embryos in the one colony indicate a true hermaphrodite condition and not a situation, as in *D. cylindrica*, in which gonads of only one sex mature in the one colony at any one time. The specimen was collected in July, so that a summer breeding season is not likely. As the species is abyssal, it is probable that sexual reproduction is not seasonal.

Remarks. Distaplia galatheae Millar, 1959, from 4410 meters in the Kermadec Trench has a similar colony from a broad base with a test of similar consistency and apparently identical larvae. However, the atrial siphon is present as a tubular or conical projection and there are other distinctions in the gonads, gut, and branchial sac.

There are several characters of *Hypsistozoa obscura* that are unusual in the genus: stomach folds, the twisted gut, and the lack of parastigmatic vessels. The condition of the posterior abdomen, position of heart and gonads, and the number of rows of stigmata indicate a close relationship with *H. fasmeriana* (Michaelsen). Unlike species of Polyclinidae, in which the gonads are also posterior to the gut, the heart of the present species is curved, is ventral to the intestine, and is not V-shaped at the end of the posterior abdomen.

Genus *Protoholozoa* new genus

Type species: *Protoholozoa pedunculata* new species

Both apertures open separately to the exterior. Atrial siphon modified. Branchial sac reduced to 2 transverse vessels. Stigmata absent. Gonads in loop of gut. Embryos develop in brood pouch. Precocious budding in embryo from epicardial stolon.

The genus is monotypic and abyssal, and is recorded from a limited area.

Protoholozoa pedunculata new species

Text figs. 17–20

Type Locality. Drake Passage, south of Tierra del Fuego: *Eltanin* Sta. 451 (4026 meters). Holotype, colony, USNM 11976.

Additional Records. Antarctic Peninsula: *Eltanin* Sta. 268 (2818 meters), 1 colony. Drake Passage: *Eltanin* Sta. 317 (3790 meters), 1 colony. Scotia Sea: *Eltanin* Sta. 690 (3446 meters), 1 colony. Southeast Pacific Basin: *Eltanin* Sta. 1154 (4709 meters), 1 colony.

Distribution. This species occurs in the southeastern limits of the Southeast Pacific Basin, through the Drake Passage to the edge of the Scotia Ridge joining the Antarctic Peninsula with South America. Depth ranges from 2818 to 5000 meters.

Description. Colony from station 451 is in the best condition and was selected as the type specimen.

Stalked colonies. The fleshy stalk 3 to 15 cm long, about 3 cm in diameter toward the base where it is widest. Head an inverted cone with the narrowest part joining the stalk. The free end of the head is concave. Head 3 to 6 cm in diameter and may be slightly longer or shorter than its diameter. The stalk length in relation to the body is variable: colony from station 317 has stalk and head of equal length and the stalk is attached to a rock. However, in a specimen from station 451 the stalk, 15 cm long, is cut and there is no indication of its total length. The test is soft, but firm, gelatinous, and completely transparent. Zooids are arranged more or less in single rows down the sides of the colony, in the surface test; both siphons are widely spaced and open separately to the exterior. Above each zooid there is a small thickening of surface test. The zooid-bearing surface test extends anteriorly beyond the central test core to form the concavity at the free end of the head. Zooids are large, about 2.00

cm long, excluding vascular stolon; the abdomen is twice the length of the thorax. The branchial opening is faintly 6-lobed; the atrial opening on the posterior third of the dorsal surface has a broad muscular upper lip and 6 deeply cleft lobes on the lower border. Siphons open to the surface with the atrial opening uppermost. Consequently, thoraces are inclined more or less at right angles to the surface with the 6 deeply cleft lobes on the lower border of the atrial opening well produced to insert into the test on the upper border of the external aperture. The abdomen of each zooid is curved obliquely downward from the angle of the thoraces. About 20 oblique muscle bands extend from the branchial opening and the dorsal surface across the sides of the thorax and join into a muscle band to the left of the ventral border along the abdomen, fading out on the vascular stolon. In specimens with thorax relaxed these muscles appear to extend transversly around the thorax. They are continuous over the dorsum but not ventrally. There are fine circular muscles around both apertures. Dorsal tubercle a simple transverse slit just anterior to the well developed prepharyngeal band. There are 6 long tentacles. In the branchial sac 2 transverse vessels extend into a broad-based triangular tongue, where they cross the dorsal membrane. There are no stigmata, but a fine connective on each side extends from the anterior border of the branchial area and joins the two transverse vessels but does not extend to the posterior border of the branchial chamber. The transverse bars are held in place by a fine membrane from the body wall. The gut loop is simple or twisted, probably depending on the state of contraction of the zooid. The stomach is large, more or less cylindrical, narrowing abruptly into a short narrow duodenal area. In the colony from station 268 the abdomen and the stomach appear contracted and the base of the stomach and duodenal area seem to be drawn up behind the stomach, in continuity with it. Stomach has 17 to 20 longitudinal folds. Gonads present in loop of gut: a cluster of about 10 testis follicles and central ovary. Oviduct and vas deferens run together up the inner side of the rectum to the base of the atrial aperture. A gastric gland may have a cylindrical trunk or spherical reservoir. Specimen from station 268 with single embryos present in free brood pouches in the test. There are few zooids in this colony, possibly because of disintegration following sexual reproduction. The colony is very damaged, however, and zooids may have been lost during handling. Heart a V-shaped tube in the base of the abdomen. Vascular stolons well developed with buds present in the region of the stolon, as in *Sycozoa* spp.

Larvae. Very large, 2.99 mm, with 3 triradiate papillae with ectodermal cups. The papillae are carried on rounded stalks like those of *Sycozoa.* Otolith present but no ocellus. There is a stolon from the esophageal region and a blastozooid and probud present in the larval test.

Biology. Embryos present in October. Buds and well developed vascular stolons present in November. Colony collected in May without zooids, buds, or embryos perhaps because of damage. There is no indication of seasonal reproductive pattern in this abyssal species.

Remarks. So many individuals of this species have been taken by the *Eltanin* from this area that it is surprising that it has not been taken before, unless its distribution is limited.

In the present species the mechanism of budding, larval budding, form of the larva, embryos liberated from the test, and the reduced number of transverse vessels indicate the family relationship with Holozoinae. Separate openings to the exterior and absence of a cloacal system suggest that this relationship is fairly primitive, as in *Atapozoa* Brewin, 1956 [*Atopozoa* Kott, 1967, and chapter 8, Phylogeny].

The species bears a superficial resemblance to *Cyathocormus* Oka, 1913. However, *C. mirabilis* has 4 rows of stigmata and a central common cloacal cavity.

Family POLYCITORIDAE Michaelsen

The family does not flourish in Antarctica; consequently, records are rare.

KEY TO GENERA OF POLYCITORIDAE

1. Zooids free or semi-embedded............................ 9
   Zooids completely embedded........................... 2
2. 3 rows of stigmata............................**Sigillina**–3
   4 or more rows of stigmata........................... 6
3. No posterior abdominal extension..................... 4
   Posterior abdominal epicardial extension............. 5
4. With smooth stomach.............Subgenus **Eudistoma**
   Stomach with 4 folds......*Subgenus **Paessleria**, p. 39
5. With smooth stomach.*Subgenus **Hyperiodistoma**, p. 40
   Stomach with 4 folds...........Subgenus **Sigillina**
6. With 4 rows of stigmata.............................. 7
   With more than 4 rows of stigmata................... 8
7. With spicules...................*Cystodytes*, p. 37
   Without spicules...........................**Tetrazona**
8. With spicules.........................**Polycitorella**
   Without spicules ....*Polycitor*, p. 37

9. With 6-lobed apertures....................*Archidistoma*
   With smooth rimmed apertures..........*Pycnoclavella*

---

* Reported from Antarctica.

Genus *Cystodytes* von Drasche, 1883

Type species: *Distoma dellechiajei* Della Valle, 1877

Four rows of stigmata; disk-shaped calcareous spicules overlap to form capsules enclosing the abdomen.

A single species of very limited distribution has been recorded from the Antarctic.

Cystodytes antarcticus Sluiter

Text fig. 21

Cystodites antarcticus Sluiter, 1912, p. 460; 1914, p. 27.—Ärnbäck, 1950, p. 26.
Cystodytes antarcticus; Van Name, 1945, p. 134.
Cystodytes dellechiajei f. *antarctica*; Millar, 1960, p. 82.

New Records. South Shetland Is.: *Staten Island* Sta. 62/63 (57 meters). Antarctic Peninsula: *Edisto* Sta. 232[4] (74 meters); *Staten Island* Sta. 66/63 (62 meters).

Previous Records.

Antarctic: Antarctic Peninsula, South Shetland Is. [Sluiter, 1912; Ärnbäck, 1950; Millar, 1960].

Distribution. Is very limited in the Antarctic Peninsula area; has been taken in from 57 to a maximum depth of 335 meters.

Description. Investing colonies, flattened, egg-shaped, disk-like, or irregular investing twigs. Up to a maximum of 6 cm in length, 1.5 cm thick. Test firm, semitransparent. Abdomina of zooids enclosed in capsule of disk-like calcareous spicules, maximum 0.3 mm diameter, with crenelated edges. Zooids in surface layer of test visible from surface. Maximum length of zooids 6 mm. Body divided into thorax and abdomen. Branchial and atrial siphon 6-lobed. Atrial siphon is especially long.

Long slender muscle bands on thorax and fine circular muscles present in a more or less continuous coat around thorax and siphons. Dorsal tubercle a ring-shaped slit. Dorsal lamina with long languets. Four rows of numerous stigmata. Esophagus long, stomach oval, smooth. Intestine with duodenal area separated from rectum by a constriction. Gonads present in loop

---

[4] U.S. Navy Antarctic Expedition, 1947–1948.

of gut: a rosette of 2 to 13 testis follicles and a large ovum may be present.

Biology. The species occurs on substrates of mud and small stones or gravel. Colonies have been collected in the summer, but no larvae have yet been taken.

Remarks. The closely related *Cystodytes dellechiajei* Della Valle (> *C. aucklandicus* Nott, 1892; *C. perspicuus* Nott, 1892) is widely distributed in the warmer waters but has also been recorded from as far south as New Zealand: Auckland [Nott, 1892; Brewin, 1948; 1951], Cook Strait region [Michaelsen, 1924; Brewin, 1960], Otago, South Island [Brewin, 1952], and Stewart Island [Brewin, 1958]; and from Tasmania: Maria Island [Kott, 1954]. All these specimens have the typical spicules of this species. In *C. antarcticus*, however, the spicules are deeply, although irregularly, indented around the border. The constancy of this character, together with the limited distribution of the *C. antarcticus*, suggests that specific rank is valid.

Genus *Polycitor* Reiner, 1804

Type species: *Polycitor crystallinus* Renier, 1804

More than 3 rows of stigmata; no spicules in the test.

The genus is rare in the Antarctic and Subantarctic and is represented by only a single record of one species of problematical affinities.

Polycitor glareosus (Sluiter)

Distoma glareosa Sluiter, 1906, p. 6.—Michaelsen, 1915, p. 467.
Tetrazona glareosa; Michaelsen, 1930, p. 481.
Polycitor glareosus; Van Name, 1945, p. 132.

New Records. None.

Previous Records.

Antarctic: Antarctic Peninsula, 30 meters [Sluiter, 1906]. Two small colonies constitute the sole record of this species.

Description. Small spherical colonies, 18 mm in diameter. Surface smooth, pale grey. Test gelatinous but firm, with bladder cells and siliceous bars often arranged in the form of 'asterisks.' Zooids visible as pale yellow spots. Both apertures 6-lobed, short, opening to the surface. Zooids short, about 2 mm long. The musculature is strong. There are 12 equal-sized tentacles. Four rows of stigmata present. The stomach

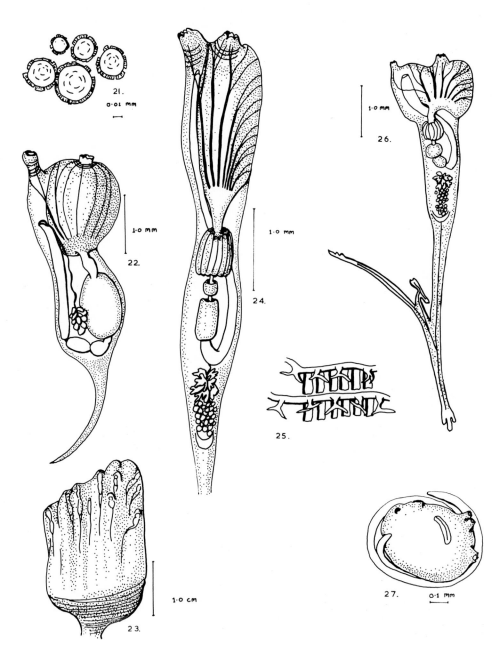

Cystodites antarcticus
21. Spicules.

Sigillina moebiusi
22. Zooid.

Tylobranchion speciosum
23. Large colony.
24. Zooid showing thoracic muscles, gut, gonads, and heart.
25. Portion of branchial sac.
26. Zooid with posterior abdominal stolon branching.
27. Larva [after Millar, 1960].

is smooth-walled. Gonads present beside the gut loop. (After Sluiter.)

Remarks. The zooids of this species are similar to those of *Cystodytes* spp., mainly because of the 4 rows of stigmata and short esophageal neck. Because specimens of *C. antarcticus* Sluiter were taken from the same locality, Van Name [1945] has suggested their synonymy, *P. glareosus* representing colonies in which the spicules have been lost. The asterisk-like siliceous spicules are probably crystals, possibly artefacts of preservation. Although the presence of gonads indicates mature colonies, the zooids are smaller than those of *C. antarcticus* and the species may not be synonymous. The short esophageal neck of this species and of *Cystodytes* spp. is found in the Holozoinae (except in *Atapozoa* sp.) but is not found in other genera of Polycitoridae.

Millar [1962] has followed Huus [1937] and Michaelsen [1930] in placing species with 4 rows of stigmata in the genus *Tetrazona*. Of these species *Polycitor vitreus* (Sars) actually has 3 rows of stigmata and belongs in the genus *Atapozoa* [Kott, 1967]. *Tetrazona porrecta* Millar, 1962, with 4 rows of stigmata is also distinguished by the position of the gonads behind the alimentary canal, and its affinities with the Polycitoridae are therefore suspect. *Polycitor glareosus* alone, with its short esophageal neck, may justify a genus *Tetrazona*, closely related to *Cystodytes* but without the calcareous plates of the *Cystodytes*.

? *Polycitor clava* (Harant and Vernières)

Polyclinum clava; Harant and Vernières, 1938, p. 9 [not *Polyclinum clava;* Herdman, 1899, p. 77].

New Records. None.

Previous Records.

Antarctic: Davis Sea, off Queen Mary Coast, 201 meters [Harant and Vernières, 1938].

Description. 'Quelques cormus,' otherwise not described. Probably a large clavate colony similar to *Polycitor giganteum:* large clavate or spherical stalked specimens up to 7 cm high and 4–5 cm wide at greatest diameter with zooids clearly visible through glassy or semitransparent test. Zooids are long. (After Harant and Vernières.)

Remarks. Herdman's specimen of *Polyclinum clava* is actually *Polycitor giganteum* [Kott, 1957]. If the zooids, as well as the colony of Harant and Vernières' specimen, resemble *P. giganteum* and lack a posterior abdomen, it could represent a probably unknown

species of antarctic Polycitoridae. The posterior abdomen may, however, have been overlooked, and the specimen could be a colony of the family Polyclinidae.

Genus *Sigillina* Savigny, 1816

Type species: *Sigillina australis* Savigny, 1816

Branchial sac with 3 rows of stigmata.

Michaelsen [1930] and Huus [1937] have divided the genus into a number of subgenera to accommodate species with or without posterior abdominal vascular extensions and stomach folds. This classification is followed here. The genus is rare in the Antarctic and the Subantarctic.

Subgenus *Paessleria* Michaelsen, 1930

Stomach smooth. Posterior abdominal vascular stolon with epicardial extension not present.

Sigillina (Paessleria) magalhaensis Michaelsen

Paessleria magalhaensis Michaelsen, 1907, p. 69; 1930, p. 490.

Polycitor (Eudistoma) magalhaensis Michaelsen, 1915, p. 461.

Sigillina (Paessleria) magalhaensis Michaelsen, 1930, p. 484 (referring to type of *Paessleria magalhaensis*) [not *Sigillina (Paessleria) magalhaensis;* Michaelsen, 1930, p. 492.—Kott, 1952, p. 71].

Polycitor magalhaensis; Van Name, 1945, p. 132.

New Records. None.

Previous Records.

Subantarctic: Strait of Magellan [Michaelsen, 1907]. For the single colony upon which this record is based, no depth was given. For a discussion of the distribution and synonymy of this species see Remarks below.

Description. Fairly large, compact colony 22 mm in diameter. Sand embedded basally. Spherical symbiotic cells embedded in upper parts of test. Zooids elongate; total length, 11 mm. A long neck present connecting thorax and abdomen. Branchial and atrial siphons 6-lobed, the atrial siphon curved and tubular with the 3 anterior lobes longer than the others. Thorax very contracted with 3 rows of stigmata in the branchial sac. The stomach is oval and may have longitudinal folds. Gonads are indistinguishable. (After Michaelsen.)

Remarks. Unfortunately, the single specimen of this species has not provided very definitive information.

The form of the atrial siphon and presence of 3 rows of stigmata suggest an affinity with *Atapozoa deerata* (Sluiter) and *Sigillina vasta* Millar [Kott, 1967].

The present species is, however, the type for the subgenus *Paessleria* Michaelsen, defined as a species lacking a posterior abdominal vascular extension into which the epicardium projects. This vessel is characteristic of *Atapozoa*.

It seems unlikely that records from the Red Sea, Seychelles, and southwestern Australia [Michaelsen, 1930; Kott, 1957] could refer to the Magellanic species. Michaelsen had no doubt that they were identical. Certainly the zooids are similar, as described. Van Name [1945] doubts the synonymy and indicates the difficulties that arise because of the lack of stable morphological characters.

Subgenus **Hyperiodistoma** Michaelsen, 1930

Stomach smooth. Posterior abdominal vascular stolon with epicardial extension present.

Sigillina (Hyperiodistoma) moebiusi
(Hartmeyer)

Text fig. 22

Colella möbiusi Hartmeyer, 1905, p. 396.
Polycitor (Eudistoma) möbiusi Hartmeyer, 1909–1911, p. 1432.
Polycitor möbiusi Hartmeyer, 1912, p. 305.
? *Eudistoma mobiusi*; Millar, 1962, p. 162.

New Records. South Shetland Is.: *Eltanin* Sta. 410 (240 meters).

Previous Records. South Africa [Hartmeyer, 1905; 1912; Millar, 1962]; Africa, east coast, Mikindani [Hartmeyer, 1905]; Madagascar, southwest coast [Hartmeyer, 1912]; Mauritius; Ilha Quirimba [Hartmeyer, 1905].

Distribution. Hartmeyer [1912] describes this as a tropical species extending south to the Cape of Good Hope. The fragment from the Antarctic, if further collections confirm the identification, suggests a wider distribution in the South Atlantic and Indian oceans.

Description. Colonies stalked, with head flattened, conical or cylindrical, maximum height 17 mm and 10 mm wide; or cushion-like colonies. From the South Shetland Islands only a portion of the colony available, embedded in a didemnid. Test very soft and semitransparent. Zooids up to 4 mm excluding vascular stolon, although Millar [1962] describes zooids up to 7 mm from South Africa. Branchial siphon terminal, 6-lobed; atrial siphon from dorsum

usually 6-lobed; however, in the present specimen the opening is extended and the lobes indistinct. Hartmeyer's specimens with strong thoracic musculature. Specimen from the Antarctic with 6 longitudinal bands extending from thorax down abdomen on to vascular stolon. Fine circular muscles around siphons do not form discrete sphincters. Three rows of branchial stigmata present with 10 to 16 per row. There are a short esophageal neck, voluminous smooth stomach, posterior stomach, and midintestinal enlargement. Gonads are present in the gut loop. A stout posterior abdominal vascular extension varies in length but is never longer than 4 mm in Antarctic specimens.

Remarks. The short esophageal neck, well developed thoracic musculature, and vascular stolon place the specimen from the South Shetland Islands in the group of species described from South Africa: *Sigillina modestum* (Sluiter) and ? *Eudistoma mobiusi* of Millar [1962]. The species is indistinguishable from ? *E. mobiusi* and may be separated from *S. modestum* (Sluiter) only by the numbers of longitudinal thoracic muscles (up to 18 in *S. modestum*). *S. illotum* (Sluiter) also has a long vascular stolon. Millar [1962] has short-waisted specimens from South Africa that he has placed in this species, which is characterized by large vesicular cells in the test. The distinctions in this genus are, however, thoroughly unsatisfactory and few stable characters exist on which to base a satisfactory classification. Even the short waist characteristic of the species might, according to Millar [1962], change at different periods in the life of the colony.

Family POLYCLINIDAE Verrill

Subfamily EUHERDMANIINAE Seeliger

This subfamily is not especially common anywhere. It is, however, well represented in Antarctica by the prolific and ubiquitous *Tylobranchion speciosum*, which is chiefly confined to the Antarctic and only rarely extends into the Subantarctic.

Several other well defined species of very limited distribution have been taken from the area.

KEY TO GENERA OF EUHERDMANIINAE

1. Stigmata lost..............***Pharyngodictyon***, p. 44
   Stigmata present.....................................2
2. With papillae or longitudinal vessels in the branchial sac. 3
   Without papillae or longitudinal vessels in the branchial sac 4
3. Heart at posterior end of posterior abdomen ....
   ....***Protopolyclinum***

Heart halfway down posterior abdomen ....
.............................*Tylobranchion, p. 41
4. Numerous rows of stigmata........................ 5
3 rows of stigmata .... Pseudodistoma
5. Testis follicles not serially arranged................ 6
Testis follicles serially arranged.................... 7
6. Zooids not embedded .... Euherdmania
Zooids embedded...................*Placentela, p. 42
7. Zooids usually separate; stomach without folds........
.... Dumus
Zooids embedded; stomach with folds......... Ritterella

---

* These genera reported from Antarctica.

Genus *Tylobranchion* Herdman, 1886

Type species: *Tylobranchion speciosum*
Herdman, 1886

Zooids open separately to the exterior. Branchial sac with biramous papillae representing internal longitudinal vessels. Gonads, heart, and epicardial sac extend posterior to the gut loop into a posterior abdomen.

Tylobranchion speciosum Herdman

Text figs. 23–27

Tylobranchion speciosum Herdman, 1886, p. 157.—
Ärnbäck, 1927, p. 5.—Kott, 1954, p. 152.—Millar, 1960, p. 84.
Tylobranchion antarcticum Herdman, 1902, p. 193.—
Sluiter, 1906, p. 10; 1914, p. 28—Hartmeyer, 1911, p. 472.—Ärnbäck, 1927, p. 8; 1950, p. 25.—
Van Name, 1945, p. 158.
? *Stereoclavella antarctica* Herdman, 1910, p. 17.
Tylobranchion weddelli Ärnbäck, 1927, p. 2; 1950, p. 23.

New Records. Weddell Sea: *Staten Island* Sta. 53/63 (55 meters); *Edisto* Sta. 20, TR 5 (384 meters), Sta. 20, TR 6 (394 meters). Scotia Sea: *Eltanin* Sta. 370 (115 meters), Sta. 732 (265 meters). South Orkney Is.: *Eltanin* Sta. 496 (234 meters), Sta. 1084 (298–403 meters). South Shetland Is.: *Eltanin* Sta. 436 (73 meters); *Staten Island* Sta. 61/63 (31 meters), Sta. 62/63 (57 meters). Antarctic Peninsula: *Edisto* Sta. 189[5] (64 meters), Sta. 28, TR 14 (129 meters), Sta. 35, TR 18 (154 meters); *Staten Island* Sta. 14/63 (45–76 meters), Sta. 66/63 (62 meters). Knox Coast: *Atka* Sta. 29 (135 meters). Ross Sea: *Edisto* Sta. 4 (400 meters), Sta. 5 (400 meters); *Burton Island* Sta. 3 (434 meters); *Staten Island* Ocean Sta. 10–1 (439 meters), Ocean Sta. 10–2 (128 meters).

---

[5] U.S. Navy Antarctic Expedition, 1947–1948.

Previous Records.

Antarctic: Circumpolar in distribution about the antarctic islands and mainland: South Georgia [Ärnbäck, 1950; Millar, 1960]; South Sandwich Is. [Millar, 1960]; Shag Rocks [Millar, 1960]; South Shetland Is. [Sluiter, 1906; 1914]; Seymour I. and Paulet I. [Ärnbäck, 1927; 1950]; Mac. Robertson Land [Kott, 1954]; Cape Adare [Herdman, 1902]; Wilhelm II Coast [Hartmeyer, 1911]; McMurdo Sound [Herdman, 1910].

Subantarctic: Kerguelen I. [Herdman, 1886]; Patagonian Shelf, Falkland Is. [Millar, 1906].

Distribution. There are only occasional records of this species from north of the antarctic convergence, as noted above. It is primarily found in the antarctic subregion and does not occur at particularly great depths; depths range from 25 to 437 meters.

Description. Colonies usually cylindrical or laterally flattened and tongue- or wedge-shaped; sessile or basally narrowed to a short stalk by which colony is attached to the substrate. Colonies may be broken up into lobes extending part of the way, or completely, to the base. Zooids in lobes or colonies number 2 or 3 to about 20 or 30, according to the diameter of the lobes or colonies. The test is firm but not hard, usually almost glassy and transparent but may be opaque, often wrinkled basally. Colonies up to 9 cm tall, 1.5 cm thick, and 7 cm long. Zooids clearly seen arranged in parallel extending the whole length of the colony. They open separately on the upper surface of the lobes and form a small protuberance of the test there. Thorax and abdomen together are 5 to 10 mm long; they may be equal but usually the abdomen is longer than the thorax. The gonads occupy the proximal part of the posterior abdomen; however, the vascular stolon with epicardial extension continues almost to the base of the colony. Both apertures have 6 shallow lobes on short siphons, the branchial terminal and the atrial antero-dorsal. From 6 to 11 longitudinal thoracic muscles continuous as either fine bands around the abdomen and posterior abdomen or as 2 bands along either side. There are 12 simple branchial tentacles, not long; 14 to 20 rows of 25 to 30 rectangular stigmata. Transverse vessels bear biramous papillae, with arms of varying length; about 2 stigmata present between consecutive papillae. Dorsal lamina is represented by pointed triangular tongues. Esophagus fairly short; stomach large and cylindrical with 12 to 19 folds. One colony from the Patagonian Shelf [Millar, 1960] has zooids without stomach folds. There is an enlarged duodenal area and midintestine in the gut loop. The rectum crosses the esophagus and extends along the branchial sac almost to the base of the atrial opening accompanied by vas deferens. The anus is smooth rimmed. Oviduct ends at the base of the peribranchial cavity. Gonads consist of a cluster of testis follicles posterior to the gut loop and a large ovary posterior to the testes. A V-shaped heart present immediately posterior to the gonads. The posterior abdomen extends beyond gonads and heart as a vascular stolon with epicardial cavity. It ends in fingerlike ampullary processes.

In one colony from the Antarctic Peninsula (*Edisto* Sta. 28, TR 14) branches from the vascular stolon extend anteriorly into developing lobes of test. They terminate in rounded ampullae with accumulations of cells.

Larvae. Berrill [1935] found large eggs (0.74 mm) in great numbers developing together in the atrial cavity. Millar [1960] found fairly immature larvae with 3 triradiate papillae with ectodermal suckers, an otolith but no ocellus. These larvae are 0.55 mm long.

Biology. Specimens collected in both July and January have been taken with larvae [Millar, 1960]. The larvae are present in the atrial cavity, where the eggs are fertilized and consequently are all at the same stage of development. It is probable that they are retained in the atrial cavity for only a very short period, as no embryos were present in the large number of colonies available from the present collection. Viviparity is therefore not very well developed.

Berrill [1935] observed, in the type colony from Kerguelen Island [Herdman, 1886], dissolution of the thorax and abdomen and evidence of constriction of the posterior abdomen to form buds. This method of budding is reminiscent of the simple strobilation involving the epicardium as in Polyclinidae. The function of the vascular stolon described above with its swollen terminal branches is not known [see also Trason, 1963, p. 309, for *Pycnoclavella*].

Ärnbäck [1927] reported this species attached to the stalk of a simple ascidian later [1950] identified as *Pyura turqueti* (< *P. georgiana*). Specimens from *Eltanin* Sta. 496 were also found attached to the stalk of *P. georgiana*, and in the *Edisto* (Sta. 5) material from Robertson Bay colonies of *T. speciosum* were found on the stalks of *Sycozoa georgiana*.

Remarks. Phylogenetically the species is closely related to Diazonidae in that it retains traces of longitudinal vessels and primitive triradiate arrangement of larval papillae and has not become viviparous to any great extent. It has, however, developed polyclinid

characters in the position of the heart and gonads, in the growth of the epicardium into a posterior abdominal extension and in the probable site and nature of its vegetative reproduction.

Despite similarities in colony form to species of *Pycnoclavella* and Clavelininae, *Tylobranchion* is distinguished by the retention of traces of internal longitudinal vessels in the branchial sac and by the formation of a posterior abdomen. Clavelininae are further distinguished by their specialized mechanism of vegetative reproduction. *Pycnoclavella* spp. show greater affinities with Polycitoridae, as they retain diazonid form of zooid, bud by abdominal strobilation, and have developed viviparity to a greater extent than either *Tylobranchion* or Clavelininae.

The extension of gonads and epicardium into the proximal part of the vascular stolon is reminiscent of *Hypsistozoa* spp.; however, the heart in *Hypsistozoa* remains in the abdomen.

Placentela Redikorzev, 1913

Type species: *Placentela crystallina*
Redikorzev, 1913

Zooids embedded; more than 3 rows of stigmata, no trace of internal longitudinal vessels. A rare genus not previously reported from the Antarctic.

Placentela translucida new species

Text figs. 32–35

Type Locality. Antarctic Peninsula: *Eltanin* Sta. 291 (370 meters). Holotype, colony, USNM 11977; paratypes, 2 colonies, USNM 11978.

Description. Colonies 7 cm high, 2 cm maximum diameter; club-shaped lobes, narrowing basally to a stalk. Test material extends out along coralline or other particles which become embedded in it. One specimen has a small accessory lobe. Surface smooth; test glassy, transparent, but firm. Zooids are packed with larvae and visible through the test. No apertures seen on surface of colony. Zooids are small, about 1 cm long. The structure of zooids in these colonies is obscured by the 20 to 30 developing embryos that fill the peribranchial cavity and the oviduct, occluding the branchial cavity and intestinal loop, which may be resorbed leaving the body wall of thorax and abdomen as a brood pouch, and the posterior abdomen from which a new zooid probably develops. Branchial and atrial siphons are short, distended, 6-lobed. Branchial lobes only sometimes apparent. In zooids packed with embryos, the branchial aperture is contracted and inconspicuous and the atrial aperture pro-

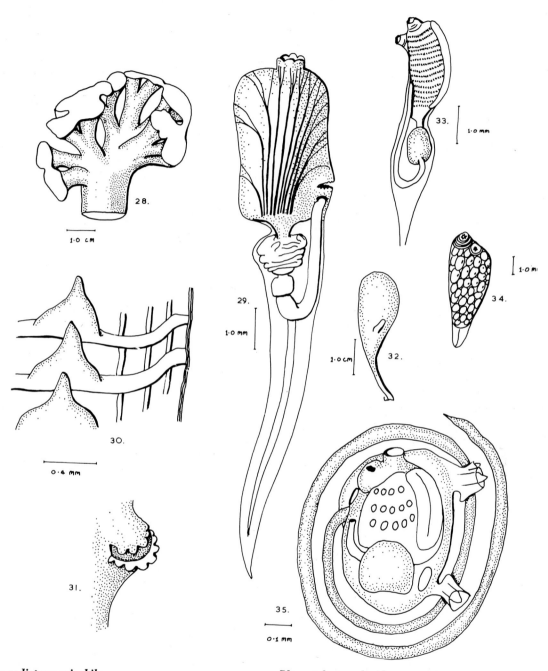

Pharyngodictyon mirabile

28. Colony.
29. Zooid showing thoracic muscles and gut.
30. Portion of left side of branchial sac and dorsal languets.
31. Atrial aperture showing lobed upper and lower lips.

Placentela translucida new species

32. Outline of colony.
33. Young zooid.
34. Zooid with thorax and abdomen obliterated by larvae.
35. Larva.

jected forward. There are 15 rows of 18 stigmata. The gut loop is short; the stomach smooth and spherical. Gonads are present in posterior abdomen behind the gut loop. Embryos are especially numerous, many at an advanced stage of development. Small regenerated zooids present in the test.

Larvae. Almost spherical, deeper than long: 0.5 mm long and 0.6 mm deep. There is an ocellus but no otolith. Three rows of definitive stigmata are present, a large spherical stomach and short gut loop. The majority of larvae have 2 median anterior adhesive papillae, but occasionally the dorsal papilla appears to divide terminally into two. These papillae comprise a deeply invaginated cone of adhesive cells. Mature larvae have single pockets on the inner side of the base of the papillary stalks. Is it possible that these pockets or invaginations force the adhesive cone to the surface or stimulate the secretion of adhesive from the cells?

Biology. The present colonies were collected in October, at the end of the antarctic winter. Small zooids in the test indicate regeneration from persisting posterior abdomina after resorption of the parent thorax and abdomen following their use as a brood pouch and eventual liberation of embryos from the test through the atrial apertures.

Remarks. The large numbers of embryos indicate a relationship with *Tylobranchion.* Unlike *Tylobranchion,* however, in which fertilization takes place in the atrial cavity, developing embryos in the present species also pack the oviduct, indicating fertilization probably takes place before the embryos reach the peribranchial cavity. This occurs in other species of Euherdmaniinae.

The larval form is typical of *Placentela* spp., *Euherdmania* spp., and *Pycnoclavella* spp., in which the larval papillae are deeply invaginated. Generally these species have only two lateral adhesive papillae, although in *Euherdmania claviformis* there may be two [Trason, 1957] or three [Berrill, 1948b] papillae, as in the present species. The larva of the present species also resembles that of *Pycnoclavella aurilucens* [Berrill, 1947a], *Pycnoclavella stanleyi* [Trason, 1963], and *Pycnoclavella minuta* Millar, 1953, in the absence of the otolith and retention of the ocellus (see chapter 8, Phylogeny).

Pharyngodictyon Herdman, 1886

Type species: *Pharyngodictyon mirabile* Herdman, 1886

Branchial sac reduced; stigmata and internal longi-

tudinal vessels lost. Zooids open separately to the exterior.

An abyssal genus of rare occurrence.

KEY TO ANTARCTIC SPECIES OF *Pharyngodictyon*

Arborescent colony......................*mirabile*, p. 44
(Kerguelen Is., South Orkney Is.)
Cylindrical colony ....*reductum*, p. 45
(South Shetland Is. ?)

Pharyngodictyon mirabile Herdman

Text figs. 28–31

Pharyngodictyon mirabile Herdman, 1886, p. 152.

New Records. South Orkney Is.: *Eltanin* Sta. 494 (1226 meters), on the western slope of the Scotia Ridge.

Previous Records.

Subantarctic: Between Kerguelen Is., and the Cape of Good Hope on the southern part of Crozet Ridge in 2928 meters [Herdman, 1886].

Distribution. Probably in the Atlantic-Indian Basin, although in waters over 1000 meters. Maximum depth of waters over the Scotia Ridge is about 2000 meters, thus allowing for the extension of the species on to the western side of the ridge, as indicated in the present collection. This allows for the possibility of an extension of its range into the Southeast Pacific Basin. It is probable, however, that the species will be taken at even greater depths, explaining the discontinuity of its records.

Description. Herdman's specimen was a small fragment. The present specimen represents a whole arborescent colony consisting of a basal stem, primary, then secondary or terminal branches expanding into mushroom-like flattened head which may coalesce with adjacent heads. Height of whole colony about 5 cm, maximum width about 5 cm, diameter of basal stalk about 1.2 cm. Test is soft, gelatinous, and semitransparent without foreign bodies. No common cloaca present.

Zooids open on to flattened surface of expanded heads, all over the surface of larger lobes, but around borders only of smaller lobes [see Herdman, 1886]. Zooids up to 15 mm long. The posterior abdomen occupying more than half of the length. Branchial siphon terminal, 6-lobed. The atrial opening on the posterior half of dorsal surface of thorax is large, bordered by upper and lower lips, fringed with 5 and 8, respectively, rounded lobes. The lobes of the zooid openings fit into corresponding protuberances of the surface of the test. There are 12 longitudinal muscle bands on either side of the thorax; these converge into 2 bands on either side of the abdomen and posterior abdomen. Circular muscles form a continuous sheet beneath longitudinal bands and are continuous with circular muscles of siphons. There are 20 simple branchial tentacles. Six wide transverse vessels present in the branchial sac, but no stigmata nor internal longitudinal vessels. Longitudinal connectives present between the transverse vessels, up to 3 in each row; these are not homologues of internal longitudinal vessels. Branchial sac is strongly adherent to the body wall. The stomach is short, almost spherical, in these specimens flattened antero-posteriorly almost obscuring the 8 folds. Anus is bilabiate. The posterior abdomen contains gonads anteriorly.

Biology. Herdman's specimen from diatom ooze; present specimen from a rocky bottom. Herdman's specimen collected in December; present specimen, in February. Both have mature gonads.

Remarks. The postero-dorsal position of the atrial opening to the surface about 2 mm away from the branchial opening causes the thorax of the zooid to be parallel to the surface rather than at right angles (which is more usual). This has led to a confusion between the longitudinal and the vertical axes of the thorax and explains Herdman's misinterpretation of the branchial sac: The vessels indicated as 'transverse' [Herdman, 1886, pl. XXI, fig. 12] are actually longitudinal connectives between the transverse vessels (which Herdman had regarded as longitudinal vessels). The specimens are thus identical in all respects and are related closely with other genera of Euherdmaniinae, except for the modification of the branchial sac usual in abyssal species.

Pharyngodictyon reductum Sluiter

Pharyngodictyon reductum Sluiter, 1906, p. 11.—Van Name, 1945, p. 76.

New Records. None.

Previous Records.

Antarctic: Washed up on beach, Booth (Wandel) Island, western Antarctica [Sluiter, 1906].

Description. More or less cylindrical, 4 cm high and 2.5 cm in diameter, attached by rootlike processes. Single terminal common cloacal aperture present. Zooids are visible through whitish transparent head arranged around cloacal aperture in an irregular circle. They are up to 9 mm long with additional posterior abdomen of 25 mm. Both apertures on short, anteriorly directed siphons, 6-lobed. Oblique muscle

bands on thorax crossing one another at right angles, and some longitudinal and transverse bands. Branchial sac with 6 transverse vessels, no stigmata, but with rudiments of internal longitudinal vessels as biramous papillae, no more than 2 per side. The stomach is small with 4 well defined folds. Gonads in anterior part of posterior abdomen, ovary anterior and testis follicles in 2 rows behind the ovary. (After Sluiter.)

Remarks. It is unusual for common cloacal apertures to exist in this subfamily where both siphons are unmodified and open to the surface independently. Sluiter has described the openings of the branchial siphons on the surface of the colony but has not mentioned the atrial openings. If, indeed, the cloacal system exists, the atrial siphons must open into a cloacal chamber beneath the terminal aperture. It is possible, however, that this aperture was an artefact and that the openings are independent on the surface of the colony. The branchial sac of Sluiter's species is reminiscent of *P. mirabile* Herdman with the same number of transverse vessels, and the biramous papillae of Sluiter's specimens may represent the connectives of *P. mirabile* Herdman. The specimens differ in form of atrial opening and number of stomach folds, and, although both clearly represent abyssal specimens of the Euherdmaniinae, probably of the same genus, they must be assigned to separate species.

The occurrence of an apparently abyssal species on the beach is puzzling. Van Name doubts that 'this form has anything to do with Herdman's *Pharyngodictyon*' and suggests that wave action has destroyed the stigmata. However, the branchial sac lacks any trace of stigmata, and, as the zooids are well protected in the test, it is unlikely that all traces of stigmata should be lost without otherwise damaging the zooids. Moreover, the condition of the branchial sac is typical of most abyssal species, and Sluiter's suggestion that it was washed up on the beach during a tempest is possible. The extension of an abyssal genus into littoral regions has been demonstrated [*Culeolus littoralis* Kott, 1956, from intertidal zone, northwest Tasmania] and may be the explanation for the littoral occurrence of *P. reductum* Sluiter.

Subfamily POLYCLININAE Adams and Adams

The subfamily is well represented by antarctic species, some very prolific and extremely variable. Although this subfamily has not been previously taken from great depths, two new abyssal species (*Aplidium abyssum, Synoicium tentaculatum*) are present in the

Eltanin collections. In one of them (*Synoicium ten-taculatum*) the stigmata are reduced in number. In neither of these species, however, are the stigmata completely lost, as they are in most primarily abyssal species.

The taxonomy of this subfamily is far from satisfactory because of the variations in colony form, the rows of stigmata, the presence of stomach folds, the length of posterior abdomen, and the arrangement of testis follicles, which are sometimes due to the age and maturity of the colony and individuals therein and sometimes due to contraction of the zooids. Similarly, the form of the atrial languet is variable and depends to some extent on the position of the zooid in relation to the common cloaca or merely represents individual variation. Even characters used for generic distinction are far from reliable. Stomach folds distinguishing *Aplidium* spp. from *Synoicium* spp. are often suppressed (e.g. *A. caeruleum*, *A. radiatum*, and *A. recumbens*), and possibly these two genera should not be separated. Similarly, although the presence of 8 branchial lobes is rare and previously confined to European genera of *Morchellium* Giard, 1872, and *Sidnyum* Savigny, 1816, colonies with exclusively 8-lobed branchial apertures have been taken with, or from the same locality as, identical colonies differing only in the 6-lobed branchial apertures of the zooids. As the larvae are also identical, the possibility of convergence in two different genera is considered unlikely. Thus, in the present work *Sidnyum antarcticum* Kott, 1954, and *Sidnyum radiatum* Kott, 1954, are considered synonyms of *Aplidium circumvolutum* (Sluiter) and *Aplidium globosum* (Herdman), respectively. In general, the identity of the species is confirmed by the larvae, but, where they are not available, the number of muscle bands and stomach folds in combination with other characters must be relied upon to identify the species. The larvae, typical of the family Polyclinidae, show a tendency to proliferation of ampullae into vesicles. These may extend well posteriorly along the dorsal and ventral borders of the body, either by proliferation from dorsal and ventral extensions of the lateral lines [Carlisle, 1952] or by proliferation from a posterior extension from the base of dorsal and ventral lateral or median ampullae at the anterior end of the zooid and from a point halfway along the ventral extent of the lateral lines, so that ventral ampullae or vesicles do not necessarily have a continuous origin. The vesicle-bearing portion of the lateral line may also separate from the body of the larva to form a stalk to which the vesicles are still attached. The mechanism of origin of these vesicles is a distinctive character of the species.

Thus, the posterior vesicles of *Aplidium radiatum* and *Aplidium caeruleum* develop from the posterior extension of the lateral ridge, whereas in *Aplidium recumbens* and *Aplidium irregulare* the posterior vesicles are developed from the backward extensions of lateral ampullae.

The following specimens, taken by the Australian Antarctic Expedition 1911–1914, in the Davis Sea off Queen Mary Coast and assigned to the family Polyclinidae, have not been identified with any species known from the area. Although they are undoubtedly species of this subfamily, the descriptions are inadequate, no figures are available, and type specimens have not been located: *Macroclinum hypurgon*; Harant and Vernières, 1938; *Macroclinum flavum*; Harant and Vernières, 1938; *Polyclinum sundaicum*; Harant and Vernières, 1938.

KEY TO GENERA OF POLYCLININAE

1. Posterior abdomen separated from abdomen by a waist.. 2
   Posterior abdomen continuous with abdomen........... 3
2. With minute papillae on transverse vessels.............
   ....**Polyclinum**
   Without minute papillae on transverse vessels..........
   ....***Aplidiopsis***, p. 71
3. With stomach folds................................. 4
   Without stomach folds.............................. 5
4. With 6-lobed branchial aperture.......***Aplidium***, p. 46
   ? With 8-lobed branchial aperture.............***Sidnyum***
5. With 6-lobed branchial aperture......***Synoicium***, p. 64
   With 8-lobed branchial aperture...........**Morchellium**

---

* These genera reported from Antarctica.

Genus *Aplidium* Savigny, 1816

Type species: *Aplidium lobatum* Savigny, 1816

Adult zooids elongate; posterior abdomen in more or less direct continuation of the thorax and abdomen. Stomach folded.

KEY TO ANTARCTIC SPECIES OF *Aplidium*

1. Branchial sac unperforated ventrally...***abyssum***, p. 47
                                        (Peru-Chile Trench)
   Branchial sac perforated ventrally................... 2
2. Posterior abdomina long and cross one another....... 3
   Posterior abdomina short and do not cross one another 5
3. With 8 to 10 longitudinal muscle bands.............. 4
   With 16 longitudinal muscle bands.......***vastum***, p. 51
                                        (circum-antarctic)
4. Atrial aperture separate from lip......***fuegiense***, p. 47
                                        (circum-subantarctic)
   Atrial lip from anterior border of aperture...........
   ....***irregulare***, p. 50
                                        (circum-subantarctic)

Aplidium abyssum new species

Text figs. 36, 37

Type Locality. Peru-Chile Trench: *Eltanin* Sta. 37 (6006 meters). Holotype, slightly battered colony, USNM 11970.

Description. Cushion-shaped colony 2 cm in diameter, fixed by a wide area of the base on small rocks and gravel. There is some mud over the surface. The test is glassy and transparent, with a few gravel particles attached to the surface. Zooids are apparently not arranged in systems.

Zooids are about 1.0 cm long. The thorax rather wide, shorter than the abdomen, and the posterior abdomen short and tapering. There are 6 branchial lobes; the atrial aperture is rounded, halfway down the thorax and protected by an undivided languet of varying length rising from the body wall anterior to

the aperture. There are 8 rows of long rectangular stigmata with 6 to 8 stigmata in each half-row. Stigmata are absent from the ventral part of the branchial sac, which is an unperforated membrane with the endostyle running down the ventral line. The dorsal lamina is a plain flat membrane with 6 large languets from the transverse vessels to the left of the membrane. The stomach is rounded in the posterior one-third of the abdomen, and has 4 distinct folds. The number of testis follicles varies, and, when most numerous, the lobes appear to be arranged more or less in double rows. The ovary, represented by a single large ovum, is present anterior to the testis, immediately behind the gut loop in the broadest part of the posterior abdomen. Fine longitudinal muscle bands are present on the thorax and extend along both sides of the abdomen and posterior abdomen.

Remarks. The species is remarkably unmodified for a specimen from this great depth. It resembles *A. quadrisulcatum* Millar, 1960, in the small number of both stomach folds and rows of stigmata. *A. quadrisulcatum* has more stigmata per row and lacks the stigmata-free unperforated membrane ventrally in the branchial sac. *Synoicium triplex* which Sluiter [1906] originally described as *Psammaplidium t.* has a similar membrane dorsally and ventrally in the branchial sac. It is possible that the stomach folds of *Psammaplidium t.* have been overlooked; however, the present specimens are also distinguished by fewer rows of stigmata and a relatively larger abdomen and smaller posterior abdomen.

Generally, species with a wide thorax have many stigmata in each row. In this species unperforated membrane in the branchial sac accounts for the width of the thorax and is the principle distinction of the species.

Aplidium fuegiense Cunningham

Text figs. 38, 39

Aplidium fuegiense Cunningham, 1871, p. 66; 1871a, p. 490.—Millar, 1960, p. 28 [not *Aplidium fuegiense*; Kott, 1954, p. 173 (< *A. vastum* Sluiter, 1912)].

Amaroucium laevigatum Herdman, 1886, p. 231.— Michaelsen, 1907, p. 28.

Atopogaster elongata Herdman, 1886, p. 173 [not *A. elongata* Herdman, 1902, p. 194].

Atopogaster elongata var. *pallida* Herdman, 1886, p. 175.

Atopogaster gigantea Herdman, 1886, p. 164.

Psammaplidium ordinatum Sluiter, 1906, p. 22.

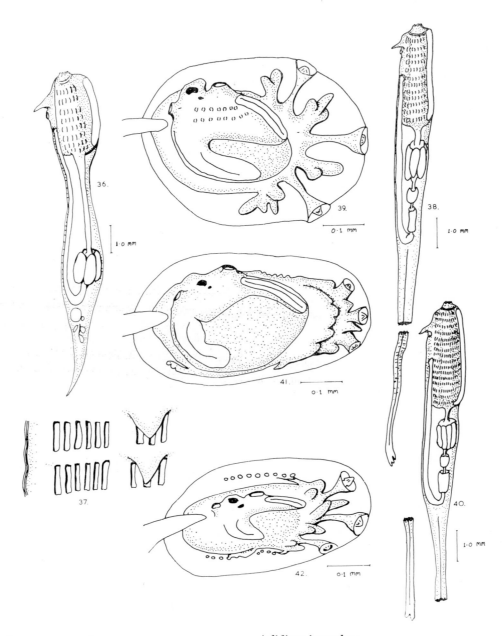

Aplidium abyssum new species
36. Zooid.
37. Portion of right side of branchial sac and dorsal languets.

Aplidium fuegiense
38. Zooid.
39. Larva.

Aplidium irregulare
40. Zooid.
41. Immature larva.
42. Mature larva.

Amaroucium fuegiense; Michaelsen, 1907, p. 28.—Hartmeyer, 1911, p. 547; 1912, p. 338; 1921, p. 275.—Van Name, 1945, p. 43.

Amaroucium variabile; Hartmeyer, 1912, p. 335 [part].

Aplidium ordinatum Sluiter, 1914, p. 35.

Amaroucium longicaudatum Sluiter, 1914, p. 33.

New Records. Drake Passage: *Eltanin* Sta. 219 (115 meters). Tierra del Fuego: *Eltanin* Sta. 222 (79 meters), Sta. 981 (40–49 meters). Falkland Is.–Burdwood Bank: *Eltanin* Sta. 339 (586 meters). Scotia Sea: *Eltanin* Sta. 370 (115 meters). South Orkney Is.: *Eltanin* Sta. 1082 (298–302 meters). Auckland I.: *Eltanin* Sta. 1425 (135–139 meters).

Previous Records.

Antarctic: Antarctic Peninsula [Sluiter, 1906; 1912]; South Georgia [Millar, 1960].

Subantarctic: Patagonian Shelf, Magellanic area, Falkland Is. [Herdman, 1886; Michaelsen, 1907; Cunningham, 1871; Millar, 1960]; Kerguelen Is. [Herdman, 1886; Hartmeyer, 1912].

Distribution. The species has usually been taken in depths between 40 and 586 meters from the Patagonian Shelf, Magellanic area, and down the Scotia Ridge as far south as South Georgia and occasionally as far as the Antarctic Peninsula. Records from the remainder of the antarctic continent are rare. The species also commonly occurs at Kerguelen Is. (18 to 183 meters) and the present record from Auckland I. confirms its distribution as circum-subantarctic.

Description. Colonies tremendously variable, from small spherical, ovoid, cylindrical, or long tapering forms. Sometimes with a short stalk; occasionally there are several lobes joined basally. Maximum diameter of colony about 28 cm; 63 cm or more in length. The test is firm at the surface but soft internally. The color of preserved specimens is usually some shade of yellow-gray. Generally, beneath the surface layer of test there is a layer of orange or yellow vesicular cells, which together with the zooids confer the yellow color to the colony. These cells are not always apparent and may be either absent or obscured by sand, which is often embedded in the surface test becoming more sparse internally, or the sand may be embedded so thickly throughout that the test becomes brittle. Zooids are arranged in the test usually at irregular and oblique angles to the surface, and the usually long posterior abdomina cross one another in the center of the colony. Inconspicuous common cloacal openings are present on the surface,

and zooids may form circular or elliptical systems or branching double rows. However, zooids are often so closely packed that all signs of systems are obscured.

Zooids are very long and thin, up to 26 mm or more. This length is due mainly to the particularly long posterior abdomen. The thorax is the widest part of the body, up to 1 mm. The branchial aperture has 6 lobes; the atrial aperture is about one-third the distance down the body and is surrounded by a small muscular sphincter. The short atrial tongue arises from the body wall anterior to the opening and may be undivided, or divided into two along its whole length, or trifid. The body musculature is very weak: transverse bands are inconspicuous and there are 8 to 10 longitudinal bands consisting of only a few fibers that extend along both sides of the abdomen and for a short distance along the posterior abdomen. There are from 10 to 20 rows of stigmata. In the present specimens the number of stigmata in each row is from 8 to 10; however, as many as 18 stigmata have been recorded for a specimen with 20 rows [*A. longicaudatum* (Sluiter, 1914)]. The stomach is comparatively voluminous in relation to the narrow and short abdomen and has from 4 to 6 well defined and uninterrupted folds. The posterior abdomen has the usual anterior ovary and testis follicles in rows in the posterior abdomen.

Larvae. Present in some specimens in the peribranchial cavity. They are small, from 0.6 to 0.9 mm long. They have, alternating with the anterior papillae, 4 median ampullae. From the base of the median ampullae in a position corresponding to the lateral line on each side of the body lateral ampullae develop first as rounded swellings, which in the mature larva are carried forward on the lengthening median ampullae. There are posterior extensions from the most ventral and dorsal median ampullae.

Remarks. The taxonomy of this species is extremely difficult. It is closely related to *A. irregulare* (Herdman) (see below, p. 50) and, because the two species occur in the same area, confusion is inevitable. The pointed condition of the free end of some colonies occurs in both species; both have long posterior abdomina crossing one another in the internal test. In both the zooids are long and narrow. However, there are fewer stomach folds in the present species, the stomach is larger, and the folds better defined; the thoracic muscle bands are finer and the atrial tongue shorter and less muscular than in *A. irregulare.* The accumulation of pigment into vesicular cells, not always evident, seems to be characteristic of *A. fue-*

giense, and, although *A. irregulare* has the same pigmentation, the cells are not present. The larval form provides the evidence that two variable species, rather than forms of a single species, are represented by *A. irregulare* and *A. fuegiense.*

There has also been considerable confusion over the characteristics of *A. fuegiense* and *A. variabile,* two widely distributed and closely related species. Millar [1960], working with the *Discovery* collections from the Magellanic area and Scotia Ridge, attempted to clear up the confusion by assigning to *A. fuegiense* all specimens with 5 or 6 stomach folds, whereas *A. variabile* was characterized by 15 stomach folds. The specimens in Millar's collection thus fall clearly into two highly variable species, which are characterized by distinctive larval forms; both species are distributed mainly in the Antarctic, although *A. variabile* has also been taken often from Kerguelen Island.

Aplidium irregulare (Herdman)

Text figs. 40–42

Amaroucium irregulare Herdman, 1886, p. 223.— Michaelsen, 1907, p. 28.

Amaroucium irregulare var. *concinnum* Herdman, 1886, p. 225.—Michaelsen, 1907, p. 28.

? *Amaroucium pallidulum* Herdman, 1886, p. 226.— Michaelsen, 1907, p. 28.

? *Amaroucium meridianum* Sluiter, 1906, p. 15.

? *Psammaplidium annulatum* Sluiter, 1906, p. 27.

? *Amaroucium* sp. Herdman, 1912, p. 318; 1915, p. 100.

Synoicium circumvolutum Kott, 1954, p. 169.

Synoicium arenaceum; Kott, 1954, p. 170 [part: Sta. 83].

New Records. Drake Passage: *Eltanin* Sta. 453 (31 meters). Off Tierra del Fuego: *Eltanin* Sta. 981 (40–49 meters). Chatham I.: *Eltanin* Sta. 1400 (436–439 meters).

Previous Records.

Antarctic: South Orkney Is., South Georgia, Antarctic Peninsula [Millar, 1960].

Subantarctic: Patagonian Shelf, Burdwood Bank, Falkland Is., Strait of Magellan [Herdman, 1886; Millar, 1960]; Kerguelen Is., Heard I., Macquarie I. [Kott, 1954].

Distribution. Generally circum-subantarctic in 0 to 500 meters, extending from the Patagonian Shelf down the Scotia Ridge to the Antarctic Peninsula, the extreme southern extent of its range.

Description. Colonies vary from low, pillow-shaped, and sessile to spherical, elongate or pointed and sessile or supported by a short wide stalk. Maximum dimension of colony up to 20 cm, sometimes divided into lobes. The color in preservative is pale creamish-yellow. The surface is smooth. There is sometimes a heavy incrustation of sand less dense below surface of test or absent or confined to the base of the colony. The test, except where it is stiffened with sand, is rather soft. Zooids are closely packed crossing one another in the test. Many cloacal openings but small and inconspicuous. Circular systems present but often obscured by crowded zooids. Zooids are set at irregular angles around the surface of the colony. Posterior abdomina are long and extend into the central test and cross one another. Zooids are small. The thorax and abdomen are each from 1.8 to 3.0 mm, and the posterior abdomen is long and narrow, from 6 or 7 mm, occasionally reaching 20 mm. The thorax is the widest part of the zooid but is rarely more than 1 mm. There are 8 fine longitudinal muscle bands and some transverse bands on each side of the thorax, where the musculature is quite strong. Longitudinal bands tend to fade out on either side of the abdomen, and the musculature on the posterior abdomen is inconspicuous. The branchial aperture has 6 pointed lobes; the atrial aperture one-third of the distance down the dorsal surface has a muscular triangular or trifid tongue from the anterior border of the opening. There are 11 to 16 rows of 12 to 18 slightly oval stigmata (10 to 23 [Millar, 1960]). There are 5 to 10 shallow stomach folds, but they may be broken or completely absent. The testis follicles are arranged in single or double rows in the long posterior abdomen.

Larvae. From 4 to 9 developing embryos present in the peribranchial cavity. Mature larvae are 0.4 to 0.7 mm long. Three anterior papillae on slender stalks alternating with 4 long median ampullae and 4 pairs of slender lateral ampullae. Epidermal vesicles develop ventrally from posteriorly extending ampullae. One series originating at the base of the anterior ampullae and the second series originating below the alimentary loop. Dorsal vesicles are in paired series connected by stalks extending from the base of the dorsal ampullae on each side of the dorsal line. A white triangular area on each side of the thorax has been observed [Millar, 1960] but is not present in larvae from the present collections.

Biology. Millar found larvae in his subantarctic material from October to July. In the present specimens larvae are present in January in the Burdwood Bank area.

Remarks. Millar [1960] suspects that this common species 'has been confused with *A. fuegiense.*' The species resemble one another in the variations of colony form, in the arrangement of zooids regularly crossing one another, and sometimes in the number of stomach folds. The larvae are distinguished by the dorsal and ventral series of epidermal vesicles in *A. irregulare* and by the atrial lip, which here rises from the anterior rim of the aperture but in *A. fuegiense* is separated from it. The body musculature of *A. fuegiense* is more delicate than that of the present species. Millar [1960] found no more than 7 stomach folds for his *A. falklandicum*, whereas for *A. irregulare* Herdman has recorded 10; for *A. pallidulum* the number is not given, but from Herdman's figure the stomach appears to have at least 7 folds. The discrepancy between *A. falklandicum* and *A. irregulare*, from the same geographic area, is not regarded here as highly significant in view of the general agreement in the test, colony shape, systems, and zooids.

A. annulatum (Sluiter) differs in the amount of embedded sand enclosing the zooids in chambers. Both stomach and body musculature suggest identity with the present species.

A re-examination of *S. circumvolutum* Kott from Kerguelen Islands has shown it to be synonymous with the present species. The larvae are identical although the ampullary vesicles had been overlooked in the earlier description [Kott, 1954, p. 169].

Aplidium vastum (Sluiter)

Text figs. 43, 44

? Amaroucium antarcticum Herdman, 1910, p. 19.
Amaroucium vastum Sluiter, 1912, p. 458; 1914, p. 32.
Aplidium fuegiense; Kott, 1954, p. 173.

New Records. Ross Sea: *Northwind* Sta. 8 (135 meters).

Previous Records. Ross Sea [Herdman, 1910]; Enderby Land, Mac. Robertson Land [Kott, 1954]; Antarctic Peninsula [Sluiter, 1912].

Distribution. Circum-antarctic in waters from 100 to 300 meters.

Description. The colonies are always massive, from 6 to 20 cm in greatest dimension. They vary from spherical or egg-shaped and fixed by a small area of their bases to more or less cylindrical and upright lobes, the head of the lobe being slightly expanded. The upright colonies are leathery and transversely wrinkled around the lower half or stalk, and the zooids open only on to the upper rounded head; in the egg-shaped or spherical colonies, however, the zooids open all around the surface. The test is firm and gelatinous and often impregnated with sand, which gives to the colony its dominant coloration in alcohol. Zooids are present in the outer layer of test, densely and irregularly arranged at various angles to the surface, and their long posterior abdomina cross one another irregularly. Sand becomes progressively less dense in the internal test. There are no systems evident.

Zooids are long, up to 12 mm of which the thorax and abdomen, of equal length, occupy about 4 mm. The thorax is the widest part of the body, about 2 mm. The branchial aperture is 6-lobed; the atrial aperture is on a short siphon one-fourth the distance down the dorsal surface and has a short tridentate lip from the upper border of the opening. There are 16 fine longitudinal muscle bands on the thorax, which extend down either side of the abdomen and posterior abdomen. The branchial sac has from 14 to 25 rows of long narrow stigmata with from 10 to 16 stigmata in each row. The stomach has 8 to 10 fairly shallow folds.

Larvae. Only immature embryos are present in colonies from Enderby Land [Kott, 1954]. The largest, with a fully developed tail, is completely spherical and 0.75 mm in diameter. No structure could be discerned. It is probable that with increasing maturity the larvae will increase in length.

Biology. The posterior abdomen of specimens collected in January in Moubray Bay appears to have completed sexual reproduction, and the posterior abdomen, without testis follicles, is in the process of invasion by granular cells.

Remarks. Although the structure of the colony and zooids resemble *A. irregulare*, both the colony and the zooids are of greater diameter; there are more thoracic muscle bands. The number of stomach folds also distinguishes the species from *A. fuegiense.*

The embryo is especially large and, allowing for an increase in length with increasing maturity, the mature larva can be expected to exceed 1 mm.

Aplidium variabile (Herdman)

Text figs. 45, 46

Amaroucium sp. Studer, 1879, p. 130.
Amaroucium variabile Herdman, 1886, p. 216.—Studer, 1889, p. 145. Hartmeyer, 1911, p. 541; 1912, p. 335.—Michaelsen, 1924, p. 388.
Aplidium variabile; Kott, 1954, p. 174.—Millar, 1960, p. 32.

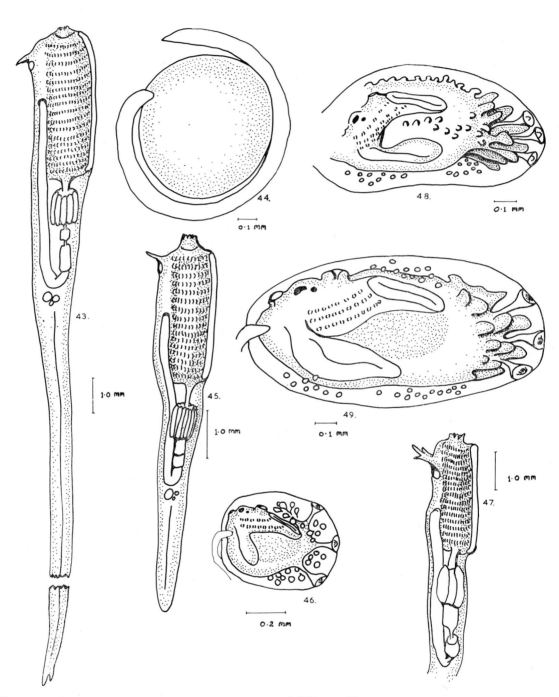

Aplidium vastum
43. Zooid.
44. Embryo.

Aplidium variabile
45. Zooid.
46. Larva [after Millar, 1960].

Aplidium radiatum
47. Zooid, thorax and abdomen only.
48. Younger larva showing origin of vesicles from lateral lines
    dorsally.
49. Mature larva.

New Records. Drake Passage: *Eltanin* Sta. 217 (110 meters), Sta. 369 (293 meters). Off Tierra del Fuego: *Eltanin* Sta. 969 (229–265 meters).

Previous Records.

Antarctic: South Georgia [Millar, 1960].

Subantarctic: Patagonian Shelf, Falkland Is. [Millar, 1960]; Kerguelen Is. [Studer, 1879; Herdman, 1886; Kott, 1954]; Chatham I., New Zealand [Michaelsen, 1924].

Distribution. Circum-subantarctic from shallow sublittoral areas to a depth of 293 meters.

Description. Colonies spherical, club-shaped, finger-like, plate-like, or wedge-shaped; sometimes stalked but often sessile. They may reach a maximum diameter of 12 cm but more often are smaller. There is often a coating of sand basally or around the stalk, but this seldom extends over the surface of the head. The test is smooth and semitransparent. Zooids are crowded in the test but are parallel to one another. Systems are indistinct. In some very narrow finger-like colonies in the present collection there is a single terminal common cloacal opening in the center of the lobe. This single opening is rare, however, and more often there are several common cloacal apertures over the surface of the colony.

Zooids sometimes have a long posterior abdomen, 4 or 5 times the length of the rest of the body. Usually the thorax is longer than the abdomen when expanded and may be as much as 3.5 mm. The abdomen is 2 mm, and posterior abdomen is about 4 mm long. The branchial siphon has the usual 6 lobes, and the atrial aperture is anterior, opposite the second row of stigmata, and has a strong muscular triangular or trifid languet. There are about 12 evenly spaced thoracic muscles on either side of the thorax; they are continuous along the sides of the abdomen and posterior abdomen. The branchial sac is long and narrow with 9 to 17 rows of 8 to 12 stigmata. The stomach is large with from 12 to 16 longitudinal folds, but most often 14 or 15. One or two of the folds may extend only part of the way down the stomach. The ovary is posterior to the gut loop and the testis follicles are arranged, as usual, in 2 rows in the posterior abdomen.

Larvae. From 4 to 10 developing embryos present in the peribranchial cavity. Immature larvae are present in several colonies in the present collection (February, Tierra del Fuego; December, Drake Passage) and were present in the B.A.N.Z.A.R.E. collection from the Kerguelen Islands [November or February, Kott,

1954]. Mature larvae have been taken only once [Millar, 1960]. They are 0.58 to 0.70 mm long and are characterized by the absence of median and lateral ampullae; epidermal vesicles are present around the 3 papillae at the anterior end of the larva.

Remarks. This species, despite its variation in colony form, is easily distinguished from other common forms in the subantarctic area by the size of the zooids, which are arranged in parallel in the colony, by the number of folds in the stomach, and especially by the larval form. It is similar to *A. multiplicatum* [Kott, 1963] from the tropical and subtropical regions of the Pacific Ocean, which also has a similar number of stomach folds, and is also similar to closely related *A. phortax* [Kott, 1963], which has a wide distribution in the Pacific including Stewart Island and Chatham Island [Michaelsen, 1924] representing the most southerly records. *A. phortax* overlaps the geographic range of the present species and could conceivably be confused; however, it has more stomach folds and the embryos develop in a true brood pouch from the thorax. See also Remarks section under *A. fuegiense*, which species has often been confused with *A. variabile*.

Aplidium loricatum (Harant and Vernières)

Amaroucium loricatum Harant and Vernières, 1938, p. 12.

New Records. Ross Sea: *Edisto* Sta. 3 (27 meters).

Previous Records. Commonwealth Bay, 644 meters [Harant and Vernières, 1938].

Distribution. Though records are few, the species apparently exists on the antarctic continental slope in the Victoria quadrant, in from 27 to 644 meters.

Description. Heads stalked, hemispherical, or clavate. Individual heads are sometimes rooted or joined to a spreading basal membrane, which extends basally and around the edges into rootlike processes that are covered with sand and undoubtedly fix the colony in a sandy substrate. On the surface of the head the test around each branchial opening is raised into 6 minute lobes, corresponding to the lobes of the branchial aperture of the zooid. The stalks are slightly leathery and transversely wrinkled externally, and the test of the rest of the head is smooth. The test of the head is soft but in the stalk region is firmer. Zooids are arranged in double rows radiating from 2 or 3 large common cloacal apertures on the upper surface. In the preserved specimen the test is semitransparent, the zooids are dark gray and confer on the whole colony a dark gray to black color. Zooids with the usual 6 branchial lobes; small atrial aperture a short distance down the dorsal surface surmounted by a small pointed languet. There are 20 longitudinal thoracic muscles extending along the sides of the abdomen and posterior abdomen almost completely surrounding them. The branchial sac is particularly wide with about 30 short stigmata in each of 10 to 16 rows. The stomach is also fairly large with 20 to 25 very fine folds sometimes interrupted along their length. The posterior abdomen has the usual arrangement of ovary anteriorly and double row of testis follicles posteriorly.

Remarks. The color, shape, and consistency of the test, together with the double rows of zooids, are especially reminiscent of *Aplidium radiatum* and *A. globosum.* The species are distinguished by the large number of thoracic muscles, the wide branchial sac, the large number of stigmata in each row, and the large number of narrow stomach folds.

Although the description of *A. loricatum* Harant and Vernières is not very detailed, the shape and color of the colony, the number of rows of stigmata, and the number of stomach folds are all similar. The records are from the same general area of the Antarctic.

Aplidium radiatum (Sluiter)

Text figs. 47–49

Psammaplidium radiatum Sluiter, 1906, p. 25.
Amaroucium radiatum; Hartmeyer, 1909–1911, p. 1471.
? *Amaroucium aurorae* Harant and Vernières, 1938, p. 11.
Aplidium radiatum; Kott, 1954, p. 173.—Millar, 1960, p. 37.

New Records. Ross Sea: *Atka* Sta. 23 (392 meters). Knox Coast: *Atka* Sta. 29 (135 meters). Davis Sea: *Burton Island* Sta. 5 (80 meters). Weddell Sea: *Edisto* Sta. 20, TR 6 (394 meters), Sta. 21, TR 7 (412 meters). Antarctic Peninsula: *Edisto* Sta. 189[6] (64 meters), Sta. 28, TR 14 (129 meters), Sta. 35, TR 18 (154 meters); *Staten Island* Sta. 9/63 (57 meters), Sta. 32/63 (46 meters). South Shetland Is.: *Staten Island* Sta. 62/63 (57 meters); *Eltanin* Sta. 435 (73 meters), Sta. 437 (311 meters), Sta. 445 (101 meters).

Previous Records. South Georgia, South Orkney Is., Antarctic Peninsula [Sluiter, 1906; Millar, 1960]; Enderby Land [Kott, 1954].

Distribution. The western Antarctic in the shelf to slope area, down to 400 meters.

---

[6] U.S. Navy Antarctic Expedition, 1947–1948.

Description. Rounded stalked heads; the stalk varies in length and may be short and almost the same diameter as the head or considerably longer and narrower than the head. Occasionally there may be more than one head from the end of a single stalk or the stalk may be absent altogether, in which case the colonies are flattened on the base. Colonies extend up to 7 cm in diameter. The outer layer of test usually has embedded sand, sometimes so dense that the test is externally almost brittle. The sand is less dense always toward the center of the colony, and the test there is soft. The color of the preserved colonies varies from gray to black; although Millar [1960] and Sluiter [1906] state that the color of the colony was due to the embedded sand, the zooids are often black. There is never black pigment in the test, which is soft and almost completely transparent. There is always a large central terminal common cloacal opening, and the zooids radiate out from it in conspicuous double rows on either side of common cloacal canals. Usually this is the only cloacal opening on each colony, but in the larger colonies a few accessory openings are developed. The zooids are especially apparent as the surface of the test is slightly raised over them and the sand is interrupted in the region of the rows of zooids. The zooids are large, the thorax 3 mm long, about the same length as the abdomen; the posterior abdomen is of variable length, up to 8 mm. The branchial aperture is 6-lobed and the atrial aperture is large, a short distance down the dorsal surface with an upper lip anterior to the well developed sphincter muscle, sometimes small and pointed but sometimes 3-lobed and occasionally almost rectangular with the free end only divided into 3-pointed lobes. Variations in the length and shape of the atrial languet depend to some extent on the position of the zooid in relation to the common cloaca and common cloacal canal [see Millar, 1960 under *Sycozoa sigillinoides*]. There are 12 or 13 strong longitudinal muscle bands in the thorax; they extend along either side of the abdomen and the posterior abdomen. The branchial sac is large and wide with 13 to 19 rows of about 20 stigmata. The stomach has 5 to 8 folds, fairly shallow, sometimes irregular, and often evident only on the anterior part of the stomach. Occasionally the stomach folds are altogether absent.

In many colonies, particularly the smaller ones, where the zooids are black, the black pigment is accumulated in round spots on either side of the endostyle, corresponding to the rows of stigmata, or sometimes at the base of the dorsal languets.

Larvae. Present in many colonies of this collection: from Wilkes Land (zooids without pigmentation) and from the Antarctic Peninsula, *Staten Island* Sta. 9/63 (zooids with black pigment) and *Edisto* Sta. TR 14 (zooids with black pigment but not accumulated into spots). The larvae from all these stations are identical, 1.2 mm long, with a comparatively short tail extending only about three-quarters of the distance around the body. Perhaps because of their size, no more than 3 embryos have been found in the peribranchial cavity of a single zooid. There are 3 anterior papillae alternating with median ampullae. Corresponding lateral ampullae and numerous smaller accessory ampullae and vesicles are present on each side, extending posteriorly in the midventral and dorsal lines from the anterior third of the body.

Biology. Although this is a fairly common antarctic species, mature embryos have not previously been taken. They are present in this collection in January from the Antarctic Peninsula and Wilkes Land, and in March from the Antarctic Peninsula. Thus the breeding period is not particularly restricted, although it may be restricted for any one colony.

Remarks. In addition to the distinctive arrangement of the systems in this species, the soft transparent internal test and robust zooids are unique. The larval form is also unique. The larval form is described here for the first time since previous records involved only colonies with immature embryos [Kott, 1954; Millar, 1960]. *A. aurorae* is quite possibly a synonym of the present form. The consistency of the test and arrangement of zooids described could represent *A. radiatum*. The zooid certainly cannot be characterized by any one condition of the atrial languet, which is variable as in the present species. Unfortunately, it has not been possible to trace the type specimen. *Psammaplidium nigrum* Herdman, 1902, from Cape Adare may possibly represent this species, in which case the range would be extended into the eastern Antarctic.

Aplidium globosum (Herdman)

Text figs. 50, 51

Amaroucium globosum Herdman, 1886, p. 219.
Synoicium arenaceum; Kott, 1954, p. 170 [part: Sta. 83].
Aplidium globosum; Kott, 1954, p. 175.
Sidnyum radiatum Kott, 1954, p. 176.
Aplidium scabellum; Kott, 1954, p. 176.

New Records. Kerguelen I.: B.A.N.Z.A.R.E. Sta. 56A, shore collection.

Previous Records. Macquarie I. [Kott, 1954], Kerguelen Is. [Herdman, 1886; Kott, 1954], intertidal to 110 meters.

Description. More or less spherical heads, fixed by a small area, sometimes produced into a stalk or long slender colonies. The test is fairly firm, yellowish-cream in alcohol, and without investing or included sand. Zooids are arranged in elliptical or circular systems around several common cloacal apertures; they are apparent from the surface as small mounds where the surface test is raised over the zooid. Maximum diameter of the colonies 4 cm. Zooids do not project into the central test and do not cross one another.

Zooids are small, 4 to 5 mm long; thorax, abdomen, and posterior abdomen of about equal length. The branchial aperture has 6 or 8 distinct pointed lobes. The atrial aperture has a stout anterior lip divided terminally into 3 distinct lobes. On the thorax there are 14 longitudinal thoracic muscles, which continue along the abdomen and are evenly disposed in fine bands around the posterior abdomen. External to the longitudinal muscles on the thorax there is an almost continuous thin sheet of fine transverse muscles. The branchial sac has 13 to 15 rows of 15 to 20 stigmata. The gut loop is long and the stomach fairly short but wide, with the wall forming 4 to 6 distinct folds. All stomach folds are not always continuous along the whole length of the stomach. The ovary is present in the anterior part of the posterior abdomen, and the testis follicles form 2 long rows behind the ovary.

Larvae. There are 3 or 4 developing embryos in the peribranchial cavity. They are small, 0.45 to 0.66 mm, with otolith and ocellus. The 3 anterior papillae on very short stalks, which lengthen with maturity, alternate with median ampullae. The lateral line on each side develops 4 anterior ampullae, and dorsal triradiate and ventral paired posteriorly directed ampullae extend from the base of the anterior ampullae. Lateral accessory lobes are present on the ventral paired posterior processes.

Remarks. The colony and the zooids resemble those of *Aplidium radiatum.* However, the systems in *A. radiatum* are more regular, and the larvae of the two species are quite distinct. The arrangement of zooids is also reminiscent of less crowded colonies of *A. fuegiense* and *A. irregulare*, but the zooids in the present species are shorter and do not cross one another in the test. The larval form of *A. irregulare* is distinct; however, both *A. fuegiense* and the present species have similar larvae distinguished only by the slightly greater size of the larvae of the former species and

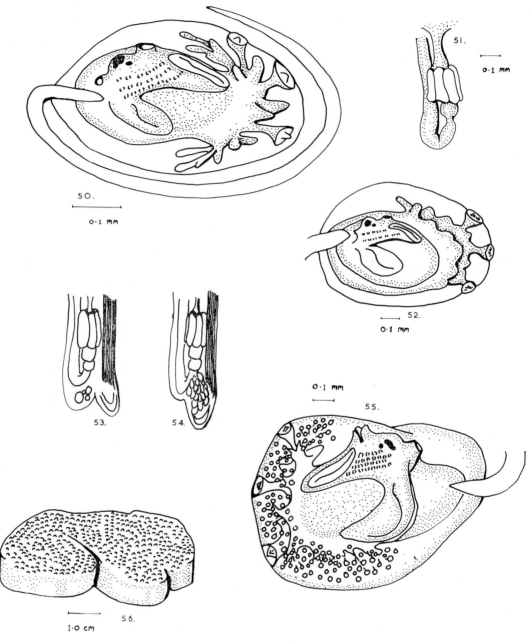

Aplidium globosum
50. Larva.
51. Gut loop.

Aplidium fuscum
52. Immature larva.

Aplidium circumvolutum
53. Abdomen and posterior abdomen contracted (♀).
54. Abdomen and posterior abdomen contracted (♂).
55. Larva.
56. Colony.

the absence of the dorsal posteriorly directed ampullae.

Colonies with exclusively 6 or 8 branchial lobes were taken from Sta. 64 by the B.A.N.Z.A.R.E. [Kott, 1954]. No other distinctions can be made between the colony and the zooids, and it has been concluded that this character represents, in these cases, an intra specific variation. Similar cases where 8 branchial lobes are present in all zooids of the colony occur in *Aplidium circumvolutum* and probably in *Synoicium giardi*.

Aplidium fuscum Herdman

Text fig. 52

Aplidium fuscum Herdman, 1886, p. 203.—Kott, 1954, p. 175.
? *Aplidium leucophaeum* Herdman, 1886, p. 205.
? *Aplidium fumigatum* Herdman, 1886, p. 211.

New Records. None.

Previous Records. All are from Kerguelen Is., 20–150 meters [Herdman, 1886; Kott, 1954].

Description. Hemispherical elongate, ovate to wedge-shaped colonies; the test hard and brittle with sand. Zooids are arranged in double rows or circular or elliptical systems and do not cross one another.

Zooids are from 10 to 15 mm long with a 1.5-mm maximum width in the thoracic region. The body wall is muscular with well developed longitudinal and transverse musculature. There are up to 20 rows of stigmata with 14 to 20 in each row. There are 4 well defined stomach folds.

Larvae. Are 0.95 mm long [see also Kott, 1954] with median ampullae alternating with the anterior papillae and corresponding lateral ampullae on each side of these. From the base of the most dorsal and ventral ampullae there is a posteriorly directed extension as in *A. globosum*.

Remarks. There is little in the colony or the zooid of this species to distinguish it from *A. globosum* except the length of the zooid. The larva is also much larger than the larva of *A. globosum*, although in other ways it is similar. It is possible that these colonies merely represent a variation of *A. globosum*. It is distinguished from *A. irregulare* by the number of stomach folds and the larval form.

Aplidium circumvolutum (Sluiter)

Text figs. 53–56

Psammaplidium circumvolutum Sluiter, 1900, p. 14.
Amaroucium circumvolutum; Michaelsen, 1924, p. 383.—Harant and Vernières, 1938, p. 10.

Amaroucium circumvolutum var. *kerguelenense,* Pérès, 1952, p. 213.
Sidnyum antarcticum Kott, 1954, p. 176.
Sidnyum punctans Kott, 1954, p. 177.
Aplidium circumvolutum; Millar, 1960, p. 25.

New Records. Drake Passage: *Eltanin* Sta. 369 (293 meters). South Shetland Is.: *Staten Island* Sta. 64/63 (86 meters); *Eltanin* Sta. 428 (662–1120 meters), Sta. 432 (935 meters), Sta. 435 (73 meters), Sta. 437 (311 meters), Sta. 439 (165 meters). South Orkney Is.: *Eltanin* Sta. 496 (234 meters), Sta. 1082 (298–302 meters). West of Macquarie I.: *Eltanin* Sta. 1417 (79–93 meters).

Previous Records.

Antarctic: South Georgia, South Shetland Is., Antarctic Peninsula [Millar, 1960], Mac. Robertson Land [Kott, 1954]; Commonwealth Bay [Harant and Vernières, 1938; Kott, 1954].

Subantarctic: Patagonian Shelf [Millar, 1960]; Falkland Is. [Millar, 1960]; Chatham I. [Sluiter, 1900]; Kerguelen Is. [Pérès, 1952]; North Island, New Zealand [Michaelsen, 1924].

Distribution. Distribution must be circumpolar in the Subantarctic and Antarctic to account for records from Chatham Island, New Zealand, Kerguelen Islands, and the Magellanic area, from which it extends down to the Scotia Ridge, South Shetland Islands, Antarctic Peninsula, and the antarctic continent. Depth range is from 39 to at least 600 meters.

Description. Colonies from 2 to 9 cm in diameter. Spherical, usually without a stalk, or rounded, pillow-shaped, or investing fixed by a large area of flattened lower surface. Dense sand present over the surface and often throughout the test, which is rather soft and may become brittle with sand. The zooids may be arranged in long complicated or double lines but often are not arranged in obvious systems. Common cloacal openings are well spaced over the surface but often are not evident. A single colony from *Eltanin* Sta. 369 in the present collection has a spherical head on a thick stalk of slightly smaller diameter, which spreads basally out over the substrate. This colony also has 4 large cloacal openings over the surface of the head. Large and smaller investing colonies from all other stations with rounded margins; the surface sometimes separated into 2 to 3 smaller areas by deep furrows, with obvious cloacal openings well spaced over the surface and zooids arranged in long, sinuous lines.

Zooids vary in length but are rarely more than 10 mm long and often smaller, especially when preserved, owing to the contraction of the strong longitudinal muscles. The thorax and abdomen are more or less of equal length in larger zooids, 2 and 3 mm, respectively, and the posterior abdomen occupies the rest of the length. Some colonies have zooids with 6 branchial lobes; however, colonies with zooids with 8 branchial lobes also occur often, particularly in the antarctic area (*Eltanin* Sta. 428, 432, 435, 437, 439) and also from *Eltanin* Sta. 496 in the subantarctic area. The atrial opening is wide, from one-third to one-half the distance down the dorsal surface; the anterior border produced into a wide rather fleshy triangular lip with accessory lobes on either side of the base, or equally divided into 3 or 4 pointed lobes. There are 10 to 20 strong muscle bands on the thorax, which extend on to the ventral surface of the abdomen and posterior abdomen to form adjacent bands or a single very broad band. The variation in the number of longitudinal bands is to some extent apparent because of the coalescence of adjacent bands in extended zooids. Contraction of the longitudinal ventral bands often draws the posterior abdomen alongside the abdomen. Transverse muscles are also well developed. There are 7 to 16 rows of 12 to 15 rectangular stigmata. The number of rows of stigmata increase from the subantarctic to the antarctic continent. The stomach is short with 5 or 6 stomach folds. The gut loop is particularly long behind the stomach. Not all the stomach folds continue along the whole length of the stomach. The internal wall is papillate and often these papillae are grouped into rounded areas. The testis follicles are few and clumped together in a tight arrangement in a short posterior abdomen, or are more numerous and arranged in a long posterior abdomen in a single or double row. The ovary is immediately behind the abdomen anterior to the testis and is minute in specimens with well developed testis. Zooids with well developed ovary and embryos have a short posterior abdomen and testis follicles are not developed.

Larvae. From 3 to 11 moderate-sized to large (0.5 to 1.3 mm) developing embryos in the peribranchial cavity. They have 3 anterior suckers with extremely numerous vesicles and ampullae proliferating from median and lateral ampullae. The largest larvae are from a colony from B.A.N.Z.A.R.E. Sta. 105, Mac. Robertson Land [Kott, 1954]. Larvae from the Antarctic Peninsula are a maximum of 0.8 mm, and for larvae from the Patagonian-Falkland area a mean length of 0.6 mm is recorded [Millar, 1960].

Biology. Regression of testis follicles apparently occurs before the ovary matures, and in any colony the male organs reach maturity before the female component. A specimen from the South Shetland Islands with larvae was taken in January. Millar [1960] had larvae in specimens from the subantarctic area in December to March. The breeding season, in the southern summer, is probably little different in the Antarctic and Subantarctic.

Remarks. The species is distinguished by the ventral muscle bands and the larvae, together with the number of stomach folds and the long gut loop, fleshy atrial lip, and arrangement of zooids. The tight sac of testis follicles is not characteristic of the species, as Michaelsen [1924] had suggested, but indicates a regression of the testis and is merely indicative of the stage reached in the sexual cycle. The species closely resembles *Synoicium pererratum* (Sluiter) and is distinguished only by the presence of stomach folds in the present species.

Differences between antarctic and subantarctic specimens in the test, length of zooid, rows of stigmata, and number and size of embryos [Millar, 1960] are confirmed in the present collection. A gradation of characters, as indicated by Millar, is present from the subantarctic area to the antarctic continent. In colonies from Commonwealth Bay and Enderby Land larvae and zooids are of a maximum size, although the larvae do not increase in numbers in the peribranchial cavity; the number of rows of stigmata are also, in these colonies, at a maximum.

As indicated in the discussion on the subfamily above, it has not been possible to separate colonies with 6-lobed branchial openings from those with 8-lobed openings. The colonies with 8 lobes show the same gradation of characters from the Subantarctic into the Antarctic as the colonies with 6 lobes.

Aplidium stanleyi Millar

Text figs. 57, 58

Aplidium stanleyi Millar, 1960, p. 41.

New Records. None.

Previous Records. Falkland Is., 210–271 meters [Millar, 1960].

Description. Low rounded heads narrowing to a sandy base. Maximum diameter 1.4 cm. There may be several of these rounded heads from the common base, which may be produced into broad lobes or finger-like processes. Test is semitransparent. Each lobe has a single terminal cloacal opening, with the zooids arranged around it in a single system.

Zooids are small, the thorax and abdomen together

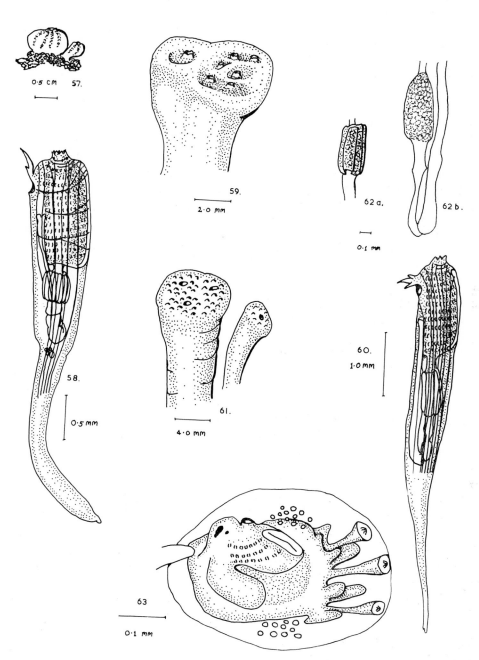

Aplidium stanleyi
57. Colony [after Millar, 1960].
58. Zooid [after Millar, 1960].

Aplidium stewartense
59. Colony.
60. Zooid.

Aplidium recumbens
61. Colony.
62a. Stomach folded.
62b. Stomach not folded showing accumulations of internal papillae in circular areas.
63. Larva.

are about 2 mm; the whole zooid does not exceed
5 mm. The branchial siphon has 6 wide lobes; the
atrial opening is small and a short distance back on
the dorsal side of the thorax with a small pointed
languet on the upper margin. There may be pointed
accessory lobes on either side of the base of the atrial
languet. There is moderate musculature on the thorax
extending along either side of the abdomen and posterior abdomen. The branchial sac has 12 to 15 rows
of about 15 stigmata. The stomach has from 20 to
24 narrow, close folds. The posterior abdomen is especially slender with the ovary anteriorly and a single
long series of testis follicles. (After Millar.)

Remarks. Millar distinguishes this species from *A.
phortax* (Michaelsen), *A. benhami* Brewin, and *A.
adamsi* Brewin [Michaelsen, 1924; Brewin, 1946]
from New Zealand by the colony and its loose attachment to the substrate and by the narrow posterior abdomen. However, both characteristics are rather variable in this genus and may not represent specific differences; further distinctions are provided by the body
wall musculature and the systems.

? *Aplidium vanhoeffeni* Hartmeyer

Aplidium vanhöffeni Hartmeyer, 1911, p. 508.

New Records. None.

Previous Record. Wilhelm II Coast, 380–385 meters
[Hartmeyer, 1911].

Description. Slender stalked colonies, a maximum of
14–15 mm long. The test is completely transparent
without any foreign particles adhering. Zooids are
apparent through the transparent test and are arranged around a central common cloaca. There is
only a single system in each colony with 2 to 6 zooids
parallel to one another. Zooids are small, total length
only 3.5 mm of which the thorax and abdomen are
each about 1 mm, with the posterior abdomen occupying the remainder of the length. The branchial siphon
has 6 lobes; the atrial aperture occurs slightly on to
the dorsal surface and has a large broad 3-lobed
tongue on the anterior rim of the aperture. There are
8 to 10 rows of stigmata in the branchial sac. The
gut forms a short loop, and the stomach has about 10
longitudinal folds that are interrupted along their
length especially on the side against the intestine. According to Hartmeyer, the gonads are not developed,
although there are larvae present in the branchial
cavity. (After Hartmeyer.)

Remarks. It is apparent that these are young colonies
despite the presence of larvae in the branchial sac.

The number of stomach folds suggests that they may
represent young colonies of *A. caeruleum,* but the
shape of the stomach and the form of the stomach
folds are distinctive and the species is probably valid.

Aplidium stewartense (Michaelsen)

Text figs. 59, 60

Macroclinum stewartense Michaelsen, 1924, p. 413.—
Harant and Vernières, 1938, p. 9.

New Records. Drake Passage: *Eltanin* Sta. 219 (115
meters).

Previous Records. Stewart I. [Michaelsen, 1924];
Macquarie I. [Harant and Vernières, 1938].

Distribution. Probably circum-subantarctic. Undoubtedly this small species has previously been confused with other species, and its distribution is probably more general than present records indicate. These
records range from 64 (Michaelsen, 1924) to 115
meters (*Eltanin* Sta. 219). The specimen identified by
Harant and Vernières (no depth given) very probably
came from fairly shallow water, inasmuch as the
Macquarie Island marine invertebrates taken in the
course of the Australian Antarctic Expedition appear
to have been 'shore-collected' [Herdman, 1923, p. 5].

Description. Pillar-like or expanded fan-shaped colonies up to 2 cm tall and from about 6 to 15 mm in
diameter at the free end. Some colonies branch and
support accessory heads from the primary stalk. The
upper surface is more or less flat-topped and slightly
expanded. The outer test is covered with sand, less
on the upper surface. The test is very delicate, especially in the region of the upper surface surrounding
the zooids, although a few sand particles may be
embedded there. In the stalk, especially toward the
base, the test is firmer. The outer rim of the flat upper
surface is raised into a rounded ridge surrounding a
central depression from the floor of which 1, 2, or 3
large or more conspicuous cloacal openings with frilly
sand-free lips protrude vertically. In larger colonies
the upper surface has a convoluted appearance, owing
to the extension of rounded ridges from the margin
across the surface, marking it off into several circular
or crescentic depressions, each with 1 or 2 cloacal
openings. When the colony contracts, the cloacal apertures are drawn down into the soft central test and
the rounded ridges tend to come together over the
top of the depressions thus protecting the openings.
The cloacal openings have frilly sand-free lips. Zooids
are tightly packed around the cloacal openings, obscuring their exact arrangement.

Zooids are not very long, up to 5 mm. The branchial openings have 6 lobes; the atrial opening has 3 pointed lobes, of which the central one is usually larger but often they are equal. There are 9 muscle bands down either side of the thorax; they extend along the abdomen and posterior abdomen as a single band on each side. There are 12 rows of about 10 stigmata. The stomach has 4 to 6 folds, but the folds are often not present, or are flattened out. The papillary lining of the stomach wall is either even or interrupted to form rounded areas. Gonads, as usual, in the posterior abdomen and consist of an anterior ovary and a double row of testis follicles.

Biology. Most probably, when the zooids contract and withdraw from the surface, the surface test in the floor of the depressions is pulled down with them into the softer internal test, thus closing the cloacal apertures and tending to pull the surrounding ridges of firm test inward.

Remarks. The regularity of zooid arrangement in single circles around conspicuous cloacal openings distinguishes this species, in which the zooids themselves are in no way remarkable. The sandy pillar-like flat-topped colonies from the New Zealand area and *A. recumbens* are very similar; in particular *A. cottrelli* [Brewin, 1957, as *Amaroucium c.*] and *A. novaezealandiae* Brewin, 1952a, from the East Cape region are distinguished from the present species only by the absence of the ridge-like development of test around the upper surface and between the systems. The condition of the stomach, apparently with structural folds that disappear when the stomach is flattened or stretched, is found in other species of *Aplidium*, and in particular in the closely related *A. recumbens* and *A. caeruleum.*

Aplidium recumbens (Herdman)

Text figs. 61–63

Amaroucium recumbens Herdman, 1886, p. 227.— Michaelsen, 1907, p. 28.
Macroclinum arenaceum Michaelsen, 1924, p. 406.
Synoicium arenaceum; Kott, 1954, p. 170 [part: Sta. 54].

New Records. South Shetland Is.: *Eltanin* Sta. 410 (240 meters). South Orkney Is.: *Eltanin* Sta. 499 (485 meters), Sta. 1084 (298–403 meters). Macquarie I.: *Eltanin* Sta. 1418 (86–101 meters).

Previous Records.
Subantarctic: Kerguelen Is. [Herdman, 1886; Kott, 1954]; Macquarie I. [Kott, 1954]; North Island, Stewart I., New Zealand [Michaelsen, 1924].

Distribution. Circum-subantarctic; the record in the South Shetland area probably represents the most southern extent of the species. Depth range is from 0 to 485 meters.

Description. Colonies are generally narrow and cylindrical, lobes joined basally, up to 5 cm high and 1.5 cm in diameter. Smaller colonies are about 1 cm high and 1 cm in diameter around the upper surface and are fixed by a small area at the base. The surface of the lobes is more or less flattened in preserved specimens; however, the test here is very loose and in the living specimens is probably raised into a mound with a central common cloacal opening. Depending on its diameter, each lobe has one or more circular areas of loose test above a cloacal cavity with a central opening. Zooids do not open around the sides of the colony. The test is impregnated with gray sand throughout. This sand stiffens the otherwise soft test and forms rigid compartments for the zooids. In the smaller colonies there are 8 or 9 zooids in circles in a circular system around the common cloacal opening, but in colonies of greater diameter the zooids are much more numerous and crowded. The zooids always lie parallel to one another in the test and the abdomina never cross.

Zooids are very small, maximum length 4 to 5 mm. The atrial opening has an anterior lip divided into 3, although the branchial opening has the usual 6 lobes. There are 10 fine longitudinal muscle bands on the thorax, which continue along each side of the abdomen and posterior abdomen. There are 10 to 15 rows of about 10 to 12 stigmata.

Minute papillae line the stomach and may be evenly distributed over the stomach wall or may be accumulated into evenly distributed rounded areas to give the appearance of areolations. The stomach sometimes has 6 distinct folds and at other times is completely without folds, but the presence or absence of folds has no correlation with the arrangement of the papillae lining the stomach. The alternative conditions of the stomach may occur in the one colony in which some of the zooids have distinctly 6 folds and others have collapsed and flattened stomachs, where the folds appear to be confined to a simple fold on either side of the suture line. Testis follicles gathered into a grape-like cluster posterior to the testis in the anterior part of the posterior abdomen.

Larvae. Known only from specimens from Kerguelen Islands and Macquarie Island [Kott, 1954] and in the present collection in specimens from Macquarie Island (*Eltanin* Sta. 1418). They are small (0.55 mm) and very plentiful in the peribranchial cavity. There are 4 median ampullae, which alternate with the anterior suckers; lateral ampullae, which develop from the base of each side of the median ampullae; and dorsal and ventral posterior projections, which support single clusters of vesicles. It is the arrangement of these vesicles that distinguishes the larvae.

Remarks. The form of the colony of this species with zooids arranged in parallel and at right angles to the upper surface on to which they open, the loose test on the surface of the lobes, and the circular systems and conspicuous common cloacal apertures are distinctive and characteristic of Herdman's colony from Kerguelen. *Synoicium arenaceum* Michaelsen was described as having 5 broad longitudinal muscle bands on the thorax. As the colonies are in every other respect identical with some in the present collection, it must be assumed that the 5 muscle bands are due to the coalescence of the more numerous very fine bands observed in other specimens. The sandy flat-topped species from New Zealand [*A. novaezealandiae* (Brewin, 1952a); *A. cottrelli* (Brewin, 1957); *A. quadrisulcatum* Millar, 1960; and *Synoicium kuranui* Brewin (see Millar, 1960)] are very closely related. Small, possibly insignificant differences in the number of longitudinal muscles, the number of stigmata, the absence of sand from the surface test, the size of the colonies, and the number of zooids involved in each system may be explained in terms of individual variation and maturity, particularly since several colonies in the present collection from the South Shetland Islands are small, typical of the ones described for *A. novaezealandiae*, *A. cottrelli*, etc. Unfortunately, larvae have not been described for this group of New Zealand related species.

The variable condition of the stomach has led to considerable confusion in the taxonomy of this and other species (e.g., *A. stewartense*). Folded or smooth stomachs occurring in zooids in the same colony in the present collection have made it possible to clarify the situation. It seems probable that the validity of separate genera for *Aplidium* spp. and *Synoicium* spp. is in doubt. Millar [1960] has questioned the separation of *S. kuranui* and *S. arenaceum* (< *Aplidium recumbens* Herdman). Although the difference depends on the development of the areolar lining of the stomach wall, the elevations in *S. kuranui* are expressed on the outer wall of the stomach, whereas in the pres-

ent species there are merely variations in distribution of papillae inside the stomach.

Aplidium caeruleum (Sluiter)

Text figs. 64–67

Amaroucium caeruleum Sluiter, 1906, p. 16.—Hartmeyer, 1911, p. 504.—Van Name, 1945, p. 45.
Aplidium caeruleum; Kott, 1954, p. 172.—Millar, 1960, p. 39.

New Records. Ross Sea: *Atka* Sta. 21 (390 meters). Weddell Sea: *Edisto* Sta. 20, TR 6 (394 meters). Antarctic Peninsula: *Staten Island* Sta. 24/63 (75 meters). South Shetland Is.: *Eltanin* Sta. 428 (662–1120 meters), Sta. 437 (311 meters).

Previous Records.

Antarctic: Antarctic Peninsula, South Shetland Is. [Sluiter, 1906; Millar, 1960]; Wilhelm II Coast, Enderby Land, Mac. Robertson Land [Hartmeyer, 1911; Kott, 1954].

Subantarctic: ? Marion I. [Millar, 1960].

Distribution. Circum-antarctic in waters of the continental shelf and slope from 75 down to about 1000 meters. Millar's doubtful record from Marion Island is from not particularly deep water and indicates perhaps that this comparatively rare species, which appears to tolerate a great range of depths, has a much wider distribution into the subantarctic area than is at present known.

Description. Colonies are usually upright, club-shaped, often evenly invested with sand externally. There may be 2 lobes or heads from a single base, or in particularly wide colonies there may be 2 inverted cone-shaped bases supporting a widely spreading upper part of the colony. The latter condition appears as though two colonies had fused in their head region but not fused basally (B.A.N.Z.A.R.E. Sta. 107, Mac. Robertson Land). Height of colonies generally about 4 cm. Increase in size mainly involves an increase in diameter. The outer layer of test is skin-like and tough, or quite brittle with sand. Internally the test is soft and in preserved specimens is pigmented bright blue [present specimens, also Sluiter, Van Name, Hartmeyer, Kott] or red [Kott]. Colorless specimens have also been recorded [Hartmeyer, Millar]. The pigmentation is not always evenly distributed and is often confined to blood vessels and membranous fibers in the test, while the matrix of the test is colorless. Where pigment is present it shines through the external layer of test, which is colorless except in the

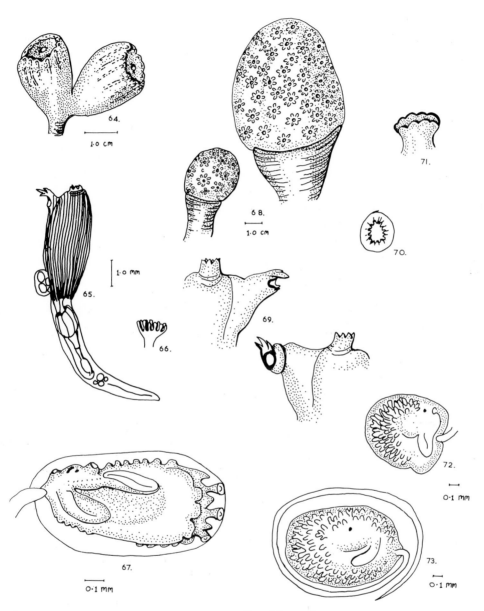

Aplidium caeruleum

64. Colony.
65. Contracted zooid showing embryos protruding through body wall (muscles shown on thorax only).
66. Anal border.
67. Larva.

Synoicium adareanum

68. Colonies.
69. Atrial apertures, showing sphincter relaxed and contracted.
70. Atrial velum.
71. Anal border.
72. Young larva.
73. Older larva.

region of zooid openings. Zooids are arranged in the test in circular systems of 6 to 15 zooids around a conspicuous central common cloaca. In narrow lobes there is only one system with the zooids arranged around the periphery of the colony; however, as the colony expands the number of systems increases from 4 or 5 in a colony 2 cm in diameter up to 20 in large colonies 6 cm in diameter (B.A.N.Z.A.R.E. Sta. 107, Mac. Robertson Land). The test above each zooid is often, but not always, conspicuously raised, but this rise may depend on the state of contraction of the zooids in preservative.

Zooids are large, often as much as 12 mm long in the contracted state and up to 3 mm wide in the thoracic region. The branchial aperture has 6 lobes. The atrial aperture, with well developed sphincter muscle, is often produced almost into a siphon with a stout languet, of varying length, sometimes divided into 3 or even 4 lobes from the anterior border of the opening. There is a narrow frilled atrial velum in the base of the atrial siphon. The musculature is well developed with about 20 longitudinal bands on the thorax extending along both sides of the ventral aspect of the abdomen and posterior abdomen. The branchial sac is wide with 6 to 20 rows of stigmata, often all with parastigmatic vessels, with parastigmatic vessels absent from the most posterior rows, or with no parastigmatic vessels. Millar [1960] suggests that 'each row crossed by a bar is later divided into two rows. This accounts for the large range in the number of rows.' However, zooids with a large number of rows are always without parastigmatic vessels, and 13 rows of stigmata with parastigmatic vessels have been counted in a specimen with a total of 20 rows. Possibly the process is a continuing one, and new parastigmatic vessels and rows of stigmata are developing from the anterior end of the zooid as the branchial sac matures posteriorly. There are about 25 stigmata in each row. The esophagus is narrow and the stomach rather 'shield-shaped' (like that of *S. giardi*), with 10 to 13 shallow folds, often broken and irregular, especially on the side against the intestine. Folds may be completely absent [Millar, 1960; Hartmeyer, 1911]. The anal border is fringed by about 12 long finger-like lobes. The posterior abdomen is often long and sturdy with the testis follicles multilobed and in double rows with a clump of ova anteriorly. The brood pouch indicated by Sluiter and Kott and discussed by other authors is due to the contraction of the body musculature, which does not involve the dorso-posterior corner of the thorax, so that in the contracted zooid developing embryos in the peribranchial cavity are forced posteriorly where they cause the body wall to bulge out between the contracted muscles.

Larvae. From 4 or 5 to 11 in the peribranchial cavity. They are large, 1.0 mm long, with 4 median ampullae alternating with anterior suckers. On each side of the median line is a row of diminishing lateral ampullae, large and corresponding with the median ampullae anteriorly and diminishing postero-ventrally to the base of the tail and postero-dorsally to the branchial aperture. Kott [1954] and Millar [1960] describe larvae with otolith but no ocellus, and in a colony from the same station Millar found the larval form with both otolith and ocellus.

Biology. Hartmeyer [1911] found colonies with developing embryos in January and July. The breeding period of this species is therefore not very restricted.

Remarks. Even where pigmentation of the test is absent, this species is unique in the consistency of the test, the arrangement and large size of zooids, and the presence of parastigmatic vessels.

Genus *Synoicium* Phipps, 1774

Type species: *Synoicium turgens* Phipps, 1774
Posterior abdomen continuous with abdomen. Stomach wall smooth or with rounded elevations.

KEY TO ANTARCTIC SPECIES OF *Synoicium*

1. Conspicuous fingerlike process protecting branchial and cloacal openings..............***tentaculatum***, p. 69
   (South Orkney Is., abyssal)
   No conspicuous fingerlike processes protecting openings.. 2
2. Stomach wall with rounded elevations................. 3
   Stomach wall smooth.................................. 4
3. Pedunculate or sessile; rounded heads......***giardi***, p. 68
   (South Georgia, Kerguelen Is.)
   Pedunculate flat-topped lobes............***kuranui***, p. 68
   (Magellanic area, New Zealand)
4. Area of plain unperforated branchial membrane dorsally and ventrally.........................***triplex***, p. 70
   (Antarctic Peninsula)
   No area of unperforated branchial membrane dorsally and ventrally..5
5. Zooids in circular systems........................... 6
   Zooids not in circular systems.......***pererratum***, p. 71
   (South Shetland Is.)
6. Colony investing; stigmata 'punch-hole'...............
   ....***kerguelenense***, p. 70
   (Kerguelen Is.)
   Colony pedunculate; stigmata rectangular............. 7
7. Large capitate colony...............***adareanum***, p. 65
   (circum-antarctic to S. Georgia)
   Small cylindrical colony............***ramulosum***, p. 66
   (Knox Coast)

Synoicium adareanum (Herdman)

Text figs. 68–73

Atopogaster elongata Herdman, 1902, p. 194 [not Herdman, 1886, p. 173 < *Aplidium fuegiense* Cunningham, 1871, p. 66; 1871a, p. 490].

Polyclinum adareanum Herdman, 1902, p. 195.— Sluiter, 1906, p. 13.

Lissamaroucium magnum Sluiter, 1906, p. 19.—Hartmeyer, 1911, p. 514.—Herdman, 1912, p. 320; 1915, p. 102.

Synoicium steineni Michaelsen, 1907, p. 33.—Hartmeyer, 1921, p. 279.

Macroclinum incertum Hartmeyer, 1909–1911, p. 1660.

Atopogaster incerta Hartmeyer, 1911, p. 512.

Macroclinum magnum Sluiter, 1914, p. 30.

Amaroucium [Synoicium] steineni Michaelsen, 1921, pp. 34, 36, 37.

Synoicium adareanum; Hartmeyer, 1921, p. 280.— Van Name, 1945, p. 59.—Kott, 1954, p. 167.— Millar, 1960, p. 45.

? *Oxycorynia mawsoni* Harant and Vernières, 1938, p. 7.

New Records. Ross Sea: *Edisto* Sta. 5 (400 meters). *Glacier* Ocean Sta. 1 (386 meters), Sta. BL-13 (125 meters). *Northwind* Sta. 8 (135 meters). *Staten Island* Ocean Sta. 10-2 (128 meters). Knox Coast: *Atka* Sta. 29 (135 meters) ; *Edisto* Sta. 45[7] (184 meters), Sta. 115[7] (184 meters). Davis Sea: *Edisto* Sta. 12[7] (274 meters). Weddell Sea: *Staten Island* Sta. 17, B 10-3 (239 meters). *Westwind* Sta. 3 (210 meters), Sta. 4 (796 meters). Antarctic Peninsula: *Edisto* Sta. 28, TD 4 (135 meters), Sta. 38, OP 17 (129 meters). *Staten Island* Sta. 14/63 (45–76 meters), Sta. 37/63 (49 meters), Sta. 66/63 (62 meters), Sta. 67/63 (38 meters). South Shetland Is.: *Staten Island* Sta. 45/63 (55 meters). *Eltanin* Sta. 410 (240 meters), Sta. 435 (73 meters), Sta. 439 (165 meters), Sta. 445 (101 meters).

Previous Records.

Antarctic: Ross Sea [Herdman, 1902; Millar, 1960]; Adélie Coast [Kott, 1954]; Wilhelm II Coast [Hartmeyer, 1911]; Enderby Land, Mac. Robertson Land [Kott, 1954]; Weddell Sea [Herdman, 1912]; Antarctic Peninsula [Sluiter, 1906; 1914]; South Shetland Is., South Georgia [Michaelsen, 1907; Millar, 1960].

Subantarctic: ? Kerguelen Is. [Kott, 1954].

Distribution. Circum-antarctic on the continental shelf

---

[7] U.S. Navy Antarctic Expedition, 1947–1948.

to slope area from 55 to 796 meters. The record from the Kerguelen Islands is doubtful and needs confirmation.

Description. Colonies usually consist of large rounded or clavate heads. The basal half is usually transversely wrinkled and leathery, representing the stalk, which is more or less continuous with the head and only slightly narrower. The maximum height of a colony is 18 cm and maximum diameter 12 cm. Colonies may consist of a single head or up to 6 heads from a single basal stalk. Occasionally a small stalked head branches from a larger stalk. The test is firm and cartilaginous, semitransparent to glassy. On the head it is smooth externally and less firm than in the stalk. Sand may be embedded in the surface test and affects the color of the colony. Preserved colonies are usually gray or pale pink-gray, the pink color being due partly to the reddish zooids. A living colony from U.S.S. *Staten Island* Sta. 67/63 is described by the collector as orange. Zooids are arranged in circular systems of 6 to 10 zooids around a conspicuous common cloaca. The systems are distributed evenly over the head.

Zooids are large, 12 to 20 mm, of which the thorax and abdomen are about 4 mm each; the length of the posterior abdomen varies. The branchial aperture is 6-lobed; the atrial aperture usually produced well forward to form a siphon with 3 lobes on the anterior rim of the aperture. These lobes may be considerably reduced or contracted, particularly when the whole siphon is extended. Often 3 small pointed lobes apparent on the posterior rim when extended. Just inside the atrial siphon there is an atrial velum, narrow and usually frilled, associated with the sphincter. The thorax has 19 to 23 longitudinal muscles, which branch and ramify to some extent, thus accounting for the variation in numbers. They extend ventrally along both sides of the abdomen and posterior abdomen. The branchial sac is very wide with 18 to 20 rows of stigmata with 20 to 30 stigmata in each row. The stomach is large and voluminous; internally it has minute regular glandular areolations but is quite smooth externally. A posterior stomach is present, lined with fine folds. The anal margin is bilabiate; the margin of each lobe is subdivided into about 5 shallow lobes. In the posterior abdomen the testis follicles are arranged in double rows, with the ovary anterior to them.

Larvae. From 1 to 8 embryos are present enclosed in isolated brood pouches in the test of the single very large specimen from the Antarctic Peninsula (*Staten Island* Sta. 67/63). These larvae are particularly robust and less elongate in relation to their dorso-ventral dimension than the larvae of most species. Sometimes they are almost spherical. Maximum length is 1.7 mm. Despite the large size of the larva, the tail is particularly slender and delicate and not very long. There is a small round otolith but no ocellus. The whole body wall, especially the anterior portion, is raised into smaller and larger ampullae, which are not apparently associated with median or lateral ridges. These ampullae obscure the particularly delicate papillae, which subsequently disappear altogether, and only a small curved definitive zooid remains in the brood pouch. These larvae mature while still enclosed in the parent test.

Biology. The mechanism whereby the embryos develop in a brood pouch enclosed in the tough internal test rather than in the peribranchial cavity of the parent zooid is not known. It may explain the lack of reports of embryos despite the numerous records of this species. It seems probable that the particularly large eggs either at some point along the course of the oviduct or in the peribranchial cavity cause a protrusion of the body wall, which, becoming isolated from the rest of the body by muscular action becomes the brood pouch, or that dissolution of the parent zooid after sexual reproduction leaves the embryos isolated in the test. Evidence for either of these processes should be present in colonies of this species but so far has not been detected. The process of dissolution after sexual reproduction is known in antarctic ascidians (see *Placentela translucida* p. 42); the isolation of a brood pouch would be merely an extension of the condition already observed in *Aplidium caeruleum.*

The mechanism whereby the offspring of the colony are liberated from the test is not known; it seems likely from the condition of mature embryos in the present colony, where tail and papillae are lost, that sexual reproduction as well as asexual reproduction produces new zooids in the parent colony. This process has also been suggested for another large antarctic species, *Distaplia cylindrica.*

Remarks. The colony shape and systems of the present species are very similar to those of *Aplidium caeruleum;* the zooids are also of a similar size, with wide thorax, strong musculature, similar modifications of the atrial aperture with anteriorly produced siphon and atrial velum. The shallow stomach folds of *A. caeruleum* are often absent altogether. The species may be distinguished, however, by the consistency of the test, the absence of parastigmatic vessels, the larger

number of stigmata in each row in the present species, and the location and form of developing embryos. *Oxycorynia mawsoni* Harant and Vernières, 1938, from Commonwealth Bay, is recognizable as a synonym of this species mainly by the colony, the shape of the stomach, and the anteriorly produced atrial siphon.

Synoicium ramulosum new species

Text figs. 74, 75

Type Locality. Knox Coast: *Edisto* Sta. 44[8] (184 meters). Holotype, colony, USNM 11971; paratypes, numerous colonies, USNM 11972.

Additional Records. Knox Coast: *Edisto* Sta. 45[8] (184 meters).

Distribution. The species is small, sandy, and inconspicuous and may have a wider distribution than is suggested by the present records. The nature of the colony suggests its special adaptation for a sandy environment, and it is possible that the distribution is especially limited.

Description. Upright, sandy, fingerlike lobes, maximum height 1.5 cm. In their basal half the lobes divide to form prop-like or horizontal branches, which facilitate the rooting of the colony in a sandy substrate. The basal half of the lobes has hairlike extensions from the surface of the test, which also facilitate their rooting. There is a thick encrustation of sand on the hairs and in the surface test of the basal half of the lobes, but the upper terminal part is naked. Terminally the test is semitransparent and swells over the anterior end of each zooid. Zooids form single circular systems of 4 to 9 individuals in each lobe, surrounding large central common cloacal openings. Branchial openings interrupt the surface around the outer rim of the terminal surface of the colony.

Zooids are about 5 mm long, contracted. The thorax, abdomen, and posterior abdomen occupy about equal parts of this total length. Six pronounced branchial lobes project into the test surrounding the aperture so that the 6 branchial lobes of each zooid are quite apparent on the surface of the colony. The atrial opening from the anterior third of the dorsal surface is on a short muscular siphon with a tripartite languet from the anterior border of the opening. The lobes of the atrial opening extend into the rim of the common cloacal opening; however, the border of the cloacal opening is entire and does not break up into lobes corresponding to those of the atrial lip. The

---

[8] U.S. Navy Antarctic Expedition, 1947–1948.

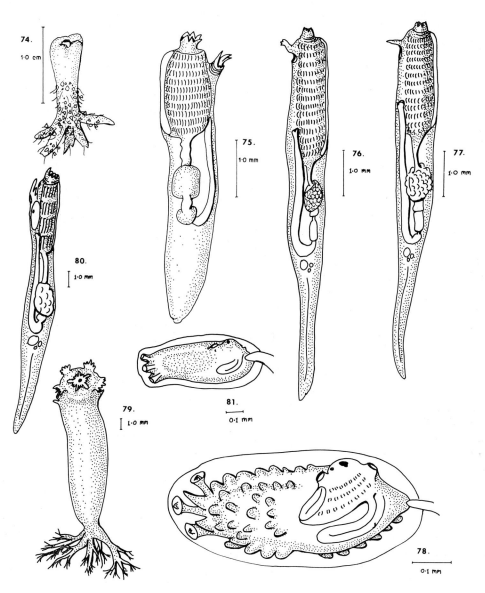

Synoicium ramulosum
74. Colony.
75. Zooid.

Synoicium kuranui
76. Zooid.

Synoicium giardi
77. Zooid.
78. Larva.

Synoicium tentaculatum
79. Colony.
80. Zooid.
81. Larva.

posterior border of the atrial opening is also produced in 3 minute lobes. There are about 30 fine longitudinal muscle bands on the thorax, which break up into fibers and anastomose over a large part of the abdomen and extend as wide bands down on either side of the posterior abdomen. There are also fine transverse muscle bands present on the thorax. There are 10 rows of 10 to 20 stigmata. The esophagus is long; the stomach is round and smooth externally with fine glandular papillae internally. There is a rounded posterior stomach in the pole of the straight gut loop. The posterior abdomen is stout and not very long. Gonads were not present in these specimens.

Remarks. This species is distinguished from other species of this genus by the short stout posterior abdomen, the form of the atrial opening, the thoracic musculature, and especially the form of the colony. The subdivision of the basal part of the upright cylindrical lobes to form rootlike branches is unusual and reminiscent of the condition in *Synoicium tentaculatum* new species. However, the reduction in stigmata and the special development of the lobes surrounding the apertures characteristic of *S. tentaculatum* has not occurred in *S. ramulosum.* The development of hairs from the surface of the test is unusual in this genus and, together with the form of the basal part of the lobes, suggests a high degree of adaptation for a life in a sandy substrate.

Synoicium kuranui Brewin

Text fig. 76

Synoicium kuranui Brewin, 1950b, p. 355.—Millar, 1960, p. 49.

New Records. Drake Passage: *Eltanin* Sta. 369 (293 meters).

Previous Records. North Island, New Zealand [Brewin, 1950b; Millar, 1960].

Distribution. Circum-subantarctic? In New Zealand the species has been taken in the sublittoral area [Brewin, 1950b] and from 84 meters off the North Island, and the present record suggests that the species may occur at other locations in the Subantarctic.

Description. Colonies consist of small stalked heads, flattened on the top, and joined together by a basal membrane. Lobes from 1.5 up to 4 cm high are known from New Zealand; however, the lobes in the present collection are only 1.5 cm tall. The stalk occupies the greater length of the lobe and is covered with sand, which is usually absent on the head. The test of the head is very soft and completely transparent,

whereas that of the stalk is harder. Zooids are arranged in circular to oval systems with up to 10 zooids in each system. There may be more than one system in each lobe.

Zooids are small, up to 9 mm long and 1 mm wide in the thoracic region. They have a 6-lobed branchial siphon and the atrial aperture has a long anterior lip, sometimes 3-lobed on the end. There are 10 to 13 longitudinal muscle bands along each side of the abdomen continuing down both sides of the abdomen and posterior abdomen. There are 10 to 14 rows of 14 to 18 stigmata. The stomach is small with low rounded external elevations. The posterior abdomen has a double row of testis follicles.

Larvae. Not yet known.

Remarks. Millar has discussed the possibility of synonymy of this species with *A. recumbens* (> *S. arenaceum*). Although *A. recumbens* shows many variations of the stomach, as yet no external elevations have been described.

Synoicium giardi (Herdman)

Text figs. 77, 78

? *Morchelloides affinis* Herdman, 1886, p. 177.
Morchellium giardi Herdman, 1886, p. 181; 1891a, p. 625.
Synoicium giardi; Lahille, 1890, p. 240.—Hartmeyer, 1909–1911, p. 1476; 1911, p. 550.—Kott, 1954, p. 169.—Millar, 1960, p. 48.

New Records. None.

Previous Records.
Antarctic: South Georgia [Millar, 1960].
Subantarctic: Kerguelen Is. [Herdman, 1886; Hartmeyer, 1911; Kott, 1954].

Distribution. It is amazing that this distinctive and not uncommon species is not represented in the present collection. It occurs in fairly shallow water and has not been taken from depths greater than 110 meters. It is commonly reported from Kerguelen Islands, and, as Millar suggests, the records from South Georgia indicate a wide distribution, probably in the Subantarctic, South Georgia representing the southern limits.

Description. Many rounded heads rising from a common base; sometimes lower and dome-shaped, 3 cm in diameter and 1.5 cm high. The test is firm and gelatinous, smooth externally and without sand or foreign particles adhering. Preserved colonies are gray to buff in color. Zooids are arranged in regular circular systems, apparent from the surface as star-shaped markings. The test is produced into 6 small evaginations around each branchial opening, which accommodate the 6 lobes of the branchial apertures. The atrial aperture on the dorsal surface is slightly produced anteriorly and has a simple pointed languet from the anterior rim. There are moderately developed longitudinal muscle bands on the thorax, which extend along the abdomen and posterior abdomen. The branchial sac has 12 to 18 rows of about 12 stigmata. The stomach has conspicuous rounded or mulberry-like elevations. The posterior abdomen is continuous with the abdomen and has anterior ovary and testis follicles in rows.

Larvae. Plentiful in the peribranchial cavity [Kott, 1954]. They are 0.66 mm long with ocellus and otolith. Four median ampullae alternate with the anterior papillae and ampullae from the lateral lines extend dorsally and ventrally, diminishing in size toward the base of the branchial aperture and base of the tail, respectively. Numerous small ampullae also develop from the body of the larva anterior to the oozooid, on both sides of the body.

Remarks. The texture and form of the colony and the larvae are similar to those of *Aplidium caeruleum;* however, the ampullae from the body of the larvae behind the lateral lines are absent in *A. caeruleum.* The stomach areolations distinguish the species from others. Although rounded systems are not apparent in Herdman's *M. affinis,* it is possible that his colony represents a variation of the present species with 8 branchial lobes.

Synoicium tentaculatum new species

Text figs. 79–81

Type Locality. South Orkney Is.: *Eltanin* Sta. 480 (2800 meters). Holotype, USNM 11973; paratype, 1 specimen USNM 11974.

Description. Narrow cylindrical flat-topped colonies about 1 cm long. The basal half of the colony divides into 4 to 6 narrow extensions or 'roots' with fine hairs along their length, which anchor the colony on the surface of small pebbles. The test is thin, transparent, and invested completely with sand, making it brittle. From 4 to 6 zooids are arranged around the periphery of the colony, forming a single system in each lobe around a central common cloacal opening. Branchial openings are just below the upper border of the colony and are protected above by a fan-like projection of 5 fingerlike hollow lobes of the test supported by a fleshy base; beneath the aperture there

is a single hollow fingerlike lobe. The common cloacal opening in the center of the flattened upper surface is surrounded by a number of fairly long fingerlike lobes, which correspond to the number of zooids in the system. Each of these longer lobes alternate with two smaller lobes, thus completing a circle around the cloacal aperture.

The zooids are small, about 6 mm long; the thorax, abdomen, and posterior abdomen of equal length. They project in parallel down through the test and into the basal hollow stalks of the root-bearing processes. There are 6 branchial lobes, long dorsally and becoming shorter toward the ventral side of the aperture, where the shortest lobe extends into the hollow test projection below the branchial opening on the surface of the colony while the longer 5 branchial lobes fit into the fingerlike projections anterior to the external aperture. The fleshy projection from the anterior border of the atrial opening and the adjacent body wall is divided into a long median lobe and 2 accessory lobes of diminishing size on either side of the median lobe. The long median lobe and immediately adjacent lateral lobes are accommodated in the hollow test projections that surround the common cloacal opening. Thus the zooids are arranged with their dorsal borders to the center of the colony. There are 12 longitudinal thoracic muscles continuing along the ventral side of the abdomen and along both sides of the posterior abdomen. There are 3 large triangular dorsal languets in the branchial sac and 4 rows of long rectangular stigmata with about 8 in each row. The gut is voluminous and the more or less spherical stomach has externally rounded elevations. There is a posterior stomach. The posterior abdomen has a double row of testis follicles and an anterior ovary.

Larvae. A single developing embryo 0.7 mm long is present in the peribranchial cavity. There are 3 anterior papillae arranged in a triangle. They are not of the usual polyclinid type with a central cone of adhesive cells but appear to be deeply invaginated cylinders, although the extent of the invagination could not be determined. There is a small otolith but no ocellus.

Remarks. This is a particularly interesting species, one of the few aplousobranch zooids adapted for abyssal conditions with few and very large stigmata in the branchial sac and a particular development of test and apertures to ensure protection of body openings. Together with these specialized characters the species retains a larval form with papillae in the primitive triradiate arrangement and with a simple deeply invaginated adhesive surface, as found in the Euherdmani-inae.

The zooid systems are simple, representing a stage not far removed from separate atrial openings to the surface. The division of the basal half of the colony into separated processes into which the zooids project may represent a condition close to *Euherdmania* spp. in which the zooids are separate. It is more probably, however, a secondary division of the colony to facilitate anchoring to the substrate. The colony most resembles the arrangement of zooids in *Synoicium pellucidum* (Ritter and Forsyth) [Van Name, 1945], but there is not the same development of protective lobes around the apertures.

Synoicium kerguelenense (Hartmeyer)

Macroclinum kerguelenense Hartmeyer, 1911, p. 547.
? *Synoicium kerguelenense*; Kott, 1957a, p. 2.

New Records.   None.

Previous Records.   Kerguelen Is., Baie de l'Observatoire [Hartmeyer, 1911]. ? Heard I., Atlas Cove [Kott, 1957a]. No depth records available; probably a shallow water species.

Description.   Irregular investing colony, 24 mm wide, 30 mm long and from 3 to 7 mm thick. Test is rather tough, but smooth and transparent and without foreign bodies encrusting or included. Zooids are not numerous and are arranged in circular systems around a common cloacal opening. Zooids are small, not more than 1.3 mm long. The branchial siphon is 6-lobed, the atrial aperture has a small undivided anterior lip. The branchial sac has 8 to 10 rows of small oval stigmata. The gut forms a short loop, stomach relatively large and smooth-walled. The posterior abdomen is of varying length.

Remarks.   Hartmeyer's colonies are young specimens and until further information is available it is difficult to determine whether the characteristic small stigmata are a specific character as present in *Aplidiopsis pyriformis* or merely represent the branchial perforations of immature zooids of another species. The abdomen of *A. pyriformis* is separated from the posterior abdomen by a marked constriction (which also occurs in *Aplidiopsis georgianum*) and this, together with a spherical colony, distinguishes it from the present species. *Synoicium kerguelenense*; Kott, 1957a; and *Polyclinum minutum* Herdman, 1886, have similar 'punch-hole' type stigmata in about 8 rows, as in Hartmeyer's species, and abdomen and posterior abdomen continuous without constriction. Both the

S. kerguelenense and the *P. minutum* are spherical and resemble the colony of *A. pyriformis*. It is possible that *S. kerguelenense* (Hartmeyer), *S. kerguelenense*; Kott, and *Polyclinum minutum* Herdman all represent a single species of variable colony form, with 'punch-hole' type stigmata and unconstricted posterior abdomen. It is equally possible that they all represent young colonies of *A. pyriformis* in which the posterior abdomen has not become constricted from the abdomen, or that they are young colonies of the same or different species without constricted posterior abdomen in which the stigmata lengthen to the usual rectangular form. Further collections of specimens at different stages of maturity should help to clarify the situation.

Synoicium triplex (Sluiter)

Psammaplidium triplex Sluiter, 1906, p. 23.
Macroclinum triplex; Hartmeyer, 1909–1911, p. 1471.
Synoicium triplex; Van Name, 1945, p. 60.

New Records.   None.

Previous Records.   Antarctic Peninsula, Schollaert Channel, from between 2 and 3 meters [Sluiter, 1906].

Description.   Two irregular colonies were present in Sluiter's material, the largest 7 by 5 cm. The surface smooth and gray. The test is tough and transparent with considerable embedded sand. No systems or common cloacal orifices were detected, and zooids lie irregularly in the test crossing one another. Zooids are up to 13 mm, of which the posterior abdomen is the greatest part. There are 6 branchial lobes, and the atrial aperture situated on the dorsal surface entirely lacks an anterior lip. There are 13 rows of stigmata and the stigmata themselves occupy only a small area in the center of each row; the rest of the width of the branchial sac is occupied by a broad lamina on either side of the endostyle and the dorsal lamina. The stomach is smooth-walled. In the posterior abdomen the ovary is anterior and the testis occupies only a short distance of the posterior abdomen in the described specimens. (After Sluiter.)

Remarks.   The colony and zooids resemble *Aplidium fuegiense* and *Aplidium irregulare*; especially the former, which often has a very small atrial languet. For the present, however, the species is considered distinct, characterized by the extensive area of plain unperforated membrane in the branchial sac. The plain stomach does not necessarily distinguish the species from *Aplidium* spp.

Synoicium pererratum (Sluiter)

Macroclinum pererratum Sluiter, 1912, p. 458; 1914, p. 30.
Synoicium pererratum; Van Name, 1945, p. 61.

New Records. Antarctic Peninsula: *Edisto* Sta. 232[9] (74 meters).

Previous Records. South Shetland Is.: 138 and 773 meters (Sluiter, 1912).

Distribution. The species is apparently rare and confined to the Antarctic Peninsula.

Description. Maximum dimensions 10 cm long and 5 to 10 mm thick. Colonies attached by the lower surface. Zooids, arranged in long curved double rows, form little elevations on the upper surface. Large common cloacal openings are present, from which double rows of zooids radiate. Sand is embedded in the surface test.

Zooids measure up to 8 mm long of which only 2.5 mm is occupied by the thorax. The posterior abdomen is relatively short and stout. There are 6 lobes on the border of the branchial aperture, and the atrial aperture has an anterior 3-lobed lip. There are 8 narrow muscle bands on the thorax, which extend down both sides of the abdomen and posterior abdomen. There are 13 to 18 rows of 12 or 13 stigmata. The stomach is large and smooth-walled. Sluiter describes the ovary as situated a little way back in the posterior abdomen with as many as 8 eggs, whereas the greater part of the posterior abdomen is occupied by testis follicles. Gonads were not developed in the present colony.

Remarks. The zooid of this species has a remarkably large number of eggs present in the ovary, and this, together with the short stout posterior abdomen and parallel arrangement of zooid in the colony, distinguishes the species. The colony and zooids most resemble those of *Aplidium circumvolutum* with the zooids not crowded and arranged in long lines, with a comparatively short posterior abdomen, and clustered testis lobes. *Aplidium circumvolutum* does extend down the Antarctic Peninsula. As yet no variation in the condition of the stomach folds has been recorded, and *S. pererratum* and *A. circumvolutum* must be considered distinct for the present.

Genus *Aplidiopsis* Lahille, 1890

Type species: *Aplidiopsis vitreus* Lahille, 1890

With a marked constriction separating abdomen from sac-like posterior abdomen.

[9] U.S. Navy Antarctic Expedition, 1947–1948.

KEY TO ANTARCTIC SPECIES OF *Aplidiopsis*

1. Small rounded 'punch-hole' stigmata 10 to 12 per row.... ....**pyriformis,** p. 71
(Kerguelen Is.)
Rectangular stigmata, 15 to 20 per row.............. 2
2. Stalked colony.....................**georgianum,** p. 73
(Patagonian Shelf, South Georgia, South Shetland Is., Antarctic Peninsula)
Investing colony.....................**discoveryi,** p. 74
(North Island, New Zealand, Patagonian Shelf)

Aplidiopsis pyriformis (Herdman)

Text fig. 82

Polyclinum pyriformis Herdman, 1886, p. 188.
Synoicium pyriformis Kott, 1954, p. 170.

New Records. None.

Previous Records. Kerguelen Is. [Herdman, 1886; Kott, 1954].

Distribution. One of the few species that seem to have a limited distribution; so far records are confined to the Kerguelen Islands, where specimens have been taken in from 18 to 110 meters.

Description. Rounded colonies on short stalks or sometimes sessile. The test is soft throughout and the stalk is not hard and leathery. Zooids are small and arranged in numerous small circular systems and do not project down into the stalk.

There are 6 branchial lobes, and the anterior atrial lip is pointed or has minute lobes on the end. There are 10 to 16 rows of 10 to 12 rounded, sometimes 'punch-hole' stigmata. The gut loop is rather wide and the stomach small and rectangular or circular, without folds or areolations. The posterior abdomen is connected by a narrow neck from an area in the loop of the gut and is not continuous with the abdomen, but the gut loop is not twisted. The posterior abdomen is sac-like and contains the testis follicles and ovary clumped together.

Larvae. Large, 0.66 mm long. They have ocellus and otolith and the usual 3 anterior papillae. However, there are no median ampullae and the stalks of the papillae rise from the anterior end of the larva very close together. There are 4 pairs of large rounded lateral ampullae on either side of the papillae. From the base of the most dorsal ampulla on each side there is a fine posterior projection that separates off from the lateral line and supports a double row or circle of vesicles above either side of the endostyle. Ventro-posteriorly there is a similar pair of vesicular clusters supported by paired stalks from the lateral line halfway along the ventral surface of the larva,

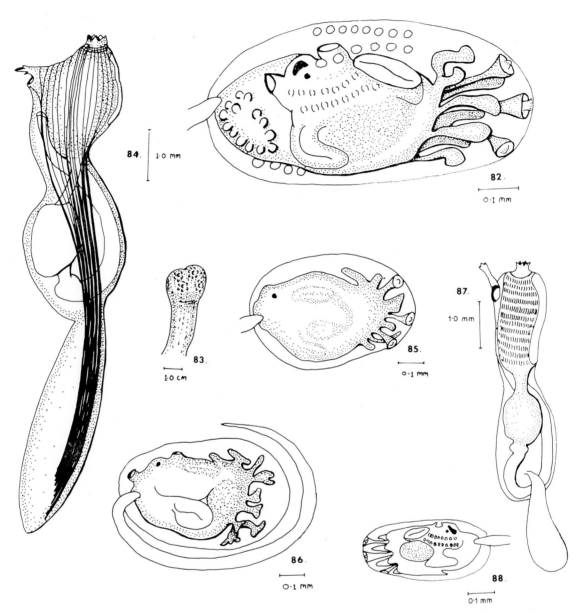

Aplidiopsis pyriformis
82. Larva.

Aplidiopsis georgianum
83. Colony.
84. Zooid showing longitudinal muscles.
85. Younger larva [after Millar, 1960].

86. Older larva showing breaking up of vesicles [after Millar, 1960].

Aplidiopsis discoveryi
87. Zooid.
88. Larva.

but no vesicles extending from the base of the ventral ampullae are present in the anterior part of the ventral surface.

Remarks. The appearance of the colony is similar to that of *Synoicium giardi,* also present in this area, and to other species from the Antarctic. The zooids themselves are distinguished by the posterior abdomen, and the larva is unique for species of this family from Antarctica.

Aplidiopsis georgianum (Sluiter)

Text figs. 83–86

Synoicium georgianum Sluiter, 1932, p. 11.—Millar, 1960, p. 47.

? *Psammaplidium retiforme* Herdman, 1886, p. 248.

? *Synoicium kohli* Sluiter, 1932, p. 14.

New Records. South Shetland Is.: *Eltanin* Sta. 410 (240 meters), Sta. 418 (426 meters), Sta. 419 (552 meters). Antarctic Peninsula: *Edisto* Sta. 38, OP 17 (129 meters).

Previous Records. Patagonian Shelf, South Georgia [Sluiter, 1932; Millar, 1960].

Distribution. Millar suggests that this species, distinct from *S. adareanum* with which it has been confused, is confined to the Subantarctic (i.e., the Patagonian Shelf and the Magellanic area), with South Georgia representing the most southern extent of its range. The present collection, however, extends the recorded range down the Scotia Ridge to the Antarctic Peninsula. The synonymy of *P. retiforme* Herdman with the present species is doubtful and consequently confirmed records of *A. georgianum* are confined, at this stage, to the one area of the Subantarctic, where it extends over the shelf and slope area from 20 to a depth of 552 meters.

Description. Colonies are usually slender and not more than 2.5 cm long. Several heads may rise from a common base with rootlike processes. The basal half of the colony or stalk may be transversely wrinkled and tough, but often there is no differentiation externally between stalk and head. The test throughout is tough, clear, and flexible with sometimes sand or shell particles adhering externally. Zooids are arranged in small circular systems of 5 to 9 around common cloacal apertures. The largest colonies have about 5 systems.

Zooids are fairly large, the abdomen and thorax both 2 to 3 mm long, while the posterior abdomen is variable, often greater than half the total length of the zooid. The branchial aperture is 6-lobed and the atrial aperture produced anteriorly with a wide 3-lobed anterior extension or languet. There may also be small pointed lobes on the posterior margin. There are 15 strong longitudinal muscle bands on the thorax, which continue along both sides of the abdomen and posterior abdomen. There are 9 to 15 rows of 15 to 20 stigmata. The stomach is large and smooth, a posterior stomach is present, and the anus is bilabiate. The posterior abdomen is joined to the abdomen by a short neck or constriction from the gut loop. The testis follicles are pear-shaped and bunched in the posterior abdomen and not serially arranged, whereas the ovary is sometimes anterior to the testis follicles and sometimes embedded in them.

Larvae. Present only in a colony from South Georgia in the *Discovery* collection [Millar, 1960]. They are present in the atrial cavities of the zooids and are 0.54 to 0.64 mm long. There are 3 anterior papillae alternating with 4 median ampullae and large dorsal and ventral ampullae. There is an otolith but no ocellus. More advanced larvae showed a breaking up of papillae and ampullae. There are no lateral ampullae.

Biology. Absence of larval ocellus and the atrophy of adhesive organs while larvae are retained in the atrial cavity suggest metamorphosis before liberation, as in the closely related *Synoicium adareanum,* in which the larvae appear to metamorphose into the adult zooid while still retained in the test of the adult colony. There are indications therefore that in both *S. adareanum* and *A. georgianum* at least some of the products of sexual reproduction are never free-swimming but contribute to the increase in the number of zooids in the parent colony. This represents a special development of viviparity.

Remarks. This species resembles *Synoicium adareanum* in colony form, systems, and nature of the test. The larvae differ in structure generally, but both lack an ocellus and show evidence of excessive retention in the parent atrial cavity or test. The atrial siphons are also similar, but this condition is shared by most species in which large zooids form small circular systems (*Aplidium caeruleum, Synoicium giardi*). There are, however, in the present species fewer rows and fewer stigmata in each row and fewer thoracic muscles and the colonies remain smaller. The shape of the abdomen also differs, but this difference could be seasonal. The species are thus clearly distinct. The questioned synonymizing of *Psammaplidium retiforme* Herdman is suggested only by the similarity of colonies of this species with Sluiter's colony of *A. georgianum* from South Georgia.

Aplidiopsis discoveryi Millar

Text figs. 87, 88

Aplidiopsis discoveryi Millar, 1960, p. 51

New Records. Off Tierra del Fuego: *Eltanin* Sta. 981 (40–49 meters).

Previous Record.

Subantarctic: North end of North Island, New Zealand, 128 meters [Millar, 1960].

Distribution. The two available records of this species suggest that it could be circumpolar in the north part of the Subantarctic. *Synoicium kuranui* has a similar distribution.

Description. The colony is sand-free, firm, and gelatinous and is fixed by the whole extent of its basal surface. The test is semitransparent. Zooids are arranged in circular systems around oval or slitlike common cloacal openings. The surface of the colony is raised into rounded areas over each system. Zooids vary from 4.5 to 7.5 mm in total length, of which the thorax, abdomen, and posterior abdomen occupy about equal parts. The atrial opening, present in the anterior third of the thorax, is rounded with a fairly long tongue-like languet from the anterior border of the opening. The tip of the atrial lobe is tridentate. There are about 10 longitudinal muscle bands on either side of the thorax, which converge posteriorly and extend as single bands along either side of the abdomen. On the posterior abdomen the single bands from both sides of the body join into a single band. There are 10 to 15 rows of 15 to 20 stigmata.

The esophagus is fairly long, the stomach rounded and smooth, and the intestine forms a fairly wide loop posterior to the stomach before crossing the esophagus. The posterior abdomen is sac-like and extends from the center of the right side of the abdomen. Gonads consist of a cluster of pear-shaped testis follicles and a group of eggs in the center of the posterior abdomen.

Larvae. Present in the specimens from Tierra del Fuego. They are small and compact (0.5 mm) with large ocellus and an otolith and with the usual 3 anterior adhesive papillae alternating with median ampullae. Lateral ampullae are present on either side of the median line.

Remarks. The species is distinguished by the flat investing form of the colony and by the stalked sac-

like posterior abdomen. The specimen in the present collection is apparently identical with Millar's [1960] specimen from the North Island of New Zealand. These widely separated records suggest that, although the species is rare, it has a wide geographic range.

Family DIDEMNIDAE Giard

Colony usually flat and encrusting, adhering to substrate by a broad base. Zooids small, arranged in complex systems and divided into thorax and abdomen. The test usually contains minute calcareous spicules of stellate form. Longitudinal thoracic muscles unite into a retractor muscle extending into the test. Budding esophageal.

The family is represented by few species in the antarctic region, although these species have a wide circumpolar distribution. One species only, *Polysyncraton chondrilla*, has a range extending from north of the subtropical convergence to the antarctic continent.

KEY TO GENERA OF DIDEMNIDAE

1. Proximal part of sperm duct spirally wound 2
   Proximal part of sperm duct straight 7
2. Branchial sac with 3 rows of stigmata . . . .
   . . . . ***Trididemnum***, p. 80
   Branchial sac with 4 rows of stigmata 3
3. 1 to 3 testis lobes . . . . ***Didemnum***, p. 74
   More than 3 testis lobes 4
4. No common cloaca; zooids open separately . . . .
   . . . . ***Sinecloaca***
   Common cloaca present into which zooids open 5
5. Without posteriorly produced atrial siphon . . . .
   . . . . ***Polysyncraton***, p. 79
   With posteriorly produced atrial siphon 6
6. Atrial siphon smooth . . . . ***Leptoclinides***, p. 82
   Atrial siphon 5-lobed . . . . ***Askonides***
7. Without spicules . . . . ***Diplosoma***, p. 82
   With spicules 8
8. Spicules tetrahedrous . . . . ***Echinoclinum***
   Spicules stellate . . . . ***Lissoclinum***

---

* These genera reported from Antarctica.

Genus *Didemnum* Savigny, 1816

Type species: *Didemnum candidum* Savigny, 1816

Proximal part of the sperm duct spirally wound around the testis, which may be a single rounded gland or two or three pyriform lobes. There are four rows of stigmata in the branchial sac. The test encloses calcareous spicules usually of stellate or spherical form.

KEY TO ANTARCTIC SPECIES OF *Didemnum*

1. Spicules especially in surface layer of test ***biglans***, p. 75
   (circum-antarctic to South Shetland Is.)

Spicules not especially in upper layer of test 2
2. Large lateral organs occupying most of length of thorax.
. . . . **trivolutum,** p. 77
(Falkland Is.)
Lateral organs do not occupy most of length of thorax . . . 3
3. Spicules up to 0.026 mm; testis usually divided . . . .
. . . . **studeri,** p. 75
(South Georgia, Magellanic area, Kerguelen Is.,
Macquarie I., Heard I., Gough I., New Zealand,
Tasmania)
Spicules up to 0.04 mm; testis usually undivided . . . .
. . . . **tenue,** p. 77
(South Georgia, Magellanic area)

Didemnum biglans (Sluiter)

Text figs. 89–91

Leptoclinum biglans Sluiter, 1906, p. 29 [not *Leptoclinum biglans* Michaelsen, 1907].
Didemnum biglans; Hartmeyer, 1911, p. 499.—Van Name, 1945, p. 91.—Kott, 1954, p. 159.—Millar, 1960, p. 57.

New Records. Ross Sea: *Atka* Sta. 23 (392 meters); *Burton Island* Sta. 3(434 meters). Antarctic Peninsula: *Staten Island* Sta. 35/63 (46 meters). South Shetland Islands: *Staten Island* Sta. 44/63 (55 meters), Sta. 64/63 (86 meters); *Eltanin* Sta. 416 (507 meters), Sta. 428 (662–1120 meters).

Previous Records.

Antarctic: Antarctic Peninsula [Sluiter, 1906; Van Name, 1945; Millar, 1960]; Enderby Land [Kott, 1954]; Wilhelm II Coast [Hartmeyer, 1911].

Distribution. Circum-antarctic with a wide depth range from 30 to at least 600 meters, i.e. from sublittoral, shelf, to slope.

Description. Encrusting colonies, maximum extent of surface about 5 cm, 3 mm thick. The test is often semitransparent with spicules only in the surface layer and absent or sparse in the remainder of the test. Spicules may also form a sparse layer in the test at the base of the common cloacal cavity. Millar [1960] records two specimens in which spicules are completely absent. In the surface layer of test the spicules are especially accumulated in the region of the branchial apertures. Spicules are 'burr-like,' 0.018 to 0.025 mm in diameter or in the present colonies (from *Eltanin* Sta. 416 and 428) larger stellate spicules up to 0.05 mm. The common cloacal cavity is thoracic but quite extensive. Abdomina of zooids are embedded in the basal test, but thoraces are isolated from one another and cross the cloacal cavity enclosed in the individual sheath of test, which is often without spicules but supports lateral organs, closely associated with

the thorax. The lateral organs contain a mass of small spicules. There are a few large 6-lobed common cloacal openings scattered over the surface of the colony. Zooids are evenly distributed and not crowded, their openings conspicuous from the surface because of the spicules crowding the branchial lobes. Zooids are small, from 1.5 to 2.5 mm long. The atrial opening is wide and when fully extended the upper border may form a small protrusion or lip. There are 4 rows of stigmata with 8 to 10 stigmata in each row. The testis may be undivided (a single lobe) or divided into 2 or 3 lobes [Millar, 1960]. The vas deferens spirals around the testis 3 to 6 times. In the only colony (*Staten Island* Sta. 44/63) in the present collection in which the testes are developed the glands are divided and the vas deferens spirals only 3 times.

Larvae. Present in the basal common test. They are 1.0 to 1.3 mm long, with ocellus and otolith; 3 median papillae; and basically 4 pairs of lateral ampullae, although these are deeply divided, almost to their base, into two.

Remarks. Although the number of testis lobes and vas deferens spirals and the spicule size and form are variable, the species is distinguished by the distribution of spicules and the nature of the common cloacal system.

Didemnum studeri Hartmeyer

Text figs. 92–94

Leptoclinum, undescribed specimens, Herdman, 1886, p. 283.
Didemnum studeri Hartmeyer, 1911, p. 538.—Van Name, 1945, p. 90.—Kott, 1954, p. 161; 1957a, p. 2.—Millar, 1960, p. 56.
Didemnum [*Leptoclinum*] *studeri* Hartmeyer, 1912, p. 322.
Didemnum studeri var. *typicum* Michaelsen, 1919, p. 23.
Didemnum studeri var. *magalhaense* Michaelsen, 1919, p. 28 [proposed by author in Remarks].
Not *Didemnum studeri* var. *africanum* Michaelsen, 1919, p. 29; 1924, p. 344.
Didemnum studeri f. *typica* Michaelsen, 1924, p. 342.
Didemnum studeri studeri Sluiter, 1932, p. 18.

New Records. Drake Passage: *Eltanin* Sta. 219 (115 meters). Scotia Sea: *Eltanin* Sta. 370 (115 meters). South Orkney Is.: *Eltanin* Sta. 1082 (298–302 meters). Off Tierra del Fuego: *Eltanin* Sta. 981 (40–49 meters). West of Macquarie I.: *Eltanin* Sta. 1417 (79–93 meters), Sta. 1418 (86–101 meters), Sta. 1419 (494–

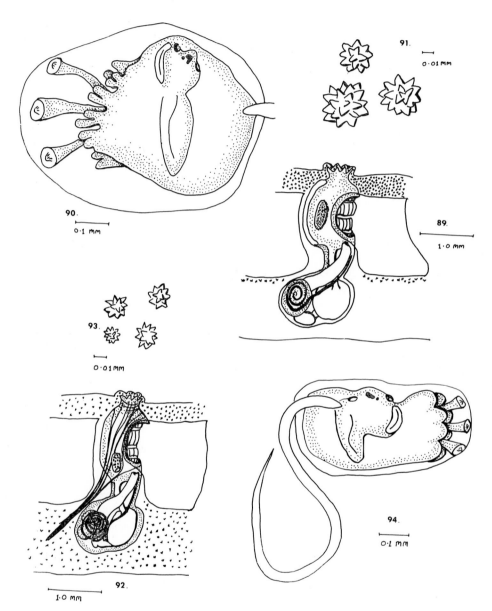

Didemnum biglans

89. Zooid in colony showing disposition of common cloacal cavities and distribution of spicules in surface and basal test.
90. Larva.
91. Spicules.

Didemnum studeri

92. Zooid in colony showing disposition of common cloacal cavities, distribution of spicules, and location of retractor muscle.
93. Spicules.
94. Larva.

714 meters), Sta. 1422 (833–842 meters), Sta. 1423 (1574–1693 meters). Auckland I.: *Eltanin* Sta. 1425 (135–139 meters).

Previous Records.

Antarctic: South Georgia [Sluiter, 1932; Millar, 1960].

Subantarctic: Magellanic area [Michaelsen, 1919; Millar, 1960]; Kerguelen Is. [Hartmeyer, 1911; Kott, 1954]; Macquarie I. [Kott, 1954]; Heard I. [Kott, 1957a]; Gough I. [Millar, 1960]; Chatham Is., Stewart I., Auckland I., New Zealand [Michaelsen, 1924].

Elsewhere: Northeastern Tasmania [Kott, 1954].

Distribution. As Van Name has indicated, the species is most common in shallower waters, from 10 to 100 meters. However, it has been taken off the South Orkney Islands in waters up to 300 meters, off Falkland Islands in 200 meters, and off Macquarie Island and Tasmania in much deeper waters ranging from 79 to 1693 meters.

Description. Colonies range from small cushion-like circular to oval colonies to thin encrusting sheets up to 7 cm, growing on kelp roots, shell fragments, or worm tubes. Preserved specimens are dirty white, pinkish, or pale buff gray, according to the number of spicules present. Spicules may be dense throughout; however, often they are more sparsely distributed. The spicules are stellate, with about 8 to 12 short blunt rays in optical section. They are from 0.015 mm or less up to 0.045 mm, often in the one colony. The cloacal system is thoracic, quite extensive; the thoraces of zooids cross the cloacal cavity independently, or in clumps or double rows. The test sheath supports lateral organs of varying size in close association with the posterior part of the thorax of the zooid. The lateral organs are sometimes large and flattened and sometimes rounded. Abdomina are enclosed in the basal test. The branchial aperture has 6 lobes, the atrial aperture is wide and simple, forming a slight anterior lip from the anterior border when fully extended. The thoracic muscles are particularly conspicuous, well separated on the thorax but converging into a band postero-dorsally, which continues for a short distance along the esophagus and then separates from the body of the zooid and extends into the test where it forms the retractor muscle. The branchial sac is narrow and small, with 4 rows of only about 5 or 6 stigmata. The testis is usually divided into 2 or 3 lobes, although Millar [1960] found 4 lobes in some of the *Discovery* specimens. The vas deferens coils around the testis lobes from 4 to 7 times.

Larvae. Present in the basal test. They are 0.6 mm long with otolith and ocellus, 3 anterior papillae, and 4 pairs of lateral ampullae.

Remarks. Although the cloacal system and condition of the testis and vas deferens could be confused with *D. biglans*, the distribution of spicules, the variation in size of the lateral organs, and the narrow branchial sac with comparatively few stigmata in each row, together with the entirely different larval form, distinguish the species. In the region of Macquarie Island this species is found investing large populations of *Corella eumyota*.

Didemnum trivolutum Millar

Text figs. 95, 96

Didemnum trivolutum Millar, 1960, p. 58.

New Records. None.

Previous Records. Falkland Is., 225–251 meters, and Patagonian Shelf, 99 meters [Millar, 1960].

Description. The colony is thin and encrusting, maximum length 10 cm, average thickness 3 mm. Pale gray or almost white because of the spicules, which are dense throughout the test. Several common cloacal openings apparent over the surface. The spicules are regularly stellate with 8 to 12 rays in optical sections, reaching 0.04 mm in diameter. Spicules formed of bundles of needle-like rays arranged in a stellate fashion are also present but in very small numbers. The common cloacal system is shallow at midthoracic level. The zooids are quite large, reaching a total length of about 2.6 mm. The branchial aperture is 6-lobed, and the large atrial aperture has a small pointed anterior lip from the upper rim. Exceptionally large lateral organs are associated with the thorax, occupying most of its length. There are 4 rows of 11 long narrow stigmata. The testis is undivided and the vas deferens makes only 3 spiral turns around it.

Remarks. The species is distinguished by the shallow cloacal cavity, the exceptionally large lateral organs, the large zooid, and the large number of stigmata in each row.

Didemnum tenue (Herdman)

Leptoclinum tenue Herdman, 1886, p. 281 [part; not Sluiter, 1898a, p. 31].

Leptoclinum asperum Sluiter, 1900, p. 19 [part].

Didemnum tenue Hartmeyer, 1912, pp. 373, 374.—Van Name, 1945, p. 90.

Didemnum studeri var. *africanum* Michaelsen, 1919, p. 29 [part]; 1924, p. 344.

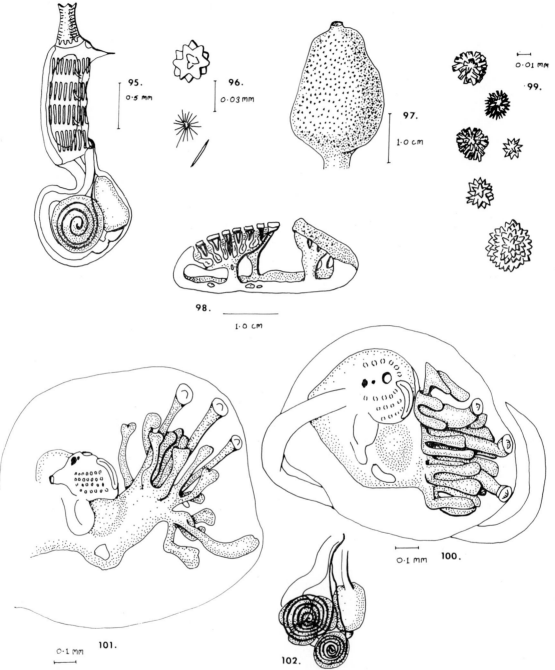

Didemnum trivolutum
95. Zooid [after Millar, 1960].
96. Spicules.

Polysyncraton chondrilla
97. Upright stalked colony.
98. Diagrammatic section through dome-shaped colony show-

ing primary posterior abdominal cloacal cavities and thoracic secondary cavities.
99. Spicules.
100. Larva.
101. Older larva.
102. Abdomen showing divided vas deferens.

? *Didemnum chilense* Ärnbäck, 1929, p. 19.—Brewin, 1950b, p. 359.

New Records. None.

Previous Records.

Antarctic: South Georgia [Van Name, 1945].

Subantarctic: Magellanic area, 450 meters [Herdman, 1886]; Chile, 50°S, 322 meters [Herdman, 1886]; Patagonian Shelf, 1100 meters [Herdman, 1886]; ? Chile, 44°S, 23 meters [Ärnbäck, 1929]; ? Great Barrier I., New Zealand [Brewin, 1950b].

Distribution. Apparently confined to the Magellanic area, Patagonian Shelf, and Chilean coast, although confirmation of its occurrence in New Zealand would indicate circum-subantarctic distribution. Depth range is from 322 to 1100 meters.

Description. Thin encrusting species with the spicules evenly distributed in varying density, stellate and up to 0.03 mm in diameter. Zooids are 'large and conspicuous.' There are 4 rows of 7 to 9 stigmata. The large testis is undivided. There are 9 to 10 spirals of the vas deferens in the specimens from New Zealand, although the number of spirals is not known from other localities. The lateral organs are small at the posterior end of the thorax.

Remarks. Millar [1960] examined Herdman's original material and distinguished *D. trivolutum* from the present species by the size of the lateral organs and spicules. Although the spicules are often not a reliable character in this family, the lateral organs constitute an adequate distinguishing character. Ärnbäck's distinction between *D. chilense* and the present species depends on characters that could be due to zooid contraction.

Genus *Polysyncraton* Nott, 1892

Type species: *Polysyncraton paradoxum* Nott, 1892

Bladder cells in superficial layer of test. With spirally wound vas deferens; large number of testis lobes. No atrial siphon.

Polysyncraton chondrilla (Michaelsen)
Text figs. 97–102

? *Leptoclinum rubicundum* Herdman, 1886, p. 305.
Didemnum chondrilla Michaelsen, 1924, p. 344.—Kott, 1954, p. 165.
Not *Polysyncraton chondrilla*; Kott, 1962, p. 296 [< ? *P. jacksoni* (Herdman), 1886].

New Records. Ross Sea: *Glacier* Sta. BL–13 (125 meters); *Northwind* Sta. 8 (135 meters). Weddell Sea: *Edisto* Sta. 20, TR 5 (384 meters), Sta. 20, TR 6 (394 meters), Sta. 21, TR 7 (412 meters). South Shetland Is.: *Staten Island* Sta. 45/63 (55 meters), Sta. 64/63 (86 meters); *Eltanin* Sta. 410 (240 meters), Sta. 428 ('sampling depth' not recorded), Sta. 432 (935 meters). Antarctic Peninsula: *Edisto* Sta. 226[10] (74 meters). Scotia Sea: *Eltanin* Sta. 732 (265 meters).

Previous Records.

Antarctic: Enderby Land [Kott, 1954].

Subantarctic: North Island, Colville Channel, Little Barrier I., and Stewart I., New Zealand [Michaelsen, 1924]; ? Kerguelen Is. [Herdman, 1886].

Distribution. Records now indicate a circum-antarctic distribution, but in the subantarctic area there are only isolated records from the Scotia Sea and the whole extent of New Zealand. The species has generally been taken in quite deep waters on the continental shelf, off Enderby Land in from 193 to 300 meters and in the vicinity of the South Shetland Islands to a depth of perhaps 935 meters. Around New Zealand, however, it is found in shallower sublittoral waters from 9 to 100 meters. The specimen from the Kerguelen Islands (37 to 110 meters) could possibly belong to this species, and, if so, a general distribution in the Subantarctic becomes more likely. There are no records of the species from the Magellanic area, despite considerable collecting there. It is possible that specimens of this inconspicuous family are generally overlooked by collectors, which would explain both the paucity of records and the very limited numbers of specimens collected from the whole area.

Description. Colonies are thick, investing, and irregularly lobed on the surface; stalked or sessile and conical; or low rounded mounds or domes fixed by the whole area of their base. The height of colonies is therefore tremendously variable, from 5 mm in encrusting or spreading mounds. The highest colony in the present collection is toadstool-shaped, 3 cm high, 2 cm in diameter. The stalk is 1 cm long and ½ cm in diameter. There is usually a single large common cloacal opening with frilled protruding lips at the apex of the colony. Spreading irregular colonies have cloacal openings at the apex of each lobe or elevation occurring over the surface. The surface test is usually packed with bladder cells and is fairly tough. Spicules occur in the layer immediately below this in fair concentration and are absent or only very sparse in the remainder of the test. Spicules

[10] U.S. Navy Antarctic Expedition, 1947–1948.

in the present collection are 'burr-like,' almost spherical with very numerous rays, usually flattened, often rounded, and occasionally pointed on the ends. One colony has typically stellate spicules with 12 rays in optical cross section, as well as the burr-like spicules. Spicules are usually small, diameter from 0.01 to 0.03 mm, rarely more. In the colony from Enderby Land [Kott, 1954] the spicules are regularly stellate and larger, 0.045 mm. Pillars of test from the basal or central test mass expand to envelop clumps of 5 to about 20 zooids supporting them against the surface test. The zooids open into fairly shallow thoracic secondary cloacal canals within the clump. These secondary canals open into the primary cloacal space that surrounds the clumps of zooids and separates the basal or central test from the surface test. The shape of the colonies is affected entirely by the development of the basal test, which may spread over a wider substrate, forming a spreading mound or irregular colony; or it may increase in thickness, expanding up into the center of the colony forming a core around which the common cloaca and the zooid-bearing surface test extend to form a conical or dome-shaped colony. Colonies are usually a shade of gray or grayish-pink, largely caused by the surface layer of bladder cells through which the spicules and zooids are seen. Some colonies have zooids in localized areas with well developed lateral organs. When these occur they considerably change the macroscopic appearance of that part of the colony, especially the color.

Zooids are large. The branchial siphon is conspicuous; the atrial aperture a wide opening. There are 4 rows of about 10 stigmata. Generally, the testis is divided into lobes with $4\frac{1}{2}$ to 6 spirals of the vas deferens around it. When the vas deferens is full of sperm it tends to unwind and there may be as few as $1\frac{1}{2}$ spirals around the testis lobes. In the present collection, colonies from the Weddell Sea have many zooids in which the vas deferens divides into 2 branches in the esophageal region; one branch spirals 4 to 6 times around 3 testis lobes and the other spirals the same number of times around a single testis lobe. A dome-shaped colony from the Drake Passage has only 2 or 3 testis lobes with $5\frac{1}{2}$ spirals of the vas deferens; some specimens from the Shetlands have 6 or 7 testis lobes with $3\frac{1}{2}$ spirals of the vas deferens. The colonies generally have only ovaries or testes developed at any one time.

Larvae. Large, up to 1.2 mm. The most mature embryos are adjacent to the cloacal cavity embedded in the basal test. Less mature embryos are embedded deeper in the basal test. They have ocellus, otolith, and 3 large anterior ampullae, which are surrounded by 8 pairs of lateral ampullae. The lateral ampullae primarily develop from the lateral lines as 4 pairs, but each of the pairs divides almost along its entire length leaving a short undivided stalk attached to, and bent at right angles to, the lateral line. The ampullae are also bent at right angles to their basal stalk, so that they are directed anteriorly. In mature embryos the ampullae straighten out, becoming long and very slender with a terminal slightly bilobed bulb.

Biology. It is possible that in this species the very extensive nature of the cloacal cavity allows for the presence of a considerably reduced number of common cloacal openings, so that the whole colony may in some instance be served by a single effluent aperture. Viviparity is well organized by the extensive nature of the central or basal test serving as a brood pouch. As the embryo is undoubtedly liberated into the common cloaca from the basal test, this further serves as an incubatory pouch protecting the early stages of the free-swimming larva. Liberated eggs from the abdomen of the zooid probably burst from the body wall and pass down the supporting pillar of test into the basal test. Vegetative reproduction, as would be imagined in species that develop into large and highly organized colonies, is prolific and in some zooids 3 series of buds are developing from the esophageal region at one time.

Genus *Trididemnum* Della Valle, 1881

Type species: *Lissoclinum tenerum* Verrill, 1871
Testis undivided; coiled vas deferens. Three rows of stigmata. Test usually with spicules. With or without an atrial siphon.

KEY TO ANTARCTIC SPECIES OF *Trididemnum*

Spicules stellate; long esophageal neck. . *auriculatum,* p. 80
       (Magellanic area, Falkland Is., Stewart I., Chile)
Spicules burr-like; short esophageal neck . . . .
. . . . *propinquum,* p. 82
       (Magellanic area)

Trididemnum auriculatum Michaelsen

Text figs. 103, 104

Leptoclinum tenue; Michaelsen, 1907, p. 39 [part].
Trididemnum auriculatum Michaelsen, 1919, p. 38.—
Van Name, 1945, p. 105.—Millar, 1960, p. 62.
Trididemnum auriculatum f. *separ* Ärnbäck, 1929, p. 16.

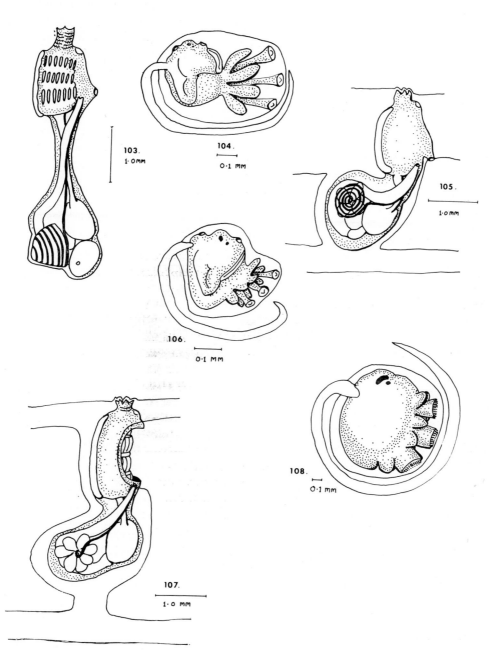

Trididemnum auriculatum
103. Zooid [after Millar, 1960].
104. Larva [after Millar, 1960].

Leptoclinides kerguelenensis
105. Zooid in colony showing disposition of cloacal cavity.
106. Larva.

Diplosoma antarcticum
107. Zooid in colony showing disposition of cloacal cavity.
108. Larva.

New Records. None.

Previous Records.

Subantarctic: Strait of Magellan [Michaelsen, 1907]; Falkland Is. [Millar, 1960]. ? Stewart I., New Zealand [Brewin, 1958].

Elsewhere: Chile [Ärnbäck, 1929].

Distribution. Limited to the Magellanic-Falkland Is. area and the Chilean coast. Ranges from fairly shallow water to a recorded maximum depth of 148 meters.

Description. Encrusting colony from 2 to 4 mm thick. On the surface 2 or 3 common cloacal openings. Stellate spicules dense in all layers of test. Spicules are fairly large, 0.037 to 0.066 mm in diameter, with rather slender conical points.

Zooids are slender with a long esophageal neck connecting the thorax and abdomen. The branchial aperture is 6-lobed; the atrial aperture is far back on the dorsal surface with a posteriorly produced short siphon. Lateral organs are large, occupying the midthoracic area. There are 3 rows of 8 to 10 stigmata. The testis follicle is undivided and the vas deferens makes 5 to 7 spiral turns around it.

Larvae. 0.5 to 0.6 mm long with ocellus and otolith, 3 median papillae, and 4 pairs of large lateral ampullae.

Remarks. Nothing is known of the common cloacal system of this species, but from the thin colony it is assumed that it is not particularly well developed. The species may be related to *T. sluiteri* Brewin, 1958, from Stewart Island (? synonym of *T. natalense* Michaelsen, 1920 [Kott, 1962], a species with a wide distribution in the southern hemisphere).

Trididemnum propinquum (Herdman)

Leptoclinum propinquum Herdman, 1886, p. 284.
Trididemnum propinquum; Hartmeyer, 1909–1911, p. 1446.—Van Name, 1945, p. 105.

New Records. None.

Previous Records.

Subantarctic: Magellanic area, 448 meters [Herdman, 1886].

Description. Thin encrusting colonies, 1 mm thick. Grayish-white color. Spicules probably burr-like, almost spherical, evenly distributed but especially thick around the branchial lobes. Zooids with short esophageal neck and 3 rows of stigmata. The vas deferens is coiled around an undivided testis follicle.

Remarks. Van Name [1945] suggests that this species cannot be separated from *T. auriculatum.* Ärnbäck [1929] distinguishes the two species mainly by the greater length of the stigmata and esophageal neck in *T. auriculatum.* These are not necessarily reliable characters. Nothing is known of the cloacal system in either.

Genus *Leptoclinides* Bjerkan, 1905

Type species: *Leptoclinides faröensis* Bjerkan, 1905

Bladder cells in surface test; spirally wound vas deferens; more than 2 testis lobes; well developed atrial siphon; 4 rows of stigmata.

Leptoclinides kerguelenensis Kott

Text figs. 105, 106

Leptoclinides kerguelenensis Kott, 1954, p. 165.

New Records. None.

Previous Records.

Antarctic: Kerguelen Is., 50 meters [Kott, 1954].

Description. Colony is thin and encrusting. Spicules are absent. The common cloacal system is extensive between surface and basal test and extends posterior to the zooids. There are no stellate pigment cells. Zooids are in the surface layer of test. They are small, with 6-lobed branchial siphon and posteriorly directed atrial siphon. There are 4 rows of stigmata with 7 or 8 stigmata in each row. The testis is divided into 4 lobes and the vas deferens coils around it 6 to 8 times.

Larvae. Small, 0.3 mm, but deeper dorso-ventrally than usual. There are an ocellus, an otolith, and 4 lateral ampullae on either side of the anterior papillae.

Remarks. The extensive posterior abdominal cloacal cavity is characteristic of this genus. The species is distinguished from others in New Zealand and Australia by the lack of stellate pigment cells and the simple gut loop.

Genus *Diplosoma* Macdonald, 1859

Type species: *Diplosoma rayneri* Macdonald, 1859

Vas deferens straight; 1 or more testis lobes. The subgenus *Lissoclinum* Verrill of this genus has not been taken from Antarctica. Subgenus *Diplosoma* has no spicules.

KEY TO ANTARCTIC SPECIES OF *Diplosoma*

With 2 testis lobes....................*longinquum*, p. 83
(Antarctic Peninsula)
With 7 or 8 testis lobes................*antarcticum*, p. 83
(Victoria quadrant)

Diplosoma (Diplosoma) longinquum (Sluiter)

Leptoclinum (Diplosoma) longinquum Sluiter, 1912, p. 460; 1914, p. 36.
Diplosoma longinquum; Van Name, 1945, p. 110.

New Records. Antarctic Peninsula: *Staten Island* Sta. 66/63 (62 meters).

Previous Records.

Antarctic: Antarctic Peninsula, 200 meters [Sluiter, 1912].

Description. Thin, fragile, encrusting colony. Test is delicate and completely transparent. There are no pigment cells or other bodies apparent in the test. Sluiter found the zooids in circular systems around common cloacal openings. The colony in the present collection is very torn and no systems were observed. The zooids extend from the basal to surface layers of thin test in their own thin sheath of test, as is usual in this genus. Zooids are about 4 mm long with a 6-lobed branchial siphon and a wide atrial aperture, which in the present colony is wide open, exposing all except the ventral part of the branchial sac. There are 4 rows of 12 to 14 long rectangular stigmata. The abdomen is slightly smaller than the thorax and the gut forms a simple rounded loop. There are no gonads in the present colony. However, Sluiter's specimens had 2 testis lobes and a straight vas deferens.

Remarks. The general appearance of this colony is reminiscent of *D. rayneri* Macdonald, completely cosmopolitan species [Kott, 1962; Rowe, 1966] but the zooids of *D. rayneri* are smaller, with fewer and shorter stigmata. Globular white bodies have not been identified in the test of the present specimen. Van Name suggests that its occurrence in Antarctica assures the validity of the species distinct from others. In view of the distribution of *D. rayneri* it would not be surprising if it also occurred in the Antarctic.

Diplosoma (Diplosoma) antarcticum new species

Text figs. 107, 108

? *Diplosoma gelatinosa;* Harant and Vernières, 1938, p. 6

Type Locality. Knox Coast, Vincennes Bay, Wilkes Land: *Atka* Sta. 29 (135 meters). Holotype, colony, USNM 11969.

Previous Records.

Antarctic: ? Commonwealth Bay, 102–110 meters [Harant and Vernières, 1938].

Description. Fragile, thin encrusting colony investing worm tube. Test is delicate and completely transparent. Zooids are supported in the common cloacal cavity in clumps held together by a pillar of tissue from the basal test which breaks up to envelop the thoraces in their own independent sheath of this test, which is interrupted only in the region of the atrial opening. They are about 3.5 mm long when not contracted. The branchial aperture is 6-lobed and the atrial aperture is wide and open. There are 4 rows of about 7 stigmata. The stomach is smooth and more or less rectangular. The gut forms a simple horizontal rounded loop. A single pair of esophageal buds are present. There is a rosette of 7 or 8 testis lobes and the vas deferens is uncoiled.

Larvae. Present in the basal test. They are particularly large, 1.5 mm long. There are 3 pairs of short lateral ampullae corresponding with the intervals between the 3 anterior papillae. The anterior papillae are particularly large with elongated areas of columnar adhesive cells such as are present in some species of Holozoinae (*Atapozoa* spp.)

Remarks. The large number of testis lobes arranged in a rosette is unusual in this genus, and the rosette arrangement is reminiscent of Holozoinae. Although the cloacal system, form of budding, and the position of the developing ova are characteristically didemnid, the form of the larval papillae and the position of the lateral ampullae suggest, more than any species of didemnid yet described, that the Didemnidae may be related phylogenetically to the Holozoinae. The only other known species of *Diplosoma* with a large number of testis lobes is *D. multifiduum* (Sluiter) from Indonesia [Sluiter, 1909]. *D. gelatinosa* Harant and Vernières is suggested as a synonym of this species mainly because its colony is similar to that of the present species and because its location is in the same general area as the present species.

Suborder PHLEBOBRANCHIA Lahille
Family CORELLIDAE Lahille
Subfamily RHODOSOMATINAE Seeliger

Straight stigmata.

Only one of the two highly specialized genera of this subfamily is present in the southern oceans. It is represented here by an abyssal species.

KEY TO GENERA OF RHODOSOMATINAE

Stigmata not reduced...................... ***Rhodosoma***
Stigmata reduced ....*****Abyssascidia***, p. 84

---

* This genus reported from Antarctica.

Genus *Abyssascidia* Herdman, 1880

Type species: *Abyssascidia wyvillii* Herdman, 1880

Stigmata reduced; branchial aperture only protected by lip of test.

In addition to the present species, only *A. pediculata* Sluiter, 1904, from 304 meters off Indonesia is known. As with other abyssal forms it is of interest that this apparently abyssal genus is represented in less deep waters in the Indonesian area (p. 206). *Abyssascidia vasculosa* Herdman, 1888, is wrongly ascribed to this genus; it belongs to the genus *Ascidia* (? < *A. meridionalis* Herdman, p. 92).

Abyssascidia wyvillii Herdman

Text fig. 109

Abyssascidia wyvillii Herdman 1880, p. 470; 1882, p. 194.—Millar 1959, p. 193.

New Records. None.

Previous Records. South of Australia, 42°42'S, 134°10'E, 4758 meters, i.e., in the South Australian Basin [Herdman, 1882]; Kermadec Trench, 5850–5900 meters [Millar, 1959]. It could be expected to extend into the South Indian Basin and Southeast Pacific Basin.

Description. Body irregularly oblong, pointed anteriorly, rounded posteriorly, and flattened dorsoventrally. It is attached by a small area of the lower ventral surface. The branchial aperture on the anterior end of the upper surface has 12 to 14 lobes. The atrial aperture, with 8 or 9 lobes is three-fourths of the way along the upper surface. Both apertures are sessile externally. The body is 0.9 to 6 cm long and 0.3 to 4 cm wide. The test is thick, firm, and semitransparent. The body wall is thin, with a few large muscle bands around the right lateral margin extending across the dorsal surface almost to endostyle on the left. Both siphons with fine circular musculature. Branchial tentacles few: 2 at each side of the anterior end of the endostyle and a few others in the usual circle. Dorsal tubercle carrot-shaped with no visible aperture. Neural ganglion at a considerable distance from the tubercle. Dorsal lamina a series of pointed languets. Branchial sac with intermediate transverse vessels and occasional stigmata extending without interruption the whole distance between primary transverse vessels. Intermediate transverse vessels present; internal longitudinal vessels without papillae. Stigmata are wide and irregular, about 3 per mesh. Meshes are almost square. A simple gut loop present on right side of

the branchial sac posteriorly. Stomach barrel-shaped with about 12 to 30 longitudinal folds. Gonad mass present on the gut loop.

Biology. Taken from red clay and pumice bottom.

Remarks. Although the relative position and nature of body musculature is similar to that of *Corynascidia suhmi*, it extends farther down the body in the present species, especially on the left.

Subfamily CORELLINAE Herdman

Represented in the Antarctic by one fairly common widely distributed species and by a widely distributed abyssal species; both extend from the Antarctic into subantarctic regions and farther. A third species known only from a single record represents a most unusual genus.

KEY TO GENERA OF CORELLINAE

1. Surface of test forms plate-like thickenings.............
   ....*Chelyosoma*
   Surface of test without plate-like thickenings........... 2
2. Branchial sac with reduced internal longitudinal vessels. 3
   Internal longitudinal vessels not reduced.............. 4
3. With regular spiral infundibula...............*Corellopsis*
   With irregular stigmata.........*Xenobranchion*, p. 87
4. Gut forms a small simple loop in the postero-dorsal
   corner of the thorax...........*Corynascidia*, p. 86
   Gut forms a curved loop across the posterior third of
   the body ....*Corella*, p. 84

---

* These genera reported from Antarctica.

Genus *Corella* Alder and Hancock, 1870

Type species: *Ascidia parallelogramma* Mueller, 1776

Gut forms a curved loop across the posterior third of the body. A network of muscles present on the left side of body.

Corella eumyota Traustedt

Text figs. 110–112

Corella eumyota Traustedt, 1882, p. 271; 1885, p. 9.—Sluiter, 1898, p. 40; 1914, p. 26; 1932, p. 3.—Michaelsen, 1900, p. 10; 1907, p. 74; 1915, p. 423; 1918, p. 50; 1922, p. 481.—Herdman, 1910, p. 16; 1923, p. 30.—Hartmeyer, 1911, p. 458; 1920, p. 132.—Van Name, 1921, p. 397; 1945, p. 212.—Ärnbäck, 1929, p. 7; 1938, p. 40.—Brewin, 1946, p. 108; 1950a, p. 344; 1956a, p. 122; 1957, p. 577; 1960, p. 119.—Kott, 1952, p. 318; 1954, p. 150.—Millar, 1960, p. 95; 1962, p. 174.—Vinogradova, 1962, p. 200.

Corella novarae von Drasche, 1884, p. 382.

Corella antarctica Sluiter, 1905b, p. 471; 1906, p. 31.

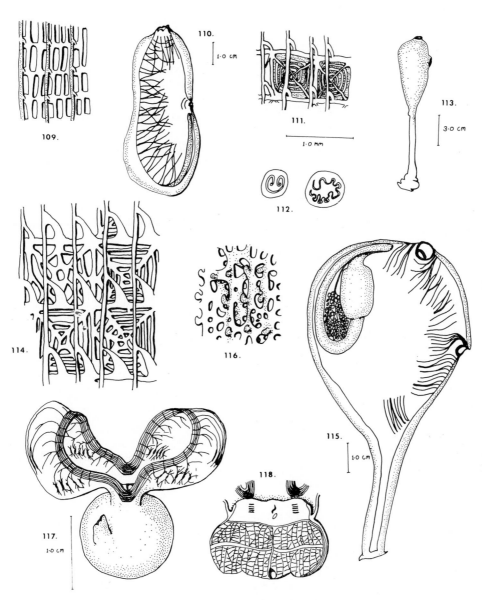

Abyssascidia wyvillii
109.   Portion of branchial sac [after Herdman, 1882].

Corella eumyota
110.   External appearance.
111.   Portion of branchial sac.
112.   Dorsal tubercles.

Corynascidia suhmi
113.   External appearance [after Herdman, 1882].
114.   Portion of branchial sac [after Van Name, 1945].

115.   External appearance showing gut, gonads, and muscula-
       ture.

Xenobranchion insigne
116.   Portion of branchial sac [after Ärnbäck, 1950].

Megalodicopia hians
117.   Body removed from test showing arrangement of muscle
       bands in branchial hoods.
118.   Prebranchial area and branchial sac bisected along ven-
       tral border showing prebranchial velum with dorsal
       ganglion, opening of dorsal tubercle.

Corella benedeni Van Beneden and Selys Longchamps, 1913, p. 9.—Ärnbäck, 1938, p. 41.

Corella dohrni Van Beneden and Selys Longchamps, 1913, p. 15.—Herdman, 1923, p. 30.—Ärnbäck, 1938, p. 41.

Corella eymyota Bovien, 1922, p. 45.

New Records. Falkland Islands-Burdwood Bank: *Eltanin* Sta. 339 (586 meters). Weddell Sea: *Edisto* Sta. 20, TR 5 (384 meters). Antarctic Peninsula: *Edisto* Sta. 28, TR 14 (129 meters); *Staten Island* Sta. 7/63 (21–31 meters). South Shetland Is.: *Staten Island* Sta. 44/63 (55 meters); *Eltanin* Sta. 418 (426 meters). Macquarie I.: *Eltanin* Sta. 1417 (79–93 meters), Sta. 1418 (86–101 meters), Sta. 1422 (833–842 meters). Auckland I.: *Eltanin* Sta. 1425 (135–139 meters). Knox Coast: *Glacier* Sta. 1 (120 meters).

Previous Records.

Antarctic: Antarctic Peninsula, South Shetland Is. [Ärnbäck, 1938; Van Beneden and Selys Longchamps, 1913; Sluiter, 1906, 1914]; Ross Sea [Millar, 1960]; Knox Coast, Wilkes Land [Herdman, 1923; Vinogradova, 1962]; Wilhelm II Coast [Hartmeyer, 1911].

Subantarctic: Falkland Is. [Ärnbäck, 1938; Millar, 1960]; Magellanic area [Michaelsen, 1900]; St. Paul I. [von Drasche, 1884]; Chatham I., Auckland I., Macquarie I. [Herdman, 1910; Michaelsen, 1922; Bovien, 1922; Kott, 1954; Brewin, 1956a].

Elsewhere: North and South Islands, New Zealand [Sluiter, 1898; Michaelsen, 1922; Brewin, 1946, 1957, 1960]; Chile, Argentina [Traustedt, 1882; Hartmeyer, 1920; Ärnbäck, 1929]; Africa [Sluiter, 1898; Michaelsen, 1915; Millar, 1962]; Tasmania, southern Australia, Southwest Australia [Kott, 1952].

Distribution. Previously the species was known from depths of 0 to 45 meters in the Subantarctic and from 40 to 644 meters in the Antarctic [Ärnbäck, 1938]. The present records extend the known depth range to a maximum of 842 meters in the Subantarctic (off Macquarie Island) and to a minimum of 21 meters in the Antarctic (off the Antarctic Peninsula). The species is therefore widely distributed on the continental shelf and slope of the Antarctic and Subantarctic and extends from these areas into cold temperate waters.

Description. Body ovate to elongate; laterally compressed. There may be a short stalk posteriorly. Largest specimen in the present collection 15 cm long, 6 cm wide. Records of specimens of this size are rare [Hartmeyer, 1920; Ärnbäck, 1938; Sluiter, 1898]; usually they are 1 to 4 cm in length.

Test delicate, completely transparent, thin and almost papery in larger specimens, thicker gelatinous test in smaller specimens. Branchial siphon terminal, 7- or 8-lobed; atrial siphon, 6-lobed, up to half the body length along dorsal surface. Both apertures almost sessile externally. The body wall is thin with circular muscles on the siphons, a network of muscles on the left, none apparent on the right, and short transverse muscles around the dorsal and ventral surfaces. There are 50 to 100 fairly long simple tentacles. The dorsal tubercle varies from a U-shaped to a C-shaped slit (turned to the right) with horns rolled in; however, the slit may become convoluted (one large specimen of 5 cm, Antarctic Peninsula Sta. 6 or 7/63).

The dorsal lamina is represented by long tongue-like languets. The branchial sac of larger specimens has regular rows of coiled stigmata, usually with secondary spirals with 30 to 60 longitudinal vessels on each side of the branchial sac supported by tall delicate papillae. In smaller specimens the branchial sac is less regular, numerous spirals of fewer turns and rudimentary spirals are formed. The gut loop and enclosed gonads form a compact mass in the posterior third of the right side of the body. As is usual when the gut is on the right, the intestinal loop turns ventrally and the upper limb extends around the posterior border of the body. The rectum crosses the esophagus and extends anteriorly to the base of the atrial siphon.

Biology. From sand, mud, gravel, and stones. Also taken in the algal (*Macrocystis*) zone [Ärnbäck, 1938]. The species is oviparous.

Remarks. Van Name [1945] and Ärnbäck [1938] present as probable the synonymy listed above. Most distinctions are based on the condition of the branchial sac, and these can be related to the age of the animal. Thus *C. dohrni*, which is 1.9 cm and has only 2 coils of the stigmata, and *C. benedeni*, which is 4 cm and has 4 to 5 coils of stigmata, represent younger and older specimens, respectively, of the same species and indicate the range of variation discussed above. The species is apparently present in large numbers attached to scallop shells over a wide area surrounding Macquarie Island (*Eltanin* Sta. 1417, 1418, 1422) in a wide range of depths from 79 to 842 meters.

Genus *Corynascidia* Herdman, 1882

Type species: *Corynascidia suhmi* Herdman, 1882

Narrow gut loop in postero-dorsal corner of the thorax. Few short radiating longitudinal muscles present.

Corynascidia suhmi Herdman

Text figs. 113–115

Corynascidia suhmi Herdman, 1882, p. 186.—Traustedt, 1885, p. 8.—Hartmeyer, 1911, p. 462; 1912, p. 277, p. 379; 1924, p. 19.—Ärnbäck, 1934, p. 75.—Van Name, 1945, p. 215.

New Records. Southeast Pacific Basin: ? Eltanin Sta. 1283 (146–174 meters). Scotia Sea: Eltanin Sta. 564 (5188 meters). South of Macquarie I.: Eltanin Sta. 1423 (1574–1693 meters).

Previous Records.
Antarctic: Wilhelm II Coast, Enderby Land [Hartmeyer, 1911, 1912].
Subantarctic: 46°46′S, 45°31′E, southwest Indian Ocean [Herdman, 1882].
Elsewhere: Between Valparaiso and Juan Fernandez Is. [Herdman, 1882]; Davis Strait and Greenland, northern hemisphere [Hartmeyer, 1924].

Distribution. This species may be expected to occur in waters below 1500 meters in all the oceans of the world from antarctic to arctic latitudes. The known depth range is from 1574 to 5188 meters.

Description. Pyriform body, 5 to 8 cm long, 2.5 to 5 cm wide, gradually narrowing to a long stalk, 5 to 7 cm long. Test is thin and semitransparent, between membranous and gelatinous. Stalk is tougher than the remainder of test. The lower end of the stalk may expand into rootlike processes and is fixed to rocks and other similar objects. Both siphons are short and tubular: the atrial siphon terminal and directed upward, and the branchial siphon one-third of the body length directed ventrally by an extension downward from the upper lip. There is an extension of the body wall into the base of the stalk. The body wall is thin, with thin, short, transverse muscles around the dorsal and anterior borders on both sides of the body, joining into wide bands on the mid-line posterior and anterior to the atrial aperture and ventral to the branchial siphon. Although the muscles dorsal to the branchial aperture join into a band as they approach the mid-line, they do not join the muscle bands of the opposite side but curve into the upper lip of the aperture. Further fine bands of muscle, similarly oriented between the siphons and on the anterior border just as the body narrows into the stalk, do not join into bands and are interrupted over the mid-line. Muscles do not extend more than one-third of the distance across the body. There are about 60 long, simple branchial tentacles, and the dorsal tubercle is oval with a simple obliquely curved or U-shaped slit. The dorsal lamina is represented by fine triangular languets. The branchial sac is very delicate, with about 30 narrow internal longitudinal vessels supported by tall triangular papillae. Stigmata coil about 3 times to form square infundibula crossed by radial vessels. In the present specimen from the Argentine Basin (Eltanin Sta. 564), the very delicate spiral stigmata and supporting radial vessels are lost and can be detected only in isolated parts of the branchial sac, generally where the sac is attached to the body wall and not subjected to strains causing these vessels to break. The stomach is oval and short. The gut forms a small, narrow loop in the dorsal corner of the terminal-free end of the body. The gonads are between and around the gut loop and consist of central ovary surrounded by testis follicle.

Biology. This species has been taken from globigerina ooze and mud [Herdman, 1882]. The gonads of the present specimens, taken in February and April, respectively, appear mature.

Remarks. Van Name [1945] described the genus Corynascidia Herdman as 'an abyssal genus closely allied to Corella and perhaps worthy of only subgeneric status.' The condition of the gut and muscles seems sufficiently constant, however, to justify generic separation. Corynascidia sedens Sluiter, 1904, from Indonesia and Corynascidia herdmani Ritter, 1913, from the Bering Sea are the only other species recorded, and both have the gut confined to a comparatively small area in the postero-dorsal corner of the body and few short radiating muscles from the region of the siphons.

Genus Xenobranchion Ärnbäck, 1950

Type species: Xenobranchion insigne Ärnbäck, 1950

Gut on right side of body. Transverse vessels are lost and stigmata very irregular; papillae persist on the branchial sac, representing remnants of longitudinal vessels.

Xenobranchion insigne Ärnbäck

Text fig. 116

Xenobranchion insigne Ärnbäck, 1950, p. 20.

New Records. None.

Previous Records. Falkland Is., 1 specimen, 10 meters [Ärnbäck, 1950].

Description. Three individuals irregularly and firmly joined by coalesced test of which the largest is 10 mm high, 9 mm broad, and compressed laterally or dorsoventrally. Test cartilaginous, semitransparent, and thin, especially basally. Surface is smooth but with a few low processes here and there. No sand or other foreign matter present on the test. Apertures on low external siphons, the branchial siphon 6-lobed and the atrial siphon with an undetermined number of lobes (6?). Body wall with well developed longitudinal and transverse muscles, especially on the left side. More than 20 long and slender branchial tentacles. Dorsal tubercle with semicircular slit, sometimes considerably wider than long. Dorsal lamina with long slender languets. The branchial sac is without folds. Stigmata are round, oval, or slit-like, irregularly oriented, often in several overlapping planes. The transverse vessels lose their regular course, although they still support numerous conical or curved papillae. A heart present in usual position above the gut loop on the right side of the branchial sac. The gut loop is horizontal. The esophagus is long; the square stomach has longitudinal folds. The intestine turns posteriorly and dorsally and crosses the esophagus to extend anteriorly as the rectum. Gonads are present in the gut loop and extend between the intestine and the body wall. (After Ärnbäck.)

Remarks. The position and course of the gut loop and the development of muscles on the left side of the body indicate that the genus belongs with the Corellidae as Ärnbäck had suggested. The branchial sac is similar to that of *Hypobythius* Moseley and other species of the Hypobythiidae [Van Name, 1945 and below] although the remnants of the longitudinal vessels remain as papillae in the branchial sac of the present genus. The condition of the stigmata here, of irregular orientation and in several planes, is rather reminiscent of *Molgula gigantea*, in which elaboration of the branchial sac has led to a breakdown of the regular spiral infudibula and interruption in the course of the transverse vessels. The process can be observed at a very early stage in some of the infundibula of *Corynascidia suhmi* Herdman [see Van Name, 1945, fig. 127]. It is more probable therefore that the immediate relationships of this genus are with forms with spiralling stigmata, i.e. Corellinae rather than with the Rhodosomatinae, in which the stigmata are straight.

Family HYPOBYTHIIDAE Sluiter

Represented in western waters below 1000 meters.

One species only, *Megalodicopia hians* Oka, 1918, has been taken from the Antarctic,

KEY TO GENERA OF HYPOBYTHIIDAE

1. Sail-like hoods either side of branchial opening......... 2
   No sail-like hoods either side of branchial opening 3
2. Stalked ....*Megalodicopia,* p. 88
   Not stalked.................................*Dicopia*
3. Size of branchial perforations not greatly varied........
   ....*Hypobythius*
   Great variation in size of branchial perforations.........
   ....*Benthascidia*

---

* This genus reported from Antarctica.

Genus *Megalodicopia* Oka, 1918

Type species: *Megalodicipia hians* Oka, 1918.

Large, stalked specimens with delicate transparent test without hairs; sail-like hoods on either side of branchial opening.

Megalodicopia hians Oka

Text figs. 117, 118

Megalodicopia hians Oka, 1918 p. 399; 1927, p. 494, fig. 592.—Tokioka, 1953, p. 235.

New Records. Weddell Sea: *Edisto* Sta. 18, TR 4 (1555 meters), Sta. 23, TR 10 (810 meters). Peru-Chile Trench: *Eltanin* Sta. 43 (5325 meters; identification doubtful).

Previous Records. Japan (Oka, 1918; Tokioka, 1953).

Distribution. There are only four records of this rare species, which, off Japan, has been taken only in 368 and 350 meters. The present records from the Weddell Sea extend the known depth range to 1555 meters; the doubtful record from the Peru-Chile Trench suggests that the species may occur in much deeper waters.

Description. Stalked and attached basally to a large stone. Two large sail-like concave hoods anteriorly dorsal and ventral to the branchial aperture with concavities facing one another. Remainder of body a spherical mass, with short lobed atrial opening protruding, slightly to the right and halfway up body. From tip of hood to base of abdomen a contracted specimen out of its test is 2.5 cm, of this length the anterior hood represents more than half. Although very much damaged, the test of the same specimen is very much larger and the extended living organism is probably also much larger. The stalk section of the test is 6 cm long, expanded slightly with rootlike processes. The test is very delicate, completely transparent, and, in these specimens, very torn. It is especially thin on the hoods. Very few muscles present on the body itself. There is a border of muscles around the margin of each hood parallel with the edge, and longitudinal muscles cross them. Musculature is not always so apparent toward the center of the lobes, where it becomes more diffuse. The circular muscles around the borders of the lobes cause appreciable concavities directed inward. The depth of these concavities may be reduced in the center, where longitudinal fibers join together to form short parallel muscle bands. Between the lateral borders and median line of the lobes on each side, a single oblique row of especially short spindle-shaped muscle bands is formed by the accumulation of longitudinal and circular fibers. There is an extension of the body wall into the stalk with a wide band of longitudinal fibers from the posterior end of the body extending along either side. Unfortunately, the present specimen is damaged posteriorly and this band of longitudinal fibers has been observed for the Japanese specimens only. Where the dorsal and ventral branchial lobes meet, the circular muscle bands thicken to form short rows of strong muscle bands parallel to one another.

The homologous structure to the branchial siphon of other species is an anterior cylindrical projection of the body, and the dorsal and ventral lobes extend from the border of this projection. The circular muscles around the border of the lobes are homologous with the circular siphonal muscles of other species of Ascidiacea. The actual opening to the branchial sac is bordered by a pronounced velum from the inner wall of the branchial siphon, which may be homologous with the tentacular ring of other ascidians. There are short parallel bands of muscle in this velum, opposite one another, in a position corresponding to the right and left sides of the opening. These are probably homologous with the circular muscle bands associated with the tentacular ring in other species. Tokioka [1953] observed tentacular membranous extensions from the border of this velum, which were not observed in the present specimen. The branchial velum extends across the top of the dish-shaped branchial sac and carries the curved slit of the dorsal tubercle on its under side and supports the dorsal tubercle and gland in the matrix of the velum. Large paired nerves from the ganglion are observed branching out across the branchial lobes. The dorsal lamina is a double membrane anteriorly and a single membrane posteriorly.

A single wide transverse vessel extends across the middle of the branchial sac. The stigmata are irregular, from triangular to rectangular. There are several accessory transverse vessels and longitudinal connectives between these, dividing the area up into irregular or rectangular meshes. The longitudinal connectives are not longitudinal vessels extending the whole length of the branchial sac. The gut loop is simple and posterior to the branchial sac. The rectum extends anteriorly to the base of the atrial siphon. Gonads are of the usual phlebobranch type in the gut loop.

Remarks. *Megalodicopia hians* Oka from Japan has been described with branchial aperture wide open, exposing the whole of the branchial sac as a concave saucer opposite the opening. A ring of sinuses with fringed rectangular tentacles [Tokioka, 1953] does not appear to be present in the antarctic specimen; however, the antarctic specimen is very damaged. The transverse vessels of the branchial sac and the dorsal lamina have not been described in the Japanese specimens but may be inconspicuous in the extended branchial sac. The hoods and their musculature, the abdomen and atrial opening, and the branchial sac are all similar. *Megalodicopia hians* is very closely related to *Dicopia* spp. (viz. *Dicopia fimbriata* Sluiter, 1905 and 1905a, and *Dicopia japonica* Oka 1913a, from Indonesia and Japan, respectively), and it is doubtful whether they should be in separate genera.

The specimens from the Peru-Chile Trench are all empty tests, 1 cm long, the anterior part of the test very thin and divided to cover the sail-like hoods typical of the species. There is a dense beard of rootlike processes on the base of the stalk.

Family Ascidiidae Herdman

Well represented in the Antarctic and elsewhere by several prolific species with a wide distribution extending into the Subantarctic and further.

Key to Genera of Ascidiidae

1. Internal longitudinal vessels without papillae...........
....***Ascidiella***
Internal longitudinal vessels with papillae.............. 2
2. Neural gland with secondary openings.........***Phallusia***
Neural gland without secondary openings.*****Ascidia,*** p. 89

* This genus reported from Antarctica.

Genus *Ascidia* Linnaeus, 1767

Type species: *Ascidia mentula* Mueller, 1776

Stigmata straight; internal longitudinal vessels with

secondary papillae. Neural gland opening on dorsal tubercle.

KEY TO ANTARCTIC SPECIES OF *Ascidia*

1. Ribs from base of tentacles; tentacles at several levels. .
..................................***challengeri,*** p. 90
(circum-antarctic, Kerguelen Is., Heard I., Tasmania)
No ribs from base of tentacles; tentacles in a single circle. 2
2. About 30 stigmata per mesh.........***translucida,*** p. 93
(Kerguelen Is., South Georgia)
5 to 13 stigmata per mesh..........***meridionalis,*** p. 92
(Patagonian Shelf, Magellanic area, South Georgia, Victoria and Enderby quadrants)

Ascidia challengeri Herdman

Text figs. 119, 120

Ascidia challengeri Herdman, 1882, p. 202; 1923, p. 28.—Ärnbäck, 1938, p. 46.—Van Name, 1945, p. 192.—Kott, 1954, p. 148.—Millar, 1960, p. 89.—Vinogradova, 1962, p. 198.
Ascidia charcoti Sluiter, 1905b, p. 471; 1906, p. 34.—Herdman, 1912, p. 314; 1915, p. 96; 1923, p. 29.
Phallusia charcoti; Hartmeyer, 1911, p. 466; 1912, pp. 286, 287.—Sluiter, 1914, p. 26.
Phallusia challengeri; Hartmeyer, 1912, p. 283.
Ascidia dispar Ärnbäck, 1938, p. 48.

New Records. Ross Sea: *Burton Island* Sta. 3 (434 meters); *Edisto* Sta. 104[11] (107 meters). Knox Coast: *Atka* Sta. 29 (135 meters). Antarctic Peninsula: *Staten Island* Sta. 6/63 (7 meters), Sta. 32/63 (46 meters), Sta. 35/63 (46 meters); *Edisto* Sta. 194[11] (64 meters), Sta. 234[11] (74 meters). South Shetland Is.: *Staten Island* Sta. 44/63 (55 meters), Sta. 45/63 (55 meters), Sta. 64/63 (86 meters); *Eltanin* Sta. 410 (240 meters), Sta. 434 (77 meters), Sta. 436 (73 meters). South Orkney Is.: *Eltanin* Sta. 1082 (298–302 meters).

Previous Records.

Antarctic: Antarctic Peninsula, South Shetland Is. [Ärnbäck, 1938; Sluiter, 1906, 1914; Millar, 1960]; South Georgia [Ärnbäck, 1938; Millar, 1960]; South Orkney Is. [Millar, 1960]; Enderby Land [Kott, 1954]; Wilkes Land [Herdman, 1923]; Davis Sea [Vinogradova, 1962]; Wilhelm II Coast [Hartmeyer, 1911]; Ross Sea [Millar, 1960].

Subantarctic: Kerguelen Is., Heard I. [Herdman, 1882; Hartmeyer, 1912; Kott, 1954; Vinogradova, 1962].

---

[11] U.S. Navy Antarctic Expedition, 1947–1948.

Elsewhere: Tasmania [Herdman, 1923; Kott, 1954].

Distribution. The species is circumpolar in the Antarctic, in from 36–637 meters. In the Subantarctic it is not recorded from the Falkland Islands-Magellanic area, although it extends to the Kerguelen Islands, Heard Island, and Tasmania. In general, it is found at its greatest depth in the Antarctic, which probably indicates only the depths at which collections have been made [Vinogradova, 1962].

Description. Largest specimen in the present collection is 5 cm long and 3 cm wide (from South Shetland Islands). Specimens up to 11 cm [Millar, 1960, from the Ross Sea] and up to 17 cm [Herdman, 1882, from Kerguelen Islands] have been recorded. The body is oblong to elongate and laterally flattened. Larger specimens taper anteriorly and are fixed posteriorly, or by part of the left side; smaller specimens have rounded margins. Living specimens, possibly of this species, have been described as purplish-black (*Staten Island* Sta. 32/63). The body surface is smooth, often with shallow longitudinal or irregular furrows. In smaller specimens part of the test, especially around the siphons, may have pointed conical processes [*A. dispar* Ärnbäck, 1938, and specimens from *Eltanin* Sta. 434, 436]. The test is firm and gelatinous, transparent or semitransparent and yellowish. Apertures, as in *A. meridionalis*, are displaced to the right. In smaller specimens they are usually sessile externally but may be produced into short siphons. The branchial siphon is 8-lobed and terminal; the atrial siphon 6-lobed and one-third of body length along the dorsum. A fine network of muscles present in the body wall, especially on the right. Short transverse muscles present around the ventral line. There are circular bands around the siphons and short radiating bands from the base of the siphons. Branchial tentacles (11 to 55) in several circles, at different levels at the base of the branchial siphon. Fine ribs extend anteriorly on the inner siphonal wall from the base of the tentacles to a flange or oral ring. Occasionally these ribs are not present [Millar, 1960], but they were observed in all specimens of the present collection. Dorsal tubercle with U-shaped slit, horns turned in or out. Ganglion only a short distance from the tubercle. Dorsal lamina smooth but may have indentations, especially posteriorly. From 30 to 60 longitudinal vessels present in the branchial sac with spatulate papillae at their junctions with the transverse vessels. Intermediate papillae present, although in small specimens they may be

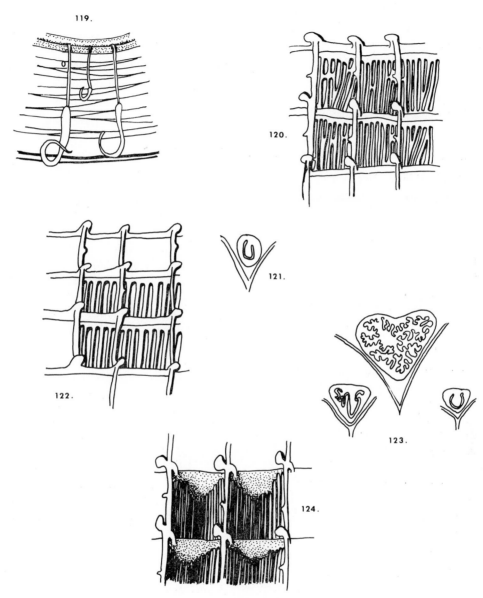

Ascidia challengeri
119. Branchial tentacles showing rib-like extensions from base.
120. Portion of branchial sac.

Ascidia meridionalis
121. Dorsal tubercle.
122. Portion of branchial sac.

Ascidia translucida
123. Dorsal tubercle [after Millar, 1960].
124. Portion of branchial sac.

absent from some parts of the sac. The branchial sac has simple primary folds between longitudinal vessels, and about 6 to 10 stigmata in each mesh. The gut forms a sometimes very open double loop in the posterior half of the body. The gonads are as usual in the gut loop.

Biology. The species has been taken from every conceivable type of substrate: clay and algae, sand and gravel, stones, broken shell, globigerina ooze.

Remarks. The distinguishing ribs extending from the base of the tentacles to the flange of the oral ring indicate a shifting back of the tentacles farther toward the base of the siphon. In other species the tentacles arise immediately from this oral ring, which is usually associated with a circular sphincter of the branchial siphon. Further distinguishing characters are the smooth dorsal lamina, the simple dorsal tubercle, and the intermediate branchial papillae. A single small damaged specimen from the Weddell Sea may be this species. One specimen from the South Orkney Islands in the present collection has 2 atrial openings, suggesting the persistence of the 2 embryonic openings of the order Enterogona.

Ascidia meridionalis Herdman

Text figs. 121, 122

Ascidia meridionalis Herdman, 1880, p. 465; 1882, p. 207; 1923, p. 28, 29.—Michaelsen, 1907, p. 74.— Van Name, 1945, p. 191.—Kott, 1954, p. 149.

Ascidia tenera Herdman, 1880, p. 467; 1882, p. 213. —Michaelsen, 1900, p. 12; 1907, p. 74.

Phallusia meridionalis; Hartmeyer, 1909–1911, p. 1403.

Ascidia parameridionalis Vinogradova, 1962, p. 199.

? *Abyssascidia vasculosa* Herdman, 1888, p. 151.

? *Bathyascidia vasculosa;* Hartmeyer, 1901, p. 166; 1912, p. 374.

New Records. Scotia Sea area north of South Georgia: *Eltanin* Sta. 732 (265 meters).

Previous Records.

   Antarctic: Davis Sea, Enderby Land, Mac. Robertson Land [Kott, 1954; Vinogradova, 1962]; Wilkes Land [Vinogradova, 1962].

   Subantarctic: Strait of Magellan [Herdman 1882]. ? South Indian (Australian-Antarctic) Basin [Herdman, 1888].

   Elsewhere: Buenos Aires [Herdman, 1882].

Distribution. The species has been taken from 100 to 500 meters off the antarctic continent and in the Magellanic area. Although records are rare, the species is present on the continental shelf and slope in the Enderby and Weddell quadrants and the Scotia Ridge to the Magellanic area off the Patagonian Shelf, where it has been recorded from a depth of 1100 meters off Buenos Aires. If Herdman's specimen from the South Indian Basin in 3,588 meters is indeed a synonym of the present species, a wide distribution in the Australian and Atlantic antarctic basins is probable, extending on to the continental shelf around the antarctic continent and north along the Scotia Ridge.

Description. Up to 15 cm long, 8 cm wide, oval, flattened. May be fixed posteriorly, ventrally, or by the left side, or by any combination of these. Apertures sessile externally. Branchial aperture 8-lobed terminal; atrial aperture 6-lobed halfway down the dorsum. The plane of the lateral flattening of the body passes slightly to the left of the dorsal line and to the right of the ventral line, so that a specimen lying on its left side presents the dorsal surface and most of the right side on its upper surface. The atrial opening in particular is thus directed away from the bottom. Test is thick and gelatinous; the surface smooth but often creased and seamed. Body wall moderately muscular with network of fine muscles on right and short transverse bands around dorsal and ventral border. Circular muscles around siphons and short radiating bands from base of siphons.

Tentacles never less than 60, simple, all from a single circle from the oral tentacular ring. The dorsal tubercle slit is crescentic with horns pointed forward or in, sometimes with simple convolutions. Dorsal lamina is ribbed and fringed by pointed languets.

Branchial sac only occasionally with conical intermediate papillae. Sometimes simple slight folding of branchial sac between longitudinal vessels. Stigmata per mesh 5 to 8 (present specimens), 8 to 9 [Herdman, 1882, Pl. XXI, Fig. 5], or 12 to 13 [Vinogradova, 1962]. The gut forms a double fairly open loop, extending more than halfway up the body. Stomach more or less rounded with internal longitudinal folds. The renal gland in the present specimens, as in Herdman's [1882], is composed of conspicuous yellow vesicles covering most of the intestine. The branchial sac often extends behind the gut.

Biology. Taken from hard ground, mud or sand, gravel or globigerina ooze.

Remarks. Van Name [1945] and Millar [1960] suggest the synonymy of this species with *A. challengeri.* The body form (especially of small individuals), body musculature, and branchial sac are in many ways similar and the dorsal tubercle in both cases is comparatively simple. However, the body of *A. meridionalis* is wider; the tentacles are more numerous and are fixed in a single circle to the oral tentacular ring; the dorsal lamina is serrated; intermediate branchial papillae are only occasional. These are characteristics of the species constantly found in all recorded specimens of all sizes and distinguish the species from *A. challengeri.* *A. parameridionalis* is distinguished from other specimens only by the number of stigmata in each mesh; however, there is considerable variation in this character. Vinogradova's larger specimens were from 9 to 16 cm with 12 to 13 stigmata per mesh; thus, it is possible that an increase in size accounts for the larger numbers of stigmata. *Bathyascidia vasculosa* (Herdman) from 3588 meters in the South Indian Basin resembles the present species in the large number of branchial tentacles, the small open gut loop, the arrangement of stigmata and branchial papillae, the body form and musculature, and the crescentic form of the dorsal tubercle. The delicacy of the branchial sac in the abyssal form, which at present provides the only distinction, could well be a result of the deep-water habitat. Further records of *A. meridionalis* from greater depth in antarctic basins could confirm this synonymy (p. 94).

Ascidia translucida Herdman

Text figs. 123, 124

Ascidia translucida Herdman, 1880, p. 466; 1882, p. 215.—Ärnbäck, 1938, p. 45.—Van Name, 1945, p. 195.—Kott, 1954, p. 149.—Millar, 1960, p. 87.
Phallusia translucida; Hartmeyer, 1912, p. 287.
Ascidia plicata Kott, 1954, p. 150.—Vinogradova, 1962, p. 197.

New Records. None.

Previous Records.

Antarctic: South Georgia [Ärnbäck, 1938; Millar, 1960].

Subantarctic: North of Kerguelen Is., 35°07'S [Vinogradova, 1962]; Kerguelen Is. [Kott, 1954; Herdman, 1882; Hartmeyer, 1912].

Distribution. The species is common only at the Kerguelen Islands and may flourish only in the subantarctic area. At South Georgia it is represented by only a few specimens. Possibly it had extended from the Kerguelen Plateau along the shallower shelf waters of the antarctic continent and

the Scotia Ridge to South Georgia. The lack of records between Kerguelen Islands and South Georgia suggests either that the species is now absent or that it is so rare that it has not been taken. Depth range is from 18 to 247 meters.

Description. Up to 29 cm long, 12 cm wide, regularly oval, laterally flattened. Branchial aperture terminal, atrial aperture one-third to one-half of the body length from the branchial aperture. Both apertures on very short siphons. Test firm, gelatinous, but not very thick, completely transparent in smaller specimens, semitransparent in large specimens. Branchial tentacles from 10 to 36 in a single circle; this number is correlated with neither longitudinal vessels nor size. Dorsal tubercle completely fills the peritubercular area, and the opening demonstrates an increasing complexity from young to older specimens [Millar, 1960]. The dorsal lamina is broad and strongly ribbed and continues beyond the esophageal opening to the end of the branchial sac. Branchial sac with primary folds between the internal longitudinal vessels; each primary fold is again slightly folded about 6 times. External to the branchial sac expansion of the outer part of the transverse bars forms a perforated sheet holding the complicated foldings of the branchial sac in place. There are about 30 stigmata in each mesh and 20 to 40 internal longitudinal vessels per side. Spatulate papillae are present at the junction of longitudinal and transverse vessels, and occasional small intermediate papillae are present. Gut loop is large, occupying the posterior two-thirds of the body length. Anal border has shallow lobes.

Remarks. Although the body externally resembles both *A. meridionalis* and *A. challengeri,* mature specimens of the present species may be easily distinguished by both branchial sac and dorsal tubercle. In younger specimens (less than 2.0 cm), in which neither the convolution of the tubercular opening nor the pleating of the branchial sac has yet occurred, the large numbers of stigmata in the meshes should distinguish the species.

Ascidia sp. ?

Record. Weddell Sea: *Edisto* Sta. 15, TD 3, west of Cape Norvegia, 71°55'S, 15°35'W.

Remarks. On January 23, 1959, the USS *Edisto* brought up in a triangular bottom dredge haul from 1280 meters a specimen of *Ascidia* that, unfortunately, was too immature for specific determination. It is mentioned here because the depth from which it

was taken exceeds by 180 meters the greatest confirmed record for *A. meridionalis* (1100 meters) off
Buenos Aires. *Bathyascidia vasculosa* (Herdman)
(? < *Ascidia meridionalis*) is reported from 3588
meters in the South Indian Basin. Consequently,
A. meridionalis may have a wider distribution at
greater depths than is at present known, and it is
possible that the present specimen represents a
juvenile of *A. meridionalis*.

Family AGNESIIDAE Huntsman
Subfamily AGNESIINAE Huus

This comparatively rare subfamily is well represented in the Antarctic by at least three reasonably
common species. Records of the family from other
than polar regions are rare, but they do occur. Characteristics of distribution indicate a very ancient
genus that has developed great specialization in isolated localities and has been especially successful
in polar regions.

KEY TO GENERA OF AGNESIINAE

1. With bifid papillae on transverse vessels.............. 2
   Branchial papillae not bifid............*Agnesia*, p. 97
2. Dorsal lamina a smooth edged membrane.............
   .... *Caenagnesia*, p. 94
   Dorsal lamina replaced by languets...*Adagnesia*, p. 99

---

* These genera reported from Antarctica.

Genus *Caenagnesia* Ärnbäck, 1938

Type species: *Caenagnesia bocki* Ärnbäck, 1938
Dorsal lamina a continuous membrane, biramous
papillae on transverse vessels. This genus is confined
to the Antarctic.

KEY TO ANTARCTIC SPECIES OF *Caenagnesia*

Large conspicuously furrowed siphons.......*schmitti*, p. 94
    (South Shetland Is., Antarctic Peninsula, Victoria Land)
Siphons not large nor conspicuously furrowed...*bocki*, p. 96
    (South Georgia to Enderby Land, Knox Coast)

Caenagnesia schmitti new species
Text figs. 125–127

Type Locality. Ross Sea area, Relay Bay, S. W.
Robertson Bay: *Edisto* Sta. 4 (400 meters). Holotype,
USNM 11968.

Additional Records. Antarctic Peninsula: *Staten
Island* Sta. 66/63 (62 meters), 1 specimen. South
Shetland Is.: *Eltanin* Sta. 428 (662–1120 meters), 1
specimen.

Distribution. In the shelf to slope area of the Antarctic. The isolated records probably represent a
circum-antarctic distribution. Depth range is from
74 to 1120 meters.

Description. Cylindrical, up to 7 cm long, 3 cm
diameter. Both apertures anterior on short siphons.
The larger 6-lobed atrial siphon is produced anterior
to the 7-lobed branchial siphon. Both are marked
along their length with furrows that correspond to
the lobes. The test is semitransparent, firm on siphons
and anterior half of body but posteriorly soft, thin,
and transversely wrinkled with fine hairs entangled
with sand and mud. Body wall with about 50
longitudinal muscle bands on each side of the body
extending from each siphon along the whole length
of the branchial sac on the right and on the left,
terminating abruptly in short branches along the
anterior border of the intestine. In the type specimen, contracted, the gut loop is alongside the posterior
third of the branchial sac forming a simple loop in
the vertical plane across the left side of the body
and the longitudinal muscles on the left extend only
to the anterior border of this loop. When the longitudinal muscles are relaxed however, they extend the
whole length of the branchial sac on the left, as
well as on the right, and the gut loop slips to a more
or less horizontal loop posterior to the branchial
sac. The thin posterior half of the test corresponds
to the highly contractile nature of the body wall and
presumably expands to accommodate the gut loop,
when, by relaxation of the longitudinal muscles, it
is released from its position alongside the branchial
sac and forms an abdomen homologous with the
abdomen of *Ciona intestinalis*. Circular muscles are
present around the siphons. Transverse muscle bands
extend along the dorsal border of the body on the
right and the left, outside the longitudinal bands
in the anterior two-thirds and inside the longitudinal
bands in the posterior one-third. Along the ventral
border transverse muscle bands are paired, one of
each pair superficial to and the other beneath the
longitudinal muscles in the anterior half of the body
length on the right and in the anterior one-third
of the body length on the left. Posterior to this,
on each side of the body respectively, the transverse
muscles are deep to the longitudinal bands. Dorsal
and ventral to both siphons these transverse muscle
bands are continuous from right to left, but elsewhere
they are interrupted across the mid-line, where they
fade out in many fine branches. The longitudinal
muscle bands are close together in a wide band in
the center of each side of the branchial, sac where
the transverse muscles do not extend.

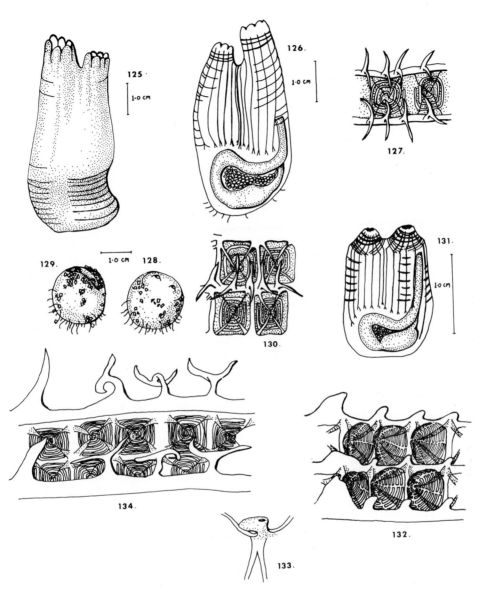

Caenagnesia schmitti new species
125. External appearance.
126. Body removed from test showing orientation of muscle bands, gut, and gonads. (Full number of muscle bands not shown).
127. Portion of branchial sac.

Caenagnesia bocki
128. External appearance, apertures extended.
129. External appearance, apertures withdrawn.
130. Portion of branchial sac.

Agnesia glaciata
131. Body removed from test showing musculature and gut.
132. Portion of branchial sac.

Adagnesia antarctica
133. Dorsal tubercle and posterior part of ganglion.
134. Portion of branchial sac.

There are numerous circular bands of muscle associated with the prepharyngeal band posterior to the tentacles. About 60 branchial tentacles are present in 4 distinct circles, the longest toward the base of the siphon. Dorsal tubercle a transverse slit directed posteriorly. Dorsal lamina an irregular edged membrane ribbed on the right side. The ribs are continuous with the transverse vessels. In one specimen the ribs of the dorsal lamina in the posterior two-thirds are extended into short languets on the free edge of the membrane. Branchial sac with about 60 transverse vessels; stigmata with 3 to 4 spirals forming about 25 infundibula in each row with occasional interstitial coils. There are 3 biramous papillae per infundibulum on the transverse vessels. The arms of the papillae are especially long and slender. Delicate radial vessels cross the spirals. The endostyle terminates at the postero-ventral corner of the pharynx and a retropharyngeal band continues across the posterior end of the branchial sac to the esophagus. Oval stomach with papillated lining. There is no differentiation of the intestine into duodenal or midintestinal regions. The intestine loops anteriorly or to the left, according to the position of the gut alongside or behind the branchial sac then dorsally and anteriorly and passes up the side of the branchial sac as the rectum, which terminates about halfway up the branchial sac. The anal margin is crenellated. Gonads present in the gut loop, consist of arborescent testis lobes surrounding and covering the ovary.

Remarks. In the strongly contractile nature of the body wall, the lack of rigidity in the posterior part of the test, the regularly cylindrical form of the body and the anterior position of the apertures, the position of the gut loop, and the form of dorsal tubercle this species strongly resembles *Ciona intestinalis* and adds weight to the argument for an origin of Agnesiidae from the Cionidae independently of the Ascidiidae. On the other hand, the branchial sac and papillae, and the short transverse muscles around the dorsal and ventral border on both sides of the body are characteristic of Agnesiidae. The species is distinguished from *Caenagnesia bocki* by the large number of transverse branchial vessels and infundibula, the greater development of longitudinal muscle bands, the interruption of transverse muscle bands across the median line, and the external appearance.

Caenagnesia bocki Ärnbäck

Text figs. 128–130

Caenagnesia bocki Ärnbäck, 1938, p. 41.—Van Name, 1945, p. 202.—Millar, 1960, p. 94.
Agnesia complicata Kott, 1954, p. 151.

New Records. Weddell Sea: *Westwind* Sta. 4 (796 meters; identification doubtful); *Edisto* Sta. 20, TR 6 (394 meters). Antarctic Peninsula: *Staten Island* Sta. 9/63 (57 meters); South Shetland Is.: *Eltanin* Sta. 437 (311 meters). Bellingshausen Sea: *Edisto* Sta. 146[12] (56 meters). Knox Coast: *Edisto* Sta. 44[12] (184 meters).

Previous Records. Antarctic Peninsula [Ärnbäck, 1938; Millar, 1960]. South Georgia [Millar, 1960]. Enderby Land [Kott, 1954].

Distribution. The species is present on the continental slope, extending rarely on to the shelf area of the antarctic continent from the Antarctic Peninsula to the eastern side of the Scotia Ridge and the antarctic continent south of the Atlantic-Indian Basin. Depth ranges from 55 to 800 meters; single specimens have been taken on two occasions in depths less than 200 meters [Millar, 1960, *Discovery* Sta. 42, and specimens from *Staten Island* Sta. 9/63]. It appears to be more commonly taken at greater depths, from 200 to 500 meters or more.

Description. Squarish to rounded oval or spherical body, laterally or dorso-ventrally flattened. Greatest dimension 1.5 to 3 cm (dorso-ventral height or antero-posterior length). A living specimen (*Staten Island* Sta. 9/63) has been described by the collector as 'reddish.'

Test usually thin, cartilaginous, and transparent but sometimes brittle and opaque with sand and mud. Fine hairlike extensions from the posterior part of the test, often long and crowded, forming a beardlike rooting system. Posterior part of test often forms a flattened keel-like structure, with or without hairs, anchoring the animal in mud [Ärnbäck, 1938]. Along the upper surface apertures are widely spaced on short siphons in an area of especially thin test without any sand. In contracted specimens this whole area is withdrawn into the body, forming a long depression embracing the siphons at either end. The anterior margins of brittle or more rigid test from both sides form two lips meeting over the top of this depression, thus protecting the apertures. Among the 6 rounded specimens from *Eltanin* Sta. 437, only one is not contracted, the lateral flattening is lost, the area corresponding to the longitudinal depression in the upper

---

[12] U.S. Navy Antarctic Expedition, 1947–1948.

surface is rounded and convex, forming the upper segment of the spherical body, the regularity interrupted only by the protruding siphons. Branchial aperture with 6 or 7 lobes; atrial aperture with 6 lobes. Body wall with well developed circular muscles around the siphon; about 20 narrow longitudinal muscle bands extending posteriorly on the right but terminating anterior to the gut loop on the left. Transverse muscles around the dorsal and ventral borders are continuous over the mid-line. No muscles present in the posterior part of body. About 50 branchial tentacles present in 4 circles, the largest tentacles in the circle nearest the base of the siphon. Dorsal tubercle with a simple pitlike opening. Dorsal lamina broad with an almost even margin. Stigmata with 3 to 6 coils, sometimes interrupted and crossed by radial vessels. There are from 12 rows of 13 or 14 spirals [Ärnbäck, 1938, specimens 1.5 cm long] up to 24 rows of 17 spirals [Kott, 1954, specimen 3 cm long]. On the transverse vessels between each row of spirals there are biramous papillae with long slender arms, 3 associated with each spiral. The gut loop is partly to the left and slightly posterior to the branchial sac. The stomach is globular and papillated internally. The anal margin has up to 18 rounded lobes. Gonads present in the gut loop and consist of a central ovary surrounded by testis lobes.

Remarks. The variation noted in the shape of the body may be explained partly by the great change effected by contraction of the body musculature causing lateral flattening. Apparently, this does not affect the posterior end of the body, where there is no musculature and where in certain specimens the 'keel-like' posterior part of the body anchors the animal [Ärnbäck, 1938]. The special modification of test to provide protective lips over the apertures is also present in specimens of *Agnesia glaciata* in the present collection (see below). This character has been previously described only by Michaelsen for *A. glaciata.* It is inconspicuous and may be overlooked either when sand is absent from the body or when the animal is not contracted (Ärnbäck's specimens were 'highly vaulted' in the anterior half of the body). *Adagnesia opaca* Kott, 1963a, is a similar sandy species of this family with a more highly developed closing mechanism over the siphons associated with greater specialization of the body musculature and a special arrangement of gonoducts to ensure viviparity. Although these mechanisms are similar in each genus, they are not present in all species, and they probably evolved independently of one another.

Caenagnesia bocki resembles *C. schmitti* in branchial sac, branchial tentacles, dorsal lamina, and branchial papillae. *C. schmitti* has many more infundibula and transverse vessels but this could be correlated with a size difference. The position of the gut is similar and the arrangement of muscles suggests that a withdrawal of the gut, as described for *C. schmitti,* may possibly occur in the present species. Although Ärnbäck describes the posterior test as thinner than the rest of the body, it is not as collapsible as in *C. schmitti.* In all the present specimens all parts of the test are equally firm, with the exception only of the area surrounding the siphons. This thin area is not present in *C. schmitti* in which the test of this part of the body is firm, and the longer and larger siphons not retractible. The interruption of transverse muscles across the mid-line, such as occurs in *C. schmitti* and *A. glaciata,* does not occur in *C. bocki,* and the longitudinal muscle bands in the former species are more numerous and better developed.

Genus *Agnesia* Michaelsen, 1898

Type species: *Agnesia glaciata* Michaelsen, 1898

Dorsal lamina absent. Without bifid branchial papillae.

Agnesia glaciata Michaelsen

Text figs. 131, 132

Agnesia glaciata Michaelsen, 1898, p. 370; 1900, p. 6; 1907, p. 75.—Van Name, 1945, p. 200.—Millar, 1960, p. 92.

Agnesia krausei Michaelsen, 1912, p. 181.

? *Agnesia himeboja* Oka, 1915a, p. 1.

? *Agnesia sabulosa* Oka, 1929a, p. 152.

Agnesia septentrionalis; Van Name, 1945, p. 200 [part: specimens from Southern California].

Agnesia capensis Millar, 1955, p. 191.

New Records. Antarctic Peninsula: *Staten Island* Sta. 27/63 (75 meters), Sta. 66/63 (62 meters). South Shetland Is.: *Staten Island* Sta. 64/63 (86 meters). Knox Coast: *Edisto* Sta. 45[13] (184 meters).

Previous Records.

Subantarctic: Tierra del Fuego, Patagonian Shelf [Michaelsen, 1898, 1912; Millar, 1960].

Elsewhere: Japan [Oka, 1915a, 1929a]; South Africa [Millar, 1955, 1960]; North Island, New Zealand [Millar, 1960]; California [Van Name, 1945].

---

[13] U.S. Navy Antarctic Expedition, 1947–1948.

Distribution. Although the rare occurrences of this species involve only single specimens, they are widespread. A distribution from the antarctic continent around the subantarctic islands into adjacent cold temperate waters of southern Africa, southern America, New Zealand, and possibly even farther to the north is indicated. Unless further collecting reveals that the species is present in much deeper waters, its occurrences are isolated ones separated from one another in sublittoral zones. Known depth range is from 13 to 184 meters.

Description. In the present specimens the body is more or less rectangular, up to 4 cm long and laterally or dorso-ventrally flattened when contracted. Both apertures present anteriorly on inconspicuous siphons. In the specimen from *Staten Island* Sta. 27/63 the siphons are placed at either end of a slit-like area of thin test, whereas the remainder of the test is rigid and brittle, with encrusted sand especially thick anteriorly. When this specimen is contracted, the body is laterally flattened and the siphons and their thin surrounding test are drawn down into the body, while the firmer test from right and left of the dorsal line closes over the top of the openings. Other specimens in the present collection are not encrusted with sand, the test is gelatinous and semitransparent, thick and firm anteriorly, and thin and flexible posteriorly. There is an area of thinner test around the base of the siphons, which, on contraction, is drawn down into the body, so that the apertures are protected by the surrounding thicker test, which forms a protective dome over the dorso-ventrally flattened body.

Body musculature well developed, with circular siphonal muscles and longitudinal bands extending as far as the gut on the left, but on the right extending only a short distance from the base of the siphons. Transverse muscles on either side of the dorsal and ventral mid-lines are continuous across the mid-line only behind the atrial siphon.

About 35 branchial tentacles present. The dorsal tubercle has a simple circular opening. A dorsal lamina is not present and primary transverse vessels are not interrupted over the mid-dorsal line. Triangular languets present to the left of the mid-line are enlarged branchial papillae. Stigmata coil up to 9 times to form conical infudibula. The coiled stigmata are interrupted in the vertical and horizontal axes [Millar, 1960] in older specimens but undivided in younger specimens. There are 6 primary transverse vessels alternating with double rows of infundibula.

There are 10 infundibula per row on each side of the dorsal line. Adjacent spirals in each row are in opposite directions. Fingerlike papillae of varying sizes, the largest dorsally, are present on the transverse vessels and correspond to the spaces between adjacent spirals except on the left of the dorsal line, where single enlarged triangular papillae develop from the transverse vessels opposite the 5 most dorsal infundibula of each row. In a single specimen (*Staten Island* Sta. 27/63) the intermediate transverse vessels bissecting double rows of infundibula are especially developed, probably with increasing size, and bear papillae corresponding to those on the primary vessels. These intermediate transverse vessels do not, however, cross the dorsal line and their papillae are smaller. Radial vessels from the corners of each coil cross each spiral and converge in the center. These help to support the infundibula. The gut loop is to the left and slightly posterior to the branchial sac. Gonads are present in the gut loop, their ducts following the course of the rectum.

Biology. The species is viviparous with developing embryos in the peribranchial cavity in February.

Remarks. The mechanism whereby the apertures are drawn into the body, where they are protected by the surrounding test, has been mentioned only by Michaelsen [1900]. It is probably effected by the longitudinal muscles radiating from the siphons. A similar mechanism occurs in *Caenagnesia bocki* (p. 96).

Van Name [1945, p. 200] has drawn attention to the similarity of *A. glaciata* and *A. septentrionalis* Huntsman, 1912, (> *A. beringia* Ritter, 1913) from British Columbia [Huntsman, 1912 and 1912a, depth not recorded] and the southeastern Bering Sea [Ritter, 1913, 27 to 78 meters]. An examination of specimens from St. Georges Sound, Pribilof Islands, from 74 meters (AMNH 1896) and from St. George Island, Alaska (USNM 10633) has shown that *A. septentrionalis* is distinguishable from *A. glaciata* by a proliferation of the number of infundibula and intermediate transverse vessels in the branchial sac of *A. septentrionalis* as figured by Van Name [1945, fig. 112, p. 201]. However, specimens dredged off Newport Harbor, California [AMNH 1570, 1571, 1572], which Van Name [1945] also considered identical with *A. septentrionalis*, are, on examination, found to be identical with *A. glaciata*. The descriptions of the branchial sac in *A. himeboja* Oka, 1915a, and *A. sabulosa* Oka, 1929a, suggest that these species from Japan are also identical with *A. glaciata* rather than with *A. septentrionalis*. Further specimens, again indistinguishable from *A. glaciata*, have recently been taken from Moreton Bay, Queensland (23 to 24 meters). *Agnesia glaciata* has, therefore, a wide distribution in sublittoral waters of the northern and southern hemispheres and is closely related to *A. septentrionalis*, which represents the genus in northern boreal waters of the Pacific Ocean.

Genus *Adagnesia* Kott, 1963a

Type species: *Adagnesia opaca* Kott 1963a

Bifid papillae on the transverse vessels. Dorsal lamina with languets.

Previously the genus was known from only a single species from Moreton Bay, Queensland [Kott 1963a] and Port Hacking, N.S.W. (unpublished record). The occurrence of the genus in Antarctica is not surprising, as the family generally flourishes here.

Adagnesia antarctica new species

Text figs. 133, 134

Type Locality. West of Macquarie I.: *Eltanin* Sta. 1418 (86–101 meters). Holotype, USNM 11966; paratypes, 2 specimens, USNM 11967.

Distribution. As with so many species adapted for free existence on a sandy bottom, the present species is covered with sand and is consequently inconspicuous. It very likely has a wide distribution in the Subantarctic and possibly could extend into the antarctic.

Description. The specimen is round and about 1.5 cm in diameter. Both apertures are sessile and are present in a longitudinal sand-free area on the upper surface and are surrounded by a rim of thickened test. Elsewhere the test is especially thin and sand-encrusted. There are about 20 circular muscles around each siphon and 35 longitudinal muscles, 20 from the branchial siphon and 15 from the atrial siphon, extending only a short distance down each side of the body. Short transverse muscles extend in rows around the body on either side of the median line. On the edge of a narrow fold around the base of the siphon there are about 15 long, simple branchial tentacles alternating with shorter ones, and a further single circle of shorter tentacles is present on the anterior surface of this fold or velum. The dorsal ganglion is long and the dorsal tubercle is extended into a fleshy tongue-like process pointing to the right. There are long pointed processes on the transverse vessels where they cross the dorsal line, as in *Agnesia* spp.

The branchial sac has 6 double rows of 11 spiral infundibula and each transverse vessel between these double rows has 8 large papillae with long, biramous arms. The gut forms a loop on the left side of the posterior part of the body enclosing the gonads. Gonads open by ducts that extend with the rectum, anteriorly toward the atrial opening.

Remarks. The species differs from the type species of this genus, *Adagnesia opaca* Kott, 1963a, in the extent to which the circular musculature around the base of the siphons is interrupted to operate the stiffened lips of test that protect the apertures. In *Adagnesia opaca* the gonoducts are directed, between the pole of the gut loop and the body wall, toward the antero-ventral corner of the body, whereas in the present species the gonoducts are directed, as is more usual in the family, toward the atrial opening. Further differences exist in the branchial sac, which in *Adagnesia opaca* has considerably more rows of infundibula and more infundibula in each row than in the present species.

Order PLEUROGONA
Suborder STOLIDOBRANCHIA Lahille

Family STYELIDAE Sluiter

Well represented in the Antarctic by several large and prolific species of *Styela* and *Cnemidocarpa*. The diverse colonial Styelidae are represented by the subantarctic genus *Alloeocarpa* and three other species, *Polyzoa opuntia*, *Polyzoa reticulata*, and *Oligocarpa megalorchis*. The genus *Polycarpa* is, however, represented by only a single record of *P. minuta* Herdman, 1882, from Kerguelen Islands.

Subfamily POLYZOINAE Hartmeyer

Zooids embedded in common test or joined by stolons and open separately to the exterior. Vegetative reproduction by pallial budding.

KEY TO GENERA OF POLYZOINAE

1. No branchial folds; few longitudinal vessels 2
   Branchial folds present or many longitudinal vessels 11
2. Stigmata transversely oriented 3
   Stigmata longitudinally oriented 4
3. Gonads on left side only; 4 longitudinal vessels . . . .
   . . . . *Berrillia*
   Gonads on both sides of the body; 3 longitudinal
   vessels . . . . *Protostyela*
4. Many small gonads 5
   Few larger gonads 8
5. Hermaphrodite gonads only present . . . . *Polyzoa*, p. 100
   Unisexual gonads present 6
6. Male gonads only on left 7
   Male and female gonads on both sides . . . .
   . . . . *Metandrocarpa*

7. Gonads in rows; female on right..*Alloeocarpa, p. 103
Gonads scattered; hermaphrodite on right. . . . .
. . . . .Theodorella
8. Gonads hermaphrodite. 9
Gonads unisexual . . . .'. . . . . .Chorizocarpa
9. Gonads on left side only . . . . .Kukenthalia
Gonads on both sides of body. 10
10. 4 internal longitudinal vessels on each side . . . .
. . . . .Symplegma
3 internal longitudinal vessels on each side. . . . .
. . . . .Botryllocarpa
11. Branchial folds suppressed; zooids sometimes solitary. .12
Branchial folds expressed; zooids never solitary. 15
12. Zooids united by stolons. . . . . .Dictyostyela
Zooids not united by stolons. 13
13. Gonads unisexual on both sides. . . . . .Psilostyela
Gonads hermaphrodite. 14
14. Gonads on right only. . . . . .Dextrocarpa
Gonads on both sides. . . . . .Monobotryllus
15. Unisexual gonads present. 16
Hermaphrodite gonads only present. 20
16. Male gonads present on both sides of the body. 17
Male gonads not present on both sides of the body. 18
17. Solely female gonads absent. . . . . .Stolonica
Solely female gonads not absent. . . . . .Amphicarpa
18. Only female gonads on left. . . . . .Arnbackia
Only male gonads on left. .19
19. Ovaries elongate. . . . .*Oligocarpa, p. 106
Ovaries not elongate. . . . . .Distomus
20. Hermaphrodite polycarps on both sides. . . . .
. . . .*Polyandrocarpa, p. 105
Hermaphrodite polycarps on right only. . . . .
. . . . .Oculinaria

———

* These genera reported from Antarctica.

Genus *Polyzoa* Lesson, 1830

Type species: *Polyzoa opuntia* Lesson, 1830
Branchial sac without folds; with 3 or more internal
longitudinal vessels. Hermaphrodite gonads forming
a row on each side near the endostyle.

KEY TO ANTARCTIC SPECIES OF *Polyzoa*

Zooids coalesce to form stalked heads. . . . . . .*opuntia*, p. 100
(South Georgia, Falkland Is., Magellanic area,
Kerguelen Is., Heard I., Campbell I.)
Stalked zooids remain discrete attached to basal stolons. . . .
. . . .*reticulata*, p. 102
(South Georgia, Falkland Is., Magellanic area,
Macquarie I., Kerguelen Is., Campbell I.)

Polyzoa opuntia Lesson

Text figs. 135–137

Polyzoa opuntia Lesson, 1830, p. 437.—Michaelsen,
1900, pp. 27, 28; 1904a, p. 58; 1907, p. 77.—
Hartmeyer, 1909–1911, p. 1372.—Van Name, 1945,
p. 236.—Ärnbäck, 1950, p. 17.—Pérès, 1952,

p. 218.—Kott, 1954, p. 147; 1957a, p. 2.—Millar,
1960, p. 96.
Goodsiria pedunculata Herdman, 1886, p. 335.
Goodsiria sp. Cunningham, 1871, p. 126.
Goodsiria coccinea Cunningham, 1871a, p. 489.—
Herdman, 1886, p. 337 [not Pfeffer, 1889, p. 4].
Colella n. sp. Pfeffer, 1889, p. 4.
Polyzoa pictonis Michaelsen, 1898, p. 368; 1900,
p. 59.
Polyzoa cunninghami Michaelsen, 1898, p. 369; 1900,
p. 28.
Polyzoa pictonis var. *waerni* Michaelsen, 1898, p. 369;
1900, pp. 27, 66.
Polyzoa coccinea Michaelsen, 1900, pp. 28, 44.—
Ärnbäck, 1950, p. 12–16 (incl. 3 forms).
Polyzoa herdmani Michaelsen, 1900, p. 29.
Polyzoa pictonis var. *georgiana* Michaelsen, 1900,
pp. 29, 63.
Polyzoa gordiana Michaelsen, 1900, p. 49.
Polyzoa lennoxensis Michaelsen, 1900, p. 56.
Polyzoa opuntia patagonica Michaelsen, 1904a, p. 59;
1907, p. 77.—Hartmeyer, 1909–1911, p. 1372.
Polyzoa opuntia pictonis Michaelsen, 1904a, p. 60;
1907, p. 78.—Hartmeyer, 1909–1911, p. 1372.
Polyzoa opuntia opuntia Michaelsen, 1904a, p. 61.
Polyzoa opuntia waerni Michaelsen, 1904a, p. 61;
1907, p. 78.—Hartmeyer, 1909–1911, p. 1372.
Polyzoa opuntia gordiana Michaelsen, 1904a, p. 63;
1907, p. 78—Hartmeyer, 1909–1911, p. 1372.—
Sluiter, 1932, p. 2.
Polyzoa opuntia coccinea Michaelsen, 1904a, p. 64;
1907, p. 78.—Hartmeyer, 1909–1911, p. 1372.—
Herdman, 1912, p. 313; 1915, p. 95.
Polyzoa opuntia lennoxensis Michaelsen, 1904a, p. 64;
1907, p. 78.—Hartmeyer, 1909–1911, p. 1372.
Polyzoa opuntia typica Michaelsen, 1907, p. 77.
Polyzoa pictonis var. *patagonica* Herdman, 1912,
p. 320; 1915, p. 102.

New Records. Off Tierra del Fuego: *Eltanin* Sta.
981 (40–49 meters).

Previous Records.
Antarctic: South Georgia [Michaelsen, 1900;
Sluiter, 1932; Ärnbäck 1950; Millar, 1960].
Subantarctic: Falkland Is. [Lesson, 1830; Cun-
ningham, 1871; Herdman, 1886, 1912; Ärnbäck,
1950; Millar, 1960]; Magellanic area [Cunningham,
1871; Michaelsen, 1900]; Kerguelen Is. [Pérès, 1952;
Kott, 1954]; Heard I. [Kott, 1954, 1957a]; Campbell
I. [Sluiter, 1932].
Elsewhere: North coast Argentina [Ärnbäck,
1950].

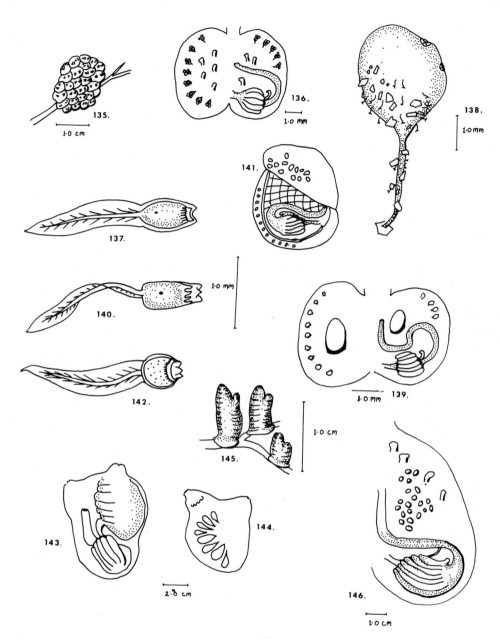

Polyzoa opuntia

135. Colony.
136. Inner body wall showing gut, gonads, and endocarps.
137. Larva [after Millar, 1960].

Polyzoa reticulata

138. External appearance with some adherent sand.
139. Inner body wall showing gut, gonads, and endocarps.
140. Larva [after Millar, 1960].

Alloeocarpa incrustans

141. Zooid, body wall reflected from left side [after Ärnbäck, 1950].
142. Larva [after Millar, 1960].

Polyandrocarpa placenta

143. Branchial sac and gut loop [after Millar, 1955].
144. Polycarps on right.

Oligocarpa megalorchis

145. Zooids external appearance.
146. Inner body wall on left showing gut and gonads.

Distribution. Generally in 4 to 50 meters, although specimens have been taken from 100 and 200 meters and in shore collecting from Heard Island. Circum-subantarctic but especially from shallower waters off the Falkland Islands-Magellanic area, extending into the antarctic area only at South Georgia. One colony has been taken from 100 meters off north Argentina [Ärnbäck, 1950, *P. coccinea* f. *fruticosa*], suggesting its occasional extension to the north.

Description. Colony of varying number of stalked heads from a common expanded basal mass or a network of anastomosing stolons by which the colony is attached to the substrate. The most common form of the head is obovate or pyriform, laterally flattened, wide and rounded at the free end and narrowing into a pedicel at the other end. Single heads up to 10 to 15 cm long, 4 to 5 cm wide, and 1.5 to 2 cm thick. Stalk is usually rather short and thick but may be slender and long (up to 5 to 6 cm). Variations in shape of the heads are considerable, sometimes even in the one colony. Small oval elevations over the ends of the zooids are evenly spaced over the surface of the heads and project to a varying extent from colony to colony. Each oval area 2.5 to 4 mm long has the two raised apertures of the zooids interrupting the surface along the long axis. Apertures are often distinctly 4-lobed or square. Color of the living colony is red, or reddish brown to flesh color, with darker oval areas over the zooids. The test is tough, and in smaller colonies slightly translucent. Tough test vessels pass from the body wall all around the zooid.

Zooids are closely attached in the colony. They are ovate, usually 4 to 5 mm long, but zooids 8 mm long have been recorded. Musculature is moderately developed with slender longitudinal bands. There are 24 to 40 or more branchial tentacles. A small circle of atrial tentacles is present. The dorsal tubercle a longitudinal ellipse with a slit-like or curved opening. Branchial sac is flat, without folds, with 8 slender internal longitudinal vessels on each side closer together dorsally. There are about 4 to 6 stigmata per mesh, and the number increases ventrally. Parastigmatic vessels are often present. The gut forms a small open loop. The stomach is short and rounded with 16 obliquely longitudinal folds and a small curved caecum from the pyloric end of the sutural ridge. There is a connective between the stomach and intestine enclosing an oval endocarp in the gut loop. The rectum is short and the anal margin more or less smooth. Gonads are hermaphrodite in a row either side of the endostyle, terminating at the intestinal loop on the left. There are 4 or 5 gonads on the left and 11 or 12 on the right. Michaelsen [1900] describes one specimen in which the row of gonads on the right extended dorsally and anteriorly from the posterior end, and Ärnbäck [1956 f. *fruticosa*] describes the right row of gonads extending completely around the dorsal and ventral margin from siphon to siphon, with the row on the left turning dorsally along the upper limb of the gut loop. Each gonad has a single sac-like testis closely attached to the body wall. The ovary is mesial to testis and consists of a small group of eggs, one usually larger than the rest. A slender vas deferens opens on top of the short oviduct. Scattered small endocarps are often present on the body wall.

Larvae. [Millar, 1960]. Ovoid trunk, about 0.8 mm long with triadiate papillae and an anterior circle of 16 (?) fingerlike ampullae. Tail 1.5 cm long with a broad fin. Single botryllid pigmented sense organ present.

Biology. The species is viviparous and embryos are present in the peribranchial cavity from December to July, i.e. well into the antarctic winter [Ärnbäck, 1950; Millar, 1960]. Specimens have been recorded from clay, sand, gravel, and shelly substrate.

Remarks. Both the colony and the zooids are, to some extent, variable. However, the zooids are always firmly embedded in common test, and the branchial sac, gut loop, and form of gonads are constant.

Polyzoa reticulata (Herdman)

Text figs. 138–140

Chorizocormus reticulatus Herdman, 1886, p. 346.—
  Pfeffer, 1889, p. 4 (40).
? *Polyzoa falclandica* Michaelsen, 1900, p. 52; 1904a,
  p. 68; 1907, p. 79.
Polyzoa falclandica var. *repens* Michaelsen, 1900,
  p. 55.
Polyzoa reticulata; Michaelsen, 1904, p. 244; 1904a,
  p. 65; 1907, p. 78.—Bovien, 1922, p. 40.—Van
  Name, 1945, p. 237.—Ärnbäck, 1950, p. 18.—
  Millar, 1960, p. 97.—Kott, 1954, p. 147.

New Records. Drake Passage: *Eltanin* Sta. 217 (110 meters), Sta. 219 (115 meters). Macquarie I.: *Eltanin* Sta. 1417 (79–93 meters), Sta. 1418 (86–101 meters), Sta. 1422 (833–842 meters).

Previous Records.

Antarctic: South Georgia [Pfeffer, 1889; Millar, 1960].

Subantarctic: Kerguelen Is. [Herdman, 1886]; Falkland Is. [Michaelsen, 1900, 1904; Ärnbäck, 1950; Millar, 1960]; Kerguelen Is. and Macquarie I. [Kott, 1954]; Patagonian Shelf [Millar, 1960]; Campbell I. [Bovien, 1922].

Distribution. This species, like *P. opuntia,* is found in the shallower waters around the Falkland Islands and South Georgia, the Magellanic area, and from Campbell Island, Macquarie Island, and Kerguelen Islands. Depth range is generally from 1 to 200 meters, but from off Macquarie Island the range is extended from shore collections to depths of 842 meters. The species appears from records to be less common than *P. opuntia,* but possibly the less robust colony may be lost or broken during collecting and inconspicuous stalked zooids may be overlooked.

Description. Colony formed of discrete stalked zooids united to basal stolons or younger zooids closely united in common test with little or no stalk. Intermediate between these conditions of the colony are specimens in the present collection (*Eltanin* Sta. 217), which are clumps of rounded zooids, each posteriorly tapering to a stalk that is confluent with the stalk of adjacent zooids, but basal stolons are not yet developed. Other zooids (*Eltanin* Sta. 219) with short thickenings of posterior test. Zooids are 4 mm high and 2.5 mm in diameter. The test is thin and leathery and may be covered with sand and hydroids. Sparse hairlike test extensions with flattened ends project among the sand grains. Branchial apertures almost terminal; the atrial aperture one-third of the body length from the branchial aperture. Both apertures are sessile. The body wall is muscular with outer circular and inner longitudinal muscle bands. Branchial tentacles are simple. There are about 12 rows of about 40 stigmata and 8 internal longitudinal vessels. The gut loop is simple or curved. The stomach short, almost spherical, with 16 longitudinal folds and a short caecum. Gonads present in a row each side of the endostyle, as in *P. opuntia,* up to 9 on the right but fewer on the left in the present specimens. Up to 3 large oval endocarps present on the body wall on each side. On the left the endocarps may be in gut loop, above gut loop, or between esophagus and rectum, or in all three positions.

Larvae. [Kott, 1954; Millar, 1960]. Oval trunk from 0.72 to 0.90 mm long. Tail from 1.0 to 1.5 mm with

a broad fin. Triradiate anterior papillae surrounded basally by a ring of 8 (4 pairs) of fingerlike ampullae. Simple pigmented botryllid sense organ present.

Biology. The species is viviparous. Developing embryos present from November to March [Millar, 1960].

Remarks. The zooid of this species is very like that of *P. opuntia.* The stalked zooids in their own discrete test distinguish the species, although there could be some confusion with younger colonies in which all zooids are embedded in common test material. The larval form of the present species, although similar to that of *P. opuntia,* has fewer anterior ampullae.

Genus *Alloeocarpa* Michaelsen, 1900

Type species: *Synstyela incrustans* Herdman, 1886 [part]

Branchial sac without folds; 5 to 16 internal longitudinal vessels. Female gonads on right, male gonads on left.

The genus is confined to the subantarctic and immediately adjacent areas. *Alloeocarpa affinis* Bovien, 1922, *A. minuta* Brewin, 1951 and 1956, from New Zealand, and *A. capensis* Hartmeyer, 1912 [Millar, 1962], from South Africa are all closely related.

KEY TO ANTARCTIC SPECIES OF *Alloeocarpa*

1. Zooids coalesce to form encrusting sheets or fleshy masses 2
   Individual zooids attached to basal membrane . . . .
   . . . . **bacca,** p. 105
                               (Islas Guaitecas, Chile)
2. 10 to 18 internal longitudinal vessels . . . **incrustans,** p. 103
                    (South Georgia, Falkland Is., Magellanic area,
                                          Patagonian Shelf)
   5 to 6 internal longitudinal vessels . . . . . . **bridgesi,** p. 104
                               (Tierra del Fuego)

Alloeocarpa incrustans (Herdman)

Text figs. 141, 142

Synstyela incrustans Herdman, 1886, p. 342 [in part; not Philippine specimens]; 1912, p. 313; 1915, p. 95 [not *Synstyela incrustans* Sluiter, 1895].

Goodsiria coccinea; Pfeffer, 1889, p. 4 (40) [not Cunningham 1871a].

Alloeocarpa incrustans; Michaelsen, 1900, p. 25; 1904a, p. 88; 1907, p. 76.—Van Beneden and Selys Longchamps, 1913, p. 41.—Van Name, 1945, p. 239.—Ärnbäck, 1950, p. 8.—Millar, 1960, p. 98.

Alloeocarpa zschaui Michaelsen, 1900, p. 32; 1904a,
p. 88; 1907, p. 76.—Sluiter, 1932, p. 2.

Alloeocarpa emilionis Michaelsen, 1900, p. 35.

? *Alloeocarpa intermedia* Michaelsen, 1900, p. 39;
1904a, p. 91; 1907, p. 77.

Alloeocarpa incrustans f. *zschaui* Ärnbäck, 1950, p. 9.

Alloeocarpa incrustans rugosa Ärnbäck, 1950, p. 10.

New Records. None.

Previous Records.

Antarctic: South Georgia [Michaelsen, 1900,
1904a; Sluiter, 1932; Ärnbäck, 1950; Millar, 1960].

Subantarctic: Falkland Is., Magellanic area [Herd-
man, 1886; Michaelsen, 1900; Ärnbäck, 1950; Millar,
1960]; Patagonian Shelf [Millar, 1960].

Distribution. Limited to shallower waters of Falkland Islands and Tierra del Fuego. This is an unusually restricted distribution for a species in the Subantarctic. Depth range is from 1 to about 150 meters.

Description. From solid fleshy masses or encrusting
sheets with furrows in the surface indicating the
limits of each zooid, to colonies in which zooids are
separate, united only by a thin basal membrane.
Brick red to lemon yellow in life but preserved specimens brown or gray. Test often leathery and wrinkled.
Both apertures are 4-lobed or sometimes short, transverse slits. Zooids sac-like, or ovate, occasionally
reaching 8 to 10 mm in length. Branchial tentacles
up to 24, of three sizes. Branchial sac with 10 to 18
internal longitudinal vessels on each side, closer
together dorsally. From 2 to 8 stigmata per mesh
on dorsal and ventral parts of the branchial sac,
respectively. The gut loop is simple and horizontal
with 16 to 20 longitudinal folds on a pyriform
stomach and a short stomach caecum from the pyloric
end of the sutural ridge. The anal margin is not
lobed. Male gonads, sometimes cleft into two or more
lobes, in a row or an irregular group of up to 20 on
the left body wall; female gonads usually more
numerous in an irregular row along the ventral border
of the right side. Each ovary consists of a few eggs
which discharge from a short oviduct of variable
diameter, often expanded distally.

Larvae. [Millar, 1960]. Trunk from 0.34 to 0.8 mm;
tail from 0.9 to 1.2 mm with a broad fin. Triradiate
papillae anteriorly surrounded by a ring of 18 to 26
ampullae. The larva is red-brown and sometimes distinct pigment spots are present on the surface. The
pigmentation obscures the single sense organ.

Biology. Species is viviparous and larvae reported in
the peribranchial chamber from February to June

from the Falkland Islands, Magellanic area, and from
November to February from South Georgia [Millar,
1960]. Thus, although there seems, on present evidence, to be a summer breeding season in South
Georgia, the specimens from the subantarctic area are
breeding for at least half the year. *Alloeocarpa
incrustans* was also taken from Falkland Islands in
July and from the Patagonian Shelf in October, but
larvae have not been reported. Colonies from South
Georgia in March and May were apparently also
free of larvae [Millar, 1960]. The species therefore
resembles both *Polyzoa opuntia* and *P. reticulata* in
the extended breeding season, which may actually be
longer since the number of colonies taken from July
to November [Millar, 1960, Table 30] are not sufficient for conclusive determination of the limits of the
breeding season.

Remarks. The form of the colony and the number
of longitudinal branchial vessels and stomach folds
are very variable, and no constant characters have
yet been described that could differentiate the species
synonymized above. Even the arrangement of the gonads is variable and 2 or 3 ovaries have been found
on the left side of the body in front of the testes [Mil-
lar, 1960]. The larval form of *A. capensis* [Millar,
1962] is identical with that of *A. incrustans* with pigment in the larval test, and a ring of 24 ampullae. The
large number of internal longitudinal vessels distinguishes the species.

Alloeocarpa bridgesi Michaelsen

Alloeocarpa bridgesi Michaelsen, 1900, p. 41; 1904a,
p. 92; 1907, p. 77.—Hartmeyer 1909–1911, p. 1374.
—Van Beneden and Selys Longchamps, 1913,
pp. 47, 49.—Van Name, 1945, p. 240.

New Records. None.

Previous Records. Tierra del Fuego [Michaelsen,
1900; Van Beneden and Selys Longchamps, 1913].

Distribution. This is an endemic species in the
shallow waters off Tierra del Fuego ranging down to
a depth of 14 meters or more.

Description. Red, encrusting colony, the zooids forming low convex elevations over the surface. Branchial
internal longitudinal vessels number 5 or 6. Male
gonads 1 to 5, each consisting of a single gland
divided into many branched lobes that are compacted
into a spherical mass from which the small sperm duct
arises. Otherwise, the species resembles *A. incrustans*.

Remarks. Although this species is recorded from the
one general area where *A. incrustans* is plentiful, the

condition of both the male gonads and the branchial sac suggest such divergence that a separate species is justified. The male gonads also distinguish the species from others closely related in adjacent areas.

Alloeocarpa bacca Ärnbäck

Alloeocarpa bacca Ärnbäck, 1929, p. 4.—Van Name, 1945, p. 240.

New Records. None.

Previous Records. Islas Guaitecas, Chile 23 meters [Ärnbäck, 1929].

Description. Individual zooids are joined by a basal membrane. Internal longitudinal branchial vessels 6 or 7. Male gonads composed of 4 or 5 coherent groups of testicular glands, each with its own short vas deferens across the top of the gut loop on the left side of the branchial sac. Either 4 or 5 ovaries around the antero-ventral part of the right side of the endostyle. 'A couple (of these) are on the left' [Ärnbäck, 1929]. The oviducts appear to be directed antero-dorsally, rather than directly toward the atrial opening, and the species is viviparous.

Remarks. Like *Alloeocarpa bridgesi*, the appearance of the colony falls within the range of variation of *A. incrustans*, and, like *A. bridgesi*, the zooids may be distinguished by the small number of internal longitudinal vessels and by the male gonads. Both *A. bridgesi* and *A. bacca* differ from *A. incrustans* in the extent to which the male gonads are subdivided and at the same time become considerably reduced in number. The species differ only in the confluence of these male glands in *A. bacca*, so that they appear continuous; however, in *A. bridgesi* the ramifications of the testis lobes are compacted into spherical masses. It is possible that the extent to which these lobes are compacted is variable, or even seasonal, and that the two species are synonymous. Ärnbäck [1929, fig. 6] does not show clearly that the bow of ovaries are, as she describes them, on the right. In her figure, however, the branchial sac is displaced and the meridian around which the body wall is bissected is oblique, rather than dorso-ventral, and passes to the left of the dorsal line and to the right of the endostyle, thus separating the ovarian area around the ventral border from the remainder of the right side of the body [see also Millar, 1962: *A. capensis*].

Alloeocarpa minuta Brewin, 1951 and 1956, from Chatham Island and North Island, New Zealand, *A. affinis* Bovien, 1922, also from Chatham Island, and

A. capensis Hartmeyer, 1912 [Millar, 1962], from South Africa . . . are closely related species in cold temperate waters, with internal longitudinal vessels, stomach folds, and number and arrangement of gonads especially the ovaries, similar to those of *A. bacca*. The testes, however, in these three species do not appear to be subdivided to any extent (in *A. capensis* a slight indentation only). *Alloeocarpa minuta* is further distinguished by a short vas deferens.

Genus *Polyandrocarpa* Michaelsen, 1904a

Type species: *Goodsiria lapidosa* Herdman, 1899
Branchial sac with 3 or 4 folds. Numerous hermaphrodite polycarps scattered over the body wall on both sides. The following doubtful record is the only one of this genus from the Antarctic region.

Michaelsen took as the type species of *Polyandrocarpa* Herdman's *Goodsiria lapidosa* '(part.)' as described in 1899, '. . . Catalogue of the Tunicata in the Australian Museum . . . .' However, Michaelsen failed to include in his generic synonymy reference to Herdman's [1891] earlier characterization of *Goodsiria* and the species *G. lapidosa*. Michaelsen did cite Herdman [1898] 'Note on the Tunicate Fauna of Australian Seas,' in which the species is merely one of a number listed.

Polyandrocarpa placenta (Herdman)

Text figs. 143, 144

Goodsiria placenta Herdman, 1886, p. 328.
Goodsiria placenta var. *fusca* Herdman, 1886, p. 333.
Not *Gynandrocarpa placenta*; Michaelsen, 1900, p. 29; 1904a, p. 30.—Van Name, 1945, p. 235 [< *Gynandrocarpa unilateralis* Michaelsen; Millar, 1962, p. 178].
? *Goodsiria* (*Gynandrocarpa*) *placenta* Herdman, 1912, p. 313; 1915, p. 95.
Polyandrocarpa placenta; Millar, 1955, p. 199.

New Records. None.

Previous Records.

   Subantarctic: ? Falkland Is. [Herdman, 1912].
   Elsewhere: Simons Bay, South Africa [Herdman, 1886; Millar, 1955].

Distribution. There are substantiated records of this species from Africa in only 18 to 37 meters. Herdman [1912] states that his single colony from the Falkland Islands 'seems to agree closely with this South African species.'

Description. Typical form of well developed colonies thick, fleshy, rounded or oval disk on a short pedicel; colonies up to 12 cm in diameter. Zooids with 3 [Herdman] or 4 [Millar] branchial folds and 6 or 7 rows of stigmata. The esophagus is short. The stomach is large with 12 to 14 longitudinal folds. The intestine and rectum form a simple S bend behind the branchial sac [Millar, 1955]. From 6 to 8 gonads on each side of the body are pear shaped or ovoid with central ovary and a row of testis follicles on each side.

Remarks. Herdman does not make it clear whether his specimen from the Falkland Islands had polycarp gonads or the single gonad of *Gynandrocarpa unilateralis*, with which Michaelsen [1900] had erroneously synonymized Herdman's original species. Possibly Herdman [1912] made his identification from the appearance of the colony only, and it could have been a large colony of *Polyzoa opuntia*.

Genus *Oligocarpa* Hartmeyer, 1911

Type species: *Oligocarpa megalorchis Hartmeyer*, 1911
    Single large testis on left side of body wall; on the right side two long ovaries near the endostyle. Branchial sac folded.

Oligocarpa megalorchis Hartmeyer

Text figs. 145, 146

Oligocarpa megalorchis Hartmeyer, 1911, p. 527.— Kott, 1954, p. 147.

New Records. Macquarie I.: *Eltanin* Sta. 1418 (86–101 meters).

Previous Records. Kerguelen Is. [Hartmeyer, 1911], Macquarie I. [Kott, 1954].

Distribution. From fairly shallow water ranges down to 101 meters in a very limited section of the subantarctic area.

Description. Zooids free standing joined by basal membrane or short stolons. Zooids cylindrical, up to 23 mm long and 14 mm wide. Distinct outer siphons. The branchial siphon terminal and the atrial siphon on dorsal border. The test is thin and leathery with deep furrows and projections in the siphonal region. Preserved specimens whitish-gray with yellow-brownish tones. The body wall is muscular. About 32 branchial tentacles of three sizes. The dorsal tubercle with a curved opening directed anteriorly. The dorsal lamina is smooth. Branchial sac with 3 low, rounded folds on each side; without parastigmatic vessels;

7 or 8 stigmata present in an average mesh but up to 12 near the endostyle. There are 8 or 9 internal longitudinal vessels on the folds and 2 to 4 between them. Only 1 or 2 internal longitudinal vessels between the dorsal lamina and the first fold.

The gut forms a large loop on the left side of the body. The stomach is longish and oval with about 16 inner folds and a short curved caecum. The rectum is long, ending in an 8-lobed anus near the base of the atrial siphon. There are two large tubular ovaries on the right side of the branchial sac. The larger elongate ovary beneath the endostyle posteriorly and extending to the end of the branchial sac. The smaller ovary is slightly lobed, completely across the posterior end of the body partly behind and partly to the right of the retropharyngeal line. Both oviducts open toward each other in the posterior part of the peribranchial cavity. Male gonad on the left side of the body consists of a single large testis, which is composed of irregularly lobed follicles building up a compact mass. In younger zooids the compact mass is not formed, and the testis is represented by well separated follicles spread over the body wall.

Biology. The orientation of the oviducts ensures viviparity, but no larvae have been taken.

Remarks. This species is reasonably conspicuous and it is surprising that further records have not occurred even in the limited area to which it may be confined (Kerguelen Islands and Macquarie Island).

Subfamily STYELINAE Herdman
Zooids solitary; usually 4 branchial folds.

KEY TO GENERA OF STYELINAE

1. Stigmata absent . . . . *Bathyoncus*, p. 125
   Stigmata present 2
2. Branchial sac without folds 3
   Branchial sac with folds 6
3. Single gonad only beneath the endostyle or on the right . . . . *Styelopsis*, p. 124
   Gonads on both sides of the body 4
4. Elongate, often V-shaped gonads . . . . *Pelonaia*
   Gonads not elongate 5
5. Almost spherical gonad, more than a single testis follicle . . . . *Dicarpa*
   Gonads not spherical; single testis follicle . . . . *Minostyela*, p. 124
6. Gonads on one side of the body only 7
   Gonads on both sides of the body 10
7. Numerous hermaphrodite polycarps on the left . . . . *Skaiostyela*
   1 or 2 polycarp-like or elongate gonads on the right 8
8. Branched elongate gonad . . . . *Dendrodoa*
   Gonad not branched 9

9. Single globular gonad .... *Podostyela*
   Paired gonads with ducts directed toward one another
   .... *Azygocarpa*
10. Numerous small hermaphrodite gonads.............
    .... *Polycarpa*, p. 107
    Gonads few, elongate or rounded 11
11. Dorsal lamina with languets .... *Hemistyela*
    Dorsal lamina smooth bordered membrane 12
12. Testis lobes mingle with ovarian tissue in gonads ......
    .... *Cnemidocarpa*, p. 107
    Testis lobes do not mingle with ovarian tissue ....
    .... *Styela*, p. 110

* These genera reported from Antarctica.

Genus *Polycarpa* Heller, 1878

Type species: *Cynthia pomaria* Savigny, 1816
Four branchial folds. Gonads in the form of numerous polycarps attached to the body wall on both sides of the body.

The following single specimen is the only record of this genus in the southern oceans.

Polycarpa minuta Herdman

Polycarpa minuta Herdman, 1881, p. 78; 1882, p. 171.

New Records. None.

Previous Records. South of Kerguelen Is., 275 meters [Herdman, 1882].

Description. Dome-shaped, convex anteriorly and posteriorly flattened, 0.6 cm long and 0.9 cm broad. Attached by the whole of the basal surface, with a test expansion at the margin continuous with the fixed surface. Apertures are anterior, not far apart, and are sessile. Surface smooth and even, the test is thin but strong. Body wall very thin and closely adherent to the test. Branchial tentacles are few and filiform. The dorsal tubercle is conspicuous with both horns coiled to the right. The branchial sac has four groups of 4 internal longitudinal vessels closely placed representing the folds. There is a single stigma in each mesh on the folds. Between the folds there are 2 internal longitudinal vessels and 6 to 8 stigmata per mesh. Gonads are flask-shaped polycarps on the inner body wall, with a funnel-like duct and rod-shaped calcareous spicules in the walls. (After Herdman.)

Remarks. This species seems definitely to belong to the genus *Polycarpa*. Although Herdman has not indicated the number of polycarps present, they are of typical form and it does not appear likely that they are reduced styelid gonads.

Genus *Cnemidocarpa* Huntsman, 1912

Type species: *Styela joannae* Herdman, 1898a
Gonads elongate; testis lobes beneath and amongst ovarian cells.

KEY TO ANTARCTIC SPECIES OF *Cnemidocarpa*

Test papillae in 2 rows from either side of branchial aperture .... *zenkevitchi*, p. 110
(Bunger Hills, Knox Coast)
Test papillae not in rows .... *verrucosa*, p. 107
(cirumpolar Antarctic, Subantarctic)

Cnemidocarpa verrucosa (Lesson)

Text figs. 147–149, Plate II

Cynthia verrucosa Lesson, 1830, p. 151. — Cunningham, 1871a, p. 488.
Ascidia verrucosa; Dujardin, 1840, p. 536.
Styela grandis Herdman, 1881, p. 67; 1882, p. 153.
Styela lactea Herdman, 1881, p. 68; 1882, p. 156; 1902, p. 192; 1912, p. 311; 1915, p. 93; 1923, p. 23.—Hartmeyer, 1927, p. 183.
Styela verrucosa; Michaelsen, 1898, p. 365; 1900, p. 86; 1907, p. 76.—Sluiter, 1914, p. 15.—Van Name, 1945a, p. 297.
Styela steineni Michaelsen, 1898, p. 365; 1900, p. 92; 1907, p. 76.
Styela spirifera Michaelsen, 1898, p. 366; 1900, pp. 83, 94; 1907, p. 76.
Styela flexibilis Sluiter, 1905b, p. 473; 1906, p. 36.
Styela spectabilis Herdman, 1910, p. 4.
Tethyum verrucosum; Hartmeyer, 1911, p. 444.
Tethyum lacteum; Hartmeyer, 1911, pp. 447, 525.
Tethyum spectabile; Hartmeyer, 1911, p. 447.
Tethyum spiriferum; Hartmeyer, 1911, p. 447.
Tethyum [Styela] steineni; Hartmeyer, 1911, p. 447.
Tethyum [Styela] lacteum; Hartmeyer, 1912, p. 250.
Cnemidocarpa verrucosa; Van Name, 1945, p. 272.—Ärnbäck, 1950, p. 5.—Pérès, 1952, p. 218.—Kott, 1954, p. 142.—Millar, 1960, p. 105.—Vinogradova, 1962, p. 202.

New Records. South Shetland Is.: *Eltanin* Sta. 434 (77 meters), Sta. 435 (73 meters), Sta. 436 (73 meters), Sta. 445 (101 meters). Antarctic Peninsula: *Edisto* Sta. 31, TD 6 (325 meters), Sta. 34, TR 17 (409 meters); *Staten Island* Sta. 6/63 (7 meters), Sta. 32/63 (46 meters), Sta. 35/63 (46 meters), Sta. 37/63 (49 meters), Sta. 67/63 (38 meters); *Edisto* Sta. 190[14] (64 meters), Sta. 193[14] (64 meters), Sta. 225[14] (74 meters), Sta. 226[14] (74 meters), Sta. 234[14] (74 meters). Bellingshausen Sea: *Edisto* Sta. 147[14]

[14] U.S. Navy Antarctic Expedition, 1947–1948.

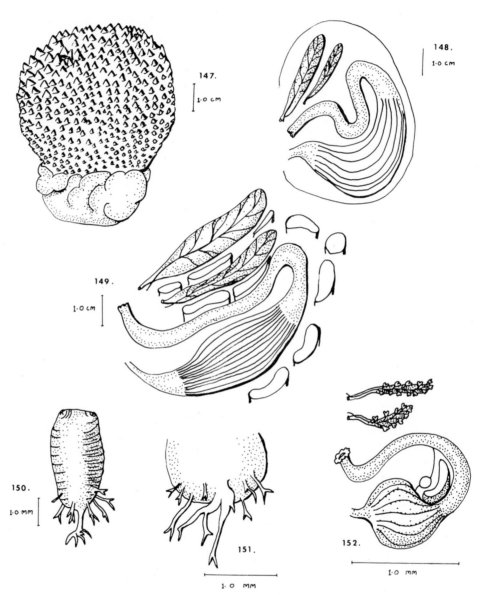

Cnemidocarpa verrucosa

147. External appearance of smaller specimens showing papillae and posterior expansion.
148. Inner body wall on left showing gut, gonads, and endocarps, small specimen.
149. Inner body wall on left showing gut, gonads, and endocarps, larger specimen.

Styela schmitti

150. External appearance.
151. Posterior end zooid, showing root processes.
152. Inner body wall, left side.

(56 meters). Knox Coast: *Edisto* Sta. 33[14] (79 meters). Ross Island, off Cape Royds, Ross Sea: *Edisto* Sta. 104 (off ship's anchorage). [McMurdo Sound, Erebus Bay, Turtle Rock, 77°45′S, 166°46′E, November 23, 1966, deep reef, 26 meters. Coll. Carleton Ray; project Physiological Ecology and Acoustics of Antarctic Seals.]

Previous Records.

Antarctic: South Georgia [Michaelsen, 1898; Ärnbäck, 1950; Millar, 1960]; South Orkney Is. [Herdman, 1912]; South Sandwich Is. [Millar, 1960]; Antarctic Peninsula [Sluiter, 1906; Millar, 1960]; Weddell Sea [Vinogradova, 1962]; Enderby Land, Mac. Robertson Land, Queen Mary Coast, Wilhelm II Coast [Hartmeyer, 1911; Kott, 1954; Vinogradova, 1962]; Adélie Coast [Herdman, 1923]; Ross Sea [Herdman, 1902].

Subantarctic: Falkland Is. [Lesson, 1830; Michaelsen, 1900; Ärnbäck 1950; Millar, 1960]; Tierra del Fuego [Michaelsen, 1898]; Kerguelen Is. [Herdman, 1882, 1910; Pérès, 1952; Kott, 1954; Vinogradova 1962]; Bouvet I., Crozet Is. [Millar, 1960]; Patagonian Shelf [Millar, 1960].

Distribution. Common in shallower waters but extending as deep as 400 meters; circumpolar in the antarctic and subantarctic areas.

Description. Large, cylindrical, ovate, or 'barrel-shaped.' The younger specimens almost cylindrical and posteriorly attached. There may be a short stalk posteriorly expanded basally where it is attached to the substrate. Largest specimens up to 18 cm long and 9 cm in diameter. The test is tough, opaque but thin and flexible, especially in larger specimens. The surface may be smooth but is usually roughened by furrows, wrinkles, and papillae. The papillae present, especially anteriorly, may be simple and conical or, in younger specimens, very pointed and often tipped with spines that may also extend over the entire surface of the papilla. In older specimens the spinous processes are often lost and the papillae expand into low, rounded, irregularly shaped wart-like swellings, which, when small and closely spaced, give the surface a granular appearance. There is tremendous variation in the form, size, number, and processes of the papillae. The test of living specimens is usually white with a rosy tinge, becoming bright yellow around the apertures. In older specimens the surface becomes stained, yellowish-brown, brown, or gray. Two living specimens from *Staten Island* Sta. 35/63 are described by the collector as 'bright yellow.' Preserved specimens often white when young but usually brownish-white, brown, or gray. Rarely any foreign matter present on the test. Both apertures square and anterior. They are sessile or on very short conical projections. The body wall is thin and closely adherent to the test. Strong inner muscle bands radiate from the siphons. Outer circular muscle bands form an open network anteriorly, but posteriorly become thin and irregular. Posteriorly in larger specimens (5 cm long), the body wall may extend into a muscle-free jelly-like extension that expands into a basal plate in the base of the stalk. This may increase in thickness to form a sort of spherical rhizome, constricted off from the rest of the body and presumably helping to anchor the individuals on a muddy bottom. From 30 to 40 branchial tentacles are of two or three sizes. The dorsal tubercle opening is more or less C-shaped and directed anteriorly, both horns often spiralling inward. The dorsal lamina is short and smooth-edged. The branchial sac with 4 well defined but low folds with wide intervals of the sac between the folds. There are 2 to 4 internal longitudinal vessels between and 6 to 15 on the folds. These are comparatively low numbers of internal longitudinal vessels for such large specimens and consequently the meshes are especially wide, with usually 20 to 30 stigmata, but occasionally as many as 40. The transverse vessels are strong and may hold the branchial sac into small secondary folds. The gut loop is variable, perhaps because of contraction or shortening of the body, and may form a simple more or less vertical loop, or the distal part of the loop involving the pyloric half of the stomach may be bent up on itself to form a secondary loop (*Eltanin*, Sta. 436). The stomach, with about 25 long plications, is always very voluminous and long, occupying most of the dorsal limb of the primary loop. The anus is distinctly lobed. There are usually on each side of the body two long cnemidocarp gonads, with male and female components mingled along their length. The male ducts extend across the surface and join a common vas deferens along the middle of the gonad, but, when the gonad is well developed, this is obscured by overlapping germinal tissues. On the left the gonads extend parallel to the gut loop or across the open interval of the secondary loop to open at varying distances from the atrial aperture. They are in a similar position on the right. There is sometimes only one gonad on each side; occasionally there may be a small third gonad. Endocarps are usually present between the gonads or between gonads and gut loop and often also in a row around the ventral border of the body.

Remarks. This conspicuous and prolific species, despite the variations in test surface, is easily distinguished by the flexible test, adherent body wall, and low widely separated folds with large number of stigmata in each mesh. The color of living specimens varies from white, white with rosy and yellow tinge, to bright yellow. It is interesting to note that two bright yellow specimens from *Staten Island* Sta. 35/63 were exactly the same color as a nudibranch taken from an adjacent station.

Cnemidocarpa zenkevitchi Vinogradova

Cnemidocarpa zenkevitchi Vinogradova, 1958, p. 1375; 1962, p. 202.

New Records. None.

Previous Records. Knox Coast, in brackish marine bays or 'oases,' 66°00′ to 66°30′S, 100°00′ to 101° 50′E. Entrances to the bays here are blocked by ice during the winter, but the entrances open during the summer. Thawing ice then causes freshening of surface water; however, at 2 or 3 meters the salinity is still 23.5‰ and here, close to the mouth of the bay, this species is found. There are also remains of fish and echinoderms in the area, but otherwise only diatoms and algae [Vinogradova, 1958].

Description. Long oval, almost cylindrical, from 3.8 to 14.3 cm long, expanded posteriorly into a fixation plate. The test is thin, becoming thicker posteriorly. It is parchment-like and translucent, covered with spines up to 0.1 mm. There is a single row of sucker-like papillae extending about one-quarter of the body length from each side of the branchial aperture. Living specimens are rosy and translucent, and preserved specimens are creamish-white or pinkish. Branchial and atrial apertures are close together anteriorly on wart-like 4-lobed siphons. The body wall is not closely adherent to the test except in the region of the papillae. There are outer circular muscle bands and inner longitudinal bands radiating from the siphons, but neither are very well developed. In its posterior third the body is a mass of white parenchymatous connective tissue extending into the basal plate. Branchial tentacles are simple, 32 or 33 in a single circle, two sizes alternating. The dorsal tubercle slit is 'horseshoe-shaped' with open interval directed anteriorly or slightly to the right, both horns spiralled inward. The dorsal lamina is short and smooth. There

are 4 branchial folds on each side of the body, with 3 or 4 internal longitudinal vessels between, and 8 to 13 on the folds. The meshes are long and there are about 80 stigmata in each mesh. The stomach is long, spindle-shaped, with 28 longitudinal folds. The gut loop is narrow, the descending limb curves up to the rectum, terminating in a bilobed anus. Two long cnemidocarp-type gonads on each side of the body above the gut loop on the left and in a similar position on the right. Endocarps are present around the gut. (After Vinogradova.)

Remarks. This interesting species, probably isolated by its especially rigorous environment, appears to be closely related to *Cnemidocarpa verrucosa*. The remarkable parenchymatous packing occupying the posterior one-third of the body and thus effecting a reduction of the general metabolic area is similar to the posterior extension into the basal plate or rhizome of *C. verrucosa* specimens in the present collection (*Eltanin* Sta. 436 from the Falkland Islands). The present species is distinguished by localization of test papillae into two lines, regularity of distribution of spines over the surface, a two-lipped anus without lobes, and the only limited adherence of the body wall to the test (in the region of the papillae only). The branchial sac is similar to, although shorter than, that of *C. verrucosa*, but the meshes are even longer than in *C. verrucosa*, with twice as many stigmata. Could the parenchymatous tissue provide a storage site for winter nourishment?

Genus *Styela* Fleming, 1822

Type species: *Cynthia canopus* Savigny, 1816

Four branchial folds per side; elongate gonads: ovary tubular; testis lobes around sides or beneath ovary or on body wall separated from the ovary but never mixed up with ovarian tissue. (See chapter 8, Phylogeny.)

This genus in Antarctica is represented by several very morphologically stable species and one particularly variable species. They are distinguished from one another largely by the gonads: one group of species representing immense developement of the ovarian tubes (*S. pfefferi*, *S. serpentina*, *S. paessleri*), and one species characterized by immense developement of testis lobes (*S. wandeli*). *Styela nordenskjoldi*, *S. grahami*, and *S. insinuosa* are distinguished by a gradual reduction of branchial folds and increase of both ♂ and ♀ components by elongation of the gonad.

Key to Antarctic Species of *Styela*

1. 7 to 10 sausage-shaped gonads on each side of the body
   .... ***ohlini***, p. 122
   (Magellanic area)
   Not more than 3 gonads on each side of the body 2
2. Without folds in the branchial sac 3
   With folds in the branchial sac 4
3. With 4 internal longitudinal vessels .... ***insinuosa***, p. 119
   (Victoria, Enderby, Weddell quadrants to
   South Georgia)
   With very numerous longitudinal vessels ***sericata***, p. 122
   (cosmopolitan, abyssal)
4. Ovarian tube branched 5
   Ovarian tube not branched 7
5. Biramous arborescent ovary with long branches; wide
   intervals between folds .... ***paessleri***, p. 121
   (Falkland Is., Tierra del Fuego, Patagonian Shelf)
   Ovary with short pinnate branches; not wide intervals
   between folds 6
6. Ovarian branches indented at the tip; gut does not spiral
   .... ***pfefferi***, p. 120
   (Davis Sea, South Georgia, South Shetland Is.,
   Kerguelen Is.)
   Ovarian branches not indented at the tip; gut spirals ..
   .... ***serpentina***, p. 120
   (Victoria, Enderby quadrants; South Shetland Is.)
7. 3 to 4 internal longitudinal vessels per fold ....
   .... ***grahami***, p. 119
   (Antarctic Peninsula, South Shetland Is.)
   More than 5 internal longitudinal vessels per fold 8
8. Testis follicles not greatly lobed .... ***schmitti***, p. 111
   (South Shetland, Tierra del Fuego, Uruguay)
   Testis follicles develop into many fan-shaped lobes 9
9. Endocarps between ovary and testis lobes .. ***wandeli***, p. 117
   (South Shetland Is.)
   Endocarps not between testis lobes and ovary ....
   .... ***nordenskjoldi***, p. 112
   (circum-antarctic, South Orkney Is., Falkland Is.,
   Patagonia, Peru-Chile Trench, South Australian Basin)

Styela schmitti Van Name

Text figs. 150–152

Styela schmitti Van Name, 1945, p. 298.
Styela schmitti f. *simplex* Millar, 1960, p. 109.

New Records. South Shetland Islands: *Eltanin* Sta.
410 (240 meters). Drake Passage: *Eltanin* Sta. 219
(115 meters).

Previous Records.

Subantarctic: Off Tierra del Fuego [Millar, 1960];
off Montevideo, Uruguay, [Van Name, 1945].

Distribution. This species is extremely inconspicuous,
coated with sand and shell. Records indicate a distribution in shallow waters on the Patagonian Shelf
probably extending along the Scotia Ridge to the
South Shetland Islands. Depth range is from 21 to
240 meters.

Description. Oval upright specimens up to 7 mm
long. Posteriorly the test is produced into a number
of rootlike processes, one of which may be longer
and thicker, forming a distinct stalk, or the rootlike
processes may branch from the stalk itself. The test
may be covered with irregular filaments or branched
hairlike extensions, especially around the apertures,
to which sand adheres, or the test may be leathery
without processes other than the root or stalk. Apertures are both sessile on anterior corners of the zooid.
Body musculature varies from diffuse (present specimens, Sta. 410) to regular tough outer circular and
inner longitudinal layers [see also Van Name, 1945].
Branchial tentacles number from 8 to 40. The dorsal
tubercle is a simple transverse or modified C-shaped
slit.

The dorsal lamina is long and undulating. The
branchial sac is reduced to varying extents from 4
folds with the most ventral fold sometimes reduced
[Van Name, 1945, and present specimens Sta. 410]
to well developed dorsal fold, rudimentary second
fold only [Millar, 1960] or rudimentary folds or
accumulation of vessels, 2 on the left, 3 on the right
(Sta. 219 present collection). The arrangement of
internal longitudinal vessels in the specimen from Sta.
219 is indicated by the formula: E. $2(3)2(6)3(7)$-
$4DL(8)5(6)5E$. This arrangement is variable, however, and in a large individual there may be about 20
closely placed internal longitudinal vessels on the first
fold, on the others usually about half that number
or less [Van Name, 1945]. Parastigmatic vessels are
present crossing meshes of 2 or 3 stigmata. The gut
forms a simple loop; the stomach is rounded to oval
with 12 to 20 folds. There is, in the present specimens, a spherical gastric gland reservoir joined by
the duct to intestine and stomach, respectively, across
the gut loop and enclosing an endocarp in the pole
of the loop. The anus has up to 15 rounded lobes on
the margin in the present specimens, but Millar
[1960] records '2 simple or slightly frilled lobes.'
There may be 1 or 2 gonads on each side of the
body, each consisting of a central sinuous and tubular
ovary surrounded along both sides and around the
blind end of the tube by separate testis follicles, sometimes lobed, each with its own duct, joining together
on the mesial surface of the ovary to empty into the
central vas deferens. The vas deferens extends
along the surface of the ovary toward the atrial opening and opens above the oviduct.

Remarks. Despite the individual variation found in
all characters of this species, the small numbers of

and arrangement of the testis follicles, together with reductions in the branchial sac and a tendency to form a stalk by the posterior extension of the test, are constant. The combination of characters distinguishes the species from all others.

Styela nordenskjoldi Michaelsen, nomen conservandum

Text figs. 153–159, Plate I

? *Cynthia magellanica* Cunningham, 1871a, p. 488.

Styela squamosa Herdman, 1881, p. 66; 1882, p. 152.

Styela flava Herdman, 1881, p. 64; 1882, p. 160.

Styela glans Herdman, 1881, p. 65; 1882, p. 162.— Hartmeyer, 1927, p. 183.—Rodrigues, 1966, p. 95.

Styela oblonga Herdman, 1881, p. 65; 1882, p. 159.— Hartmeyer, 1927, p. 183.—Van Name, 1945, p. 299.

Styela nordenskjoldi Michaelsen, 1898, p. 365; 1900, p. 97; 1907, p. 76.—Van Name, 1945, p. 303.

? *Styela canopus* var. *magalhaensis* Michaelsen, 1898, p. 367.

Styela curtzei Michaelsen, 1900, p. 94.

Styela milleri Ritter, 1907, p. 21.—Van Name, 1945, p. 308.—Millar, 1959, p. 196; 1964, p. 62.

Tethyum nordenskjöldi; Hartmeyer, 1909–1911, p. 1359.

Tethyum [Styela] nordenskiöldi Michaelsen, 1912, p. 124.

Tethyum curtzei; Hartmeyer, 1909–1911, p. 1359.

Styela rotunda Herdman, 1910, p. 6.—Kott, 1954, p. 142.—Vinogradova, 1962, p. 201.

? *Tethyum canopus* var. *magalhaense* Hartmeyer, 1911, p. 22.—Coifmann, 1933, p. 5.

Tethyum gaussense Hartmeyer, 1911, p. 448.

Tethyum drygalskii Hartmeyer, 1911, p. 452.

Tethyum flavum; Hartmeyer, 1912, pp. 374, 378.

Tethyum glans; Hartmeyer, 1912, pp. 374, 378.

Tethyum oblongum; Hartmeyer, 1912, pp. 374, 378.

Tethyum tholiforme Sluiter, 1912, p. 455.

Styela drygalskii; Sluiter, 1914, p. 17.

Styela tholiformis Sluiter, 1914, p. 18.—Hartmeyer, 1927, p. 191.—Van Name, 1945, p. 306.

Styela magalhaensis; Ärnbäck, 1929, p. 3.—Kott, 1954, p. 145.—Millar, 1960, p. 112.

Cnemidocarpa drygalskii; Van Name, 1945, p. 270.— Millar, 1960, p. 104.

Ypsilocarpa nordenskjoldi; Ärnbäck, 1950, p. 4.

Styela papillata Kott, 1954, p. 143.

Cnemidocarpa nordenskjoldi; Millar, 1960, p. 101.

? *Cnemidocarpa barbata* Vinogradova, 1962, p. 202.

? *Cnemidocarpa bifurcata* Millar, 1964, p. 60.

New and Previous Records. See Tables 1 and 2. In addition to occurrence and depth range, some information on habitus and comparative morphology is given.

Distribution. From the western side of the Antarctic Peninsula, South Shetland Islands, and the eastern Antarctic as far as McMurdo Sound in depths ranging from 115 to 126 meters. There are no records from the antarctic continent between Charcot Island and the Ross Sea, but this is probably due to a lack of collecting. The species extends along the Scotia Ridge to the Magellanic area in depths as shallow as 37 meters. It occurs farther to the north along both sides of the American continent: On the east it has been taken from 600 meters off the Río de la Plata, and on the west coast it extends through the deep waters of the Peru-Chile Trench and farther north off California at depths from 825 to 5000 meters. It has not been taken from the shelf region of subantarctic islands, although Hartmeyer records possibly young specimens of this species from St. Paul Island in the Indian Ocean and Herdman described synonymous species from the South Australian Basin in 4758 meters.

Description. There is tremendous variation in the form of this species from almost spherical, attached by a small area of the posterior surface or fixed by a beard of rootlike processes, to conical, dome-shaped, or completely dorso-ventrally flattened, attached by a spreading base. The test is thin and tough, the surface may be raised into rounded papillae or round to polygonal flattened scale-like elevations with or without sand. Without sand these elevations appear to be accompanied by localized stiffening of the test, giving a 'grainy,' roughened effect. Where these elevations are especially developed around the siphons, the surface may appear leathery but generally they merely stiffen the thin test. When encrusted with sand the elevations of test are higher and appear as low 'warts.' One dorso-ventrally flattened specimen (*Burton Island* Sta. 3) has a partly 'warty' test posteriorly with sand encrustations, but anteriorly around the siphons the test has typically scale-like thickenings and no sand. From the South Orkney Islands region (*Eltanin* Sta. 494) identical dorsoventrally flattened specimens were taken, two with a scaly sand-free test and one with 'warty' sandencrusted test. Small specimens may also have fine hairs over the body surface to which particles of sand adhere [Kott, 1954, as *S. magalhaensis*; Ritter, 1907; Millar, 1964, as *S. milleri*; and specimens from *Eltanin* Sta. 43]. Specimens with warty elevations

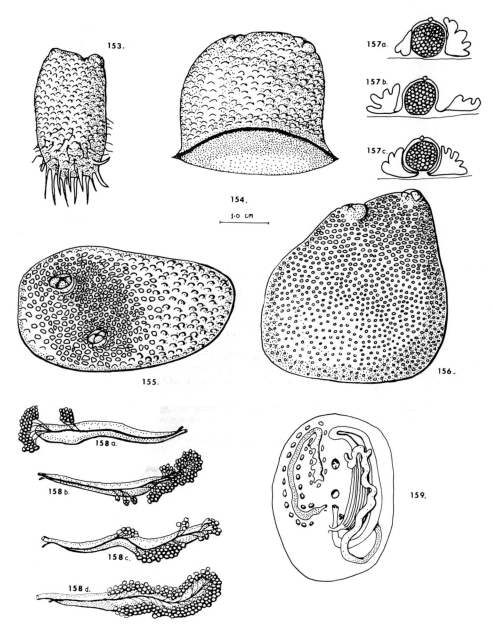

Styela nordenskjoldi

153. Upright specimen, *Eltanin* Sta. 43/52; wartlike swellings and hairs.

154. Dome-shaped specimen, Sta. 29 B.A.N.Z.A.R.E.; wartlike swellings on test.

155. Flattened specimen; wartlike swellings and plate-like thickenings anteriorly.

156. Globular specimen *Eltanin* Sta. 370; minute plate-like thickenings.

157. Section through gonads showing varying disposition of testis lobes in relation to ovary: (*a*) Flattened specimen *Burton Island* Sta. 3 and *Eltanin* Sta. 344; (*b*) many mature specimens; (*c*) upright specimens *Eltanin* Sta. 43 and stalked specimen *Eltanin* Sta. 494.

158. Gonads from various individuals: (*a*) Upright specimen *Eltanin* Sta. 45; (*b*) flattened specimen, *Eltanin* Sta. 494; (*c*) many mature specimens; (*d*) dome-shaped specimen B.A.N.Z.A.R.E. Sta. 29.

159. View from ventral surface, through body wall of a flattened specimen showing shift in relative position of gut loop and gonad due to flattening of body. Endocarps on right only showing.

and sand have not been recorded larger than 3 cm; specimens larger than this up to 5 cm diameter, either globular or irregular (*Eltanin* Sta. 370), or completely dorso-ventrally flattened (*Eltanin* Sta. 344) have scale-like thickenings in the test. Rooted specimens have been taken up to 2.2 cm, usually with sandy elevated surface; however, scale-like thickenings also occur [Van Name, 1945, as *S. milleri*]. Generally, the test is thicker when wart-like elevations occur. In the region of the scale-like or papilliform thickenings minute spherical transparent globules clumped together into morulae are accumulated in the superficial layer of test. They have not been detected in any specimens in which there is an incrustation of sand. The apertures are 4-lobed on low papillae, or completely sessile. They are usually fairly close together anteriorly; however, the dorsal aspect of the body is usually expanded in both upright and flattened forms, so that the apertures are rarely central on the upper surface. Living specimens, when not obscured by sand, are orange. Preserved specimens are usually some shade of brown, yellowish-brown, or whittish-yellow. The body wall is fairly closely adherent to the test and is fairly thin, with inner radiating longitudinal muscles, not always clearly differentiated into bands, and outer circular muscle fibers. The muscles are well developed on

the anterior half of the body but fade out posteriorly or cease abruptly halfway down at a point corresponding to the greatest diameter of the body, especially in dorso-ventrally flattened individuals. There are 20 to 40 branchial tentacles of varying sizes. The dorsal tubercle varies from a conspicuous C-shaped slit to a minute longitudinal slit deep in the peritubercular area. Dorsal lamina is smooth edged and wavy or slightly pectinate. The branchial sac is distinctive with 4 low rounded folds and numerous internal longitudinal vessels close together, especially on the folds. Dorsal folds are best developed. The internal longitudinal vessels are not always completely straight, but often are minutely undulating. There are 5 to 12 internal longitudinal vessels between the folds and up to 26 on the folds. In smaller specimens some folds may be suppressed, and then there are more internal longitudinal vessels on or between the existing folds. There are usually from 2 to 5 stigmata per mesh, although there may be more in certain parts of the branchial sac. The stomach is oval to elongate, roomy, longitudinally folded in 15 to 25 ridges. A short pyloric caecum is often present. The gut loop is a long horizontal curve which may extend on to the right side of the body beneath the endostyle. It is always loosely attached to the body wall, and especially in dorso-ventrally flattened forms the

TABLE 1. *Styela nordenskjoldi,* New Records

Specimens	Occurrence and Depth in Meters	Shape*	Internal Longitudinal Vessels between Folds†	Gut Loop	Longest Dimension, cm	Position of Testis Lobes
Eltanin Sta. 43 [part]	Peru-Chile Trench (5234–5314)	Da	3–6 (10–20)	Not across endostyle	2	On sides of ovary
Eltanin Sta. 43 [part]	Peru-Chile Trench (5234–5314)	Da	3–6 (10–20)	Not across endostyle	1.2–2	On body wall
Eltanin Sta. 344	Falkland Is. (119)	AAb	3–8 (10–20)	Across endostyle	5	On sides of ovary
Eltanin Sta. 370	Falkland Is. (104–115)	Bb	5–10 (10–20)	Across endostyle	5	On sides of ovary
Eltanin Sta. 494	South Orkney Is. (1226)	AAb AAa	2–5 (8–20)	Not across endostyle	2–3	On body wall
Eltanin Sta. 439	NW of South Shetland Is. (128–165)	Da	3–4 (8–15)	Not across endostyle	0.5	On body wall
Eltanin Sta. 981	Off Tierra del Fuego (40–49)	Aa	3–4 (10–15)	Not across endostyle	1.5	Beneath ovary
Burton I. Sta. 3	Ross Sea (434)	AAb-a	3–8 (10–20)	Not across endostyle	4	On sides of ovary

* Key to abbreviations:

    A, dome-shaped specimens.
   AA, specimens flattened (dorso-ventrally).
    B, globular or irregular specimens fixed by a smaller basal area.
    C, stalked specimens.
    D, rooted specimens.
    a, outer cuticle raised into warty elevations.
    b, scale-like thickenings in test.

† Numbers in parentheses are the number of longitudinal vessels on folds.

TABLE 2. *Styela nordenskjoldi* and synonyms, *Previous Records*

Species	Occurrence and Depth in Meters	Shape*	Internal Longitudinal Vessels between Folds†	Gut Loop	Longest Dimension, cm	Position of Testis Lobes
nordenskjoldi Michaelsen, 1898	Magellanic area (90)	AAb	4–6 (10–12)	Across endostyle	. . .	Beneath ovary
curtzei Michaelsen, 1898	Magellanic area (37)	AAa	1–3 (6–13)	Not across endostyle	. . .	Beneath ovary
nordenskjoldi Van Name, 1945	Magellanic area (18.4–55)	Ab to AAb	4–6 (10–12)	Not across endostyle	5	Beneath ovary
nordenskjoldi Van Name, 1945	Magellanic area (18.4–55)	Ab AAb	4–6 (10–12)	Not across endostyle	5	On body wall
magalhaensis Michaelsen, 1898	Magellanic area (183)	Aa	4 (20)	Not across endostyle	. . .	On body wall
nordenskjoldi Ärnbäck, 1950	Magellanic area (10–22)	Bb	. . .	Across endostyle	. . .	On sides of ovary
nordenskjoldi Millar, 1960	Magellanic area (0–170)	Ab AAb	. . .	Across endostyle	1.0–5.0	On sides of ovary
magalhaensis Millar, 1960	Patagonian Shelf (99–110)	Aa	4–6 (13–15)	Not across endostyle	1.1	On body wall
magalhaensis Millar, 1960	South Georgia (230–250)	Ab	3–8 (11–14)	Not across endostyle	1.5	On body wall
tholiformis Sluiter, 1914	Antarctic Peninsula (460)	AAa	6 (6)	Not across endostyle	2.2	On body wall
drygalskii Millar, 1960	Antarctic Peninsula (259–354)	AAb	. . .	Not across endostyle	2.5	On sides of ovary
oblogna, glans, flava Herdman, 1882	Off Río de la Plata (1097)	Aa Aa AAb	7 (5–10)	Not across endostyle	1.5–3.5	On body wall
milleri; see Van Name, 1945	California to Peru (825–4322)	Da to AAb	?	Not across endostyle	2.2	On body wall
drygalskii Van Name, 1945	Panama, Pacific (3281)	?Ab	?	?	. . .	On body wall
? *bifurcata* Millar, 1964	West Panama (3570)	E	8–23 (15–33)	Not across endostyle	2	On sides of ovary
? *milleri* Millar, 1964	West Panama (3570)	Da	?	Not across endostyle	3	On sides of ovary
squamosa Herdman, 1882	South of Australia (4758)	Ab	?	Not across endostyle	2	On sides of ovary
rotunda Herdman, 1910; Kott, 1954; Vinogradova, 1962	McMurdo Sd. (183) Enderby (300) Knox Coast (660)	Bb	11 (24)	Not across endostyle	2–3	On sides of ovary
drygalskii Hartmeyer, 1911	Wilhelm II Coast 300–385	Ab AAb	4–6 (5–20)	Not across endostyle	2	On sides of ovary
gaussense Hartmeyer, 1911	Wilhelm II Coast (385)	B— C—	4–6 (8–14)	Not across endostyle	1–1.2	On sides of ovary
magalhaensis Kott, 1954	Mac. Robertson Land (1266)	Aa	3–7 (10–16)	Not across endostyle	1.0	On body wall
papillata Kott, 1954	Mac. Robertson Land (456) Kemp Coast (603)	Ba	4–7 (10–26)	Not across endostyle	. . .	Beneath ovary
barbata Vinogradova, 1962	Knox Coast (639)	Da	4–13 (10–24)	Not across endostyle	1.0	Beneath ovary

* See key to abbreviations Table 1.
† Numbers in parentheses are number of longitudinal vessels on folds.

body folds around a plane just anterior to the gut loop, which remains in the base while the rectum curves over the outer margin of the body and extends in the mid-line along the upper surface to the atrial opening. The anal border varies from 2 or 3 lobes to 6 lobes, which may themselves be subdivided to give a maximum of 12 rounded lobes.

Gonads are long and sinuous ovarian tubes with pear-shaped testis follicles closely applied to the sides and around the ends in a continuous or interrupted line. Sometimes they form a double row beneath the ovary. There are 1 or 2 gonads on each side of the body; sometimes subdivided into two branches [Kott, 1954, as *S. papillata*]. On the left the gonads are anterior to the gut loop, or on the body wall covered by the gut loop on their mesial surface. The testes mature as varying numbers of these follicles increase in size and usually form clumps around the ends, or around the ends and along the sides of the ovaries. Enlargement of the testes involves enormous growth of the outer border of each lobe upward and outward from the ovary until the seminal ducts, curving around the ovary to join the vas deferens on its mesial surface, are completely obscured for most of their length by the testis follicles. Well developed testis follicles are fan-shaped, at right angles to the ovary, their upper or mesial surface deeply indented to give the appearance of many rounded lobes. These indentations may actually develop and subdivide the follicles; however, generally the fan shape is maintained and often it may be observed more closely by transmitted light than by dissection. Development of testis lobes along both sides of the end of the ovary may suppress that end of the ovary, leading to the condition in which double rows of testis follicles appear to extend out from the end of the ovary [Sluiter, 1914, as *S. tholiformis*, and specimens from *Eltanin* Sta. 494]. There is either a series of small flat-topped endocarps parallel to the gonads on both sides or, less usual, larger endocarps in a comparable position but less regularly arranged.

Biology. The variations in shape of this species may be at least partly explained by the shape of the substrate on which they develop. Ärnbäck [1950] observed that specimens with an expanded base were fixed in most cases, to stones, shell, or algae. The dorso-ventrally flattened specimens in the present collection are fixed to large scallop shells or rock or around coral particles. The upright specimens are fixed to small rocks or pebbles, and the concave basal surface described by Hartmeyer [1911] is

limited by the size of the particle to which the animal is fixed. Although in many other species the test may grow over or among the substrate, here there seems to be a tendency for the whole posterior half of the test to flatten itself on to a broad uninterrupted substrate, thus pulling the animal down and stretching it flat across the surface. This occurs only where the substrate is continuous. Where the surface is an interrupted one (e.g. composed of pebbles or sand), the upright habit is maintained and only the immediately posterior part of the test is fixed. Stalked specimens from deeper stations are probably a special development for a soft muddy substrate, whereas rooted specimens, taken especially from depths of over 1000 meters, are obviously suited for a substrate of diatomaceous ooze, from which in fact they have invariably been collected. The varying condition of the surface test may be associated with age and the presence of sand. Either the hardening of the wart-like protuberances causes the loss of sand embedded in their surface, or the presence of sand inhibits the formation of the scale-like thickenings. Neither the function nor the nature of the accumulations of morulae in surface scales is known. The biological significance of the various conditions of gonads is difficult to assess; no size correlation has been found with gonad condition, and the largest specimens with simple pear-shaped, immature ♂ follicles closely applied to the sides of the ovary are common. Unless these large specimens represent individuals that are reaching sexual maturity for the first time, which is unlikely, it must be assumed that testis follicles expended in one breeding season are reformed at the ends of the seminal ducts close to the ovarian tube. Michaelsen [1900] under the name of *S. canopus* var. *magalhaensis* describes immature testis follicles developing in the body wall. This development has not been observed in the present collection nor in previous descriptions, in which immature follicles are closely applied along the sides or beneath the ovary. All specimens where testes form clumps or wide margins around the ovaries are mature.

Remarks. The above synonymy is based, within wide limits, on form and thickness of test, form of gonads, and the low folds and wide intervals of the branchial sac. Millar [1960] separated *C. nordenskjoldi* from *C. drygalskii* by the number of stomach folds and the crossing of the endostyle by the gut loop. However, large and identical 'drygalskii' flattened forms with 19 stomach folds have the gut loop crossing well over into the right side of the body or confined to the left side. No correlation of variables (number of stomach folds, extent of gut, body shape, size of dorsal tubercle, depth, or geographical distribution) was found and the morphological variations must be considered intraspecific. The variation of body shape is probably due to a specific tendency to spread over a surface. *Styela schmitti* [see Van Name, 1945, and below], a closely related species, also has a tendency for the test surface to flatten on to the substrate as in the present species.

The range of variation in the test and shape of *S. milleri* [see Van Name, 1945] bring this species within the limits of variation for *S. nordenskjoldi* and the internal structure also varies in the same way. Ritter's [1907] type specimen of *S. milleri* had hairs and is similar to *S. magalhaensis* [Kott, 1954]. If hairs developed from the external test are indeed a variation to be found in this species, the identity of *Cnemidocarpa bifurcata* Millar, 1964, is suspect. *C. bifurcata* is surrounded by a feltwork of hair and its tubular ovary is branched, thus providing the only, not very reliable, distinctions from *S. nordenskjoldi*. *Styela papillata* Kott, 1954, also has a branched ovary, but otherwise is identical with *S. nordenskjoldi*.

The great variability in the surface test presumably has enabled the species to adjust to many environmental conditions and may explain the very wide geographical and vertical range recorded. Conversely, the wide geographic separation of specimens with similar test modifications argues against the significance of these modifications as specific characters.

Styela sericata Herdman, 1888, off Kerguelen and at many localities in the Indian Ocean and Tasman Sea [Millar, 1959] is also closely related but is distinguished by the absence of branchial folds. Van Name [1945] suggested that *Styela bythia* Herdman, 1881 and 1882, taken with *S. squamosa* (< *S. nordenskjoldi*) from the South Australian Basin and from the Tasman Sea and the Kermadec Trench [Millar, 1959] might be identified with *S. tholiformis*, a synonym of the present species. However, the languets on the dorsal lamina clearly distinguish it and suggest a relationship with the genus *Pyura*. The branchial tentacles have not yet been described.

It is interesting that in this collection (*Eltanin* Sta. 494) a specimen of *Pyura squamata* was taken with three flattened specimens of *S. nordenskjoldi*. Hartmeyer [1911] also took the two species off Wilhelm II Coast in 350 to 380 meters, and Millar [1960] records a single specimen of *Pyura squamata* taken

with three flattened specimens of *Cnemidocarpa drygalskii* (< *S. nordenskjoldi*). Furthermore, these specimens represent the only records of *P. squamata* in the Antarctic.

The present species is also closely related to *S. orbicularis* Sluiter, 1904, from Indonesia, 1200 meters. Although this distribution seems unlikely, there are a number of other species with a similar distribution (see chapter 9, Zoogeographical Discussion).

Styela wandeli (Sluiter)

Text figs. 160, 161

Tethyum wandeli Sluiter, 1911, pp. 37, 38.—Hartmeyer, 1911, pp. 456, 457.

Tethyum (Styela) quidni Sluiter, 1912, p. 456.

Styela wandeli Sluiter, 1914, p. 18.—Van Name, 1945, p. 307.

Styela quidni Sluiter, 1914, p. 22.—Van Name, 1945, p. 307.

New Records. Antarctic Peninsula: *Edisto* Sta. 189[15] (64 meters), Sta. 193[15] (64 meters), Sta. 226[15] (74 meters), Sta. 232[15] (74 meters), Sta. 234[15] (74 meters); *Staten Island* Sta. 67/63 (38 meters). South Shetland Is.: *Staten Island* Sta. 62/63 (57 meters). Bellingshausen Sea: *Edisto* Sta. 162[15] (56 meters).

Previous Records.

Antarctic: South Shetland Is., Booth (Wandel) I. [Sluiter, 1911, 1914].

Distribution. Limited to the Bellingshausen Sea and adjacent South Shetland Islands and Antarctic Peninsula area in shallow waters up to 75 meters.

Description. Conical body fixed by flat base, or with a short stalk. The outer surface of the test is leathery and pink with transverse wrinkles. The outer cuticle is raised into minute mammillations or scale-like polygonal areas, which are not obvious to the naked eye. Specimens 1 to 2.0 cm high. The stalk is slightly narrower than the body and expands over the substrate. Both apertures are present anteriorly on short siphons, close together. The body wall has inner radiating longitudinal muscle bands and an outer layer of circular fibers. There are only about 12 to 30 branchial tentacles, some or all quite large. The dorsal tubercle is horseshoe-shaped, the open interval directed anteriorly. The branchial sac has 4 low rounded folds with 8 to 17 internal longitudinal vessels on the folds and 4 or 5 between with 4 to

---

[15] U.S. Navy Antarctic Expedition, 1947–1948.

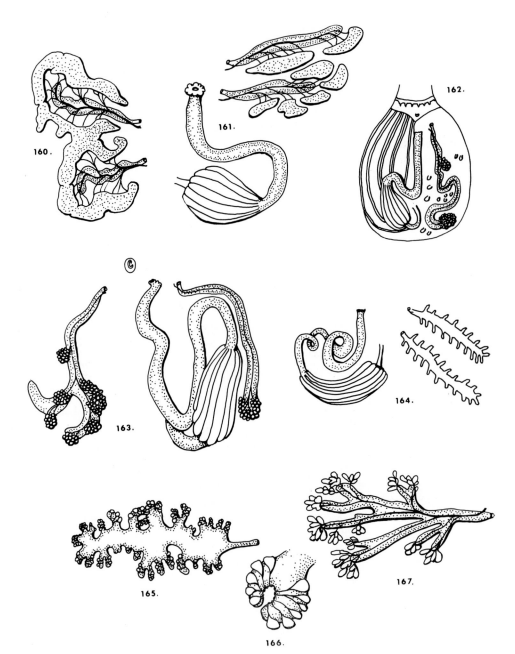

Styela wandeli
160. Gonads with coalesced clumps of testis lobes.
161. Inner body wall on left side showing gut and gonads
      with discrete clumps of testis lobes.

Styela grahami
162. Inner body wall [after Sluiter, 1914].

Styela insinuosa
163. Gut and gonads.

Styela serpentina
164. Gut loop and gonads [after Sluiter, 1914].

Styela pfefferi
165. Gonads from parietal surface [after Millar, 1960].
166. Tip of gonad branches from parietal side showing course
      of seminal ducts [after Millar, 1960].

Styela paessleri
167. Gonad from mesial surface [after Millar, 1960].

8 stigmata in each mesh. The stomach is oval with 24 folds and a very small pyloric caecum. The gut loop is comparatively short and the intestine turns anteriorly and dorsally almost as soon as it leaves the stomach to form the horizontal narrow loop. The rectum is fairly long and terminates in 6 anal lobes near the atrial opening. There are 2 gonads on each side of the body, each comprising a tubular ovary, separated by an interval of body wall from very numerous testis follicles in coalesing lobes. There is usually not room between the 2 ovaries on each side for two continuous series of testis lobes, and the lobes associated with the most posterior ovary of each pair are interrupted by the continuous series of male lobes of the anterior gonad. This is indicated only by the course of the seminal ducts on to the mesial surface of the ovary. In one specimen the testis lobes anterior to the gonads on the right are completely absent. Tall endocarps are present on the body wall, some between the testis and the ovary.

Remarks. The species is probably closely related to *S. nordenskjoldi.* In addition to the huge development of testis lobes and their separation from the sides of the ovary, however, the species is distinct in the appearance of the leathery test, the presence of 24 stomach folds (always ?), the small number and large size of the tentacles, and the presence of 2 pairs of gonads on each side (always ?). The combination of the characters is sufficient to maintain the species as distinct from *S. nordenskjoldi.*

Styela grahami Sluiter

Text fig. 162

Styela grahami Sluiter, 1905b, p. 473; 1906, p. 39; 1914, p. 17.—Van Name, 1945, p. 305.
Tethyum grahami Hartmeyer, 1911, p. 456.

New Records. None.

Previous Records.

Antarctic: Antarctic Peninsula, South Shetland Is. [Sluiter, 1905b; 1914].

Distribution. Sluiter found the species fairly common in the Antarctic Peninsula and South Shetland Islands area (13–21 specimens) in depths up to 110 meters. It has not been taken since.

Description. Cylindrical, attached posteriorly. Up to 9 cm high, 4 cm wide. Surface furrowed, divided into small areas. Yellowish-gray color. Test thin, tough, and leathery. Both apertures short, directed anteriorly. Body wall with moderate musculature. Branchial tentacles 10 to 20, according to the size

of the individual. Dorsal tubercle horseshoe-shaped, horns spirally inrolled. Dorsal lamina narrow and smooth-edged. Branchial sac with 4 narrow folds with only 3 or 4 internal longitudinal vessels separated by wide flat intervals with numerous internal longitudinal vessels. However, these vessels are not closely spaced and there are 12 or more stigmata per mesh. The gut forms a double, almost vertical loop similar to that of *Styela insinuosa.* One elongate and sinuous tubular ovary on each side of the body. Small groups of testis follicles occur at random on the sides of the ovary. Small, upright endocarps are present over inner surface of body wall.

Remarks. Although the external appearance, gut, and course of gonads resemble *S. insinuosa,* the species is distinguished by the large number of internal longitudinal vessels and by the accumulation of the testis follicles into larger and less frequent groups than in *S. insinuosa.*

Styela insinuosa (Sluiter)

Text fig. 163

Tethyum insinuosum Sluiter, 1912, p. 457.
Styela insinuosa Sluiter, 1914, p. 24.—Herdman, 1923, p. 25.—Van Name, 1945, p. 304.—Kott, 1954, p. 141.—Millar, 1960, p. 111.

New Records. Weddell Sea: *Edisto* Sta. 21, TR 7 (412 meters). Antarctic Peninsula: *Edisto* Sta. 180[16] (156–193 meters).

Previous Records.

Antarctic: South Georgia [Millar, 1960]; South Shetland Is. [Sluiter, 1912]; Commonwealth Bay [Herdman, 1923; Kott, 1954]; Queen Mary Coast [Herdman, 1923].

Distribution. Probably circum-antarctic on the continental shelf in from 75 to 400 meters.

Description. More or less cylindrical, up to 5.3 cm high and 2 cm in diameter. The surface is covered by low circular to elongate wartlike swellings. The color in preservative pinkish, yellowish-gray, or brown. Apertures both anterior and adjacent on short tubular siphons. Body wall with inner longitudinal, middle circular, and outer longitudinal layers of muscle. There are 16 to 32 tentacles. The slit of the dorsal tubercle is C-shaped with inrolled horns, the open interval directed anteriorly. Kott [1954] recorded a large square dorsal ganglion with 3 pairs of anterior and 2 pairs of posterior nerves, i.e. a

---

[16] U.S. Navy Antarctic Expedition, 1947–1948.

very conspicuous nervous system. There are no folds and only 4 large internal longitudinal vessels each side of the branchial sac, which may be slightly pleated (as in certain *Ascidia* spp.). The stomach is a longish oval with 20 to 35 long folds, placed vertically or obliquely. The primary gut loop is vertical, the first limb formed by the pyloric part of the stomach and the ascending intestine; the second limb formed by descending intestine until it turns dorsally and anteriorly and ascends toward the atrial opening to form the second loop. The anal border has 12 to 15 distinct lobes. There are single gonads on each side of the body, or 2 gonads on the right and 1 on the left. Gonads comprise a long tubular ovary and interrupted groups of testis follicles along the sides of the ovary, especially around the posterior end. Anteriorly, the ovarian tube is straight; posteriorly, it may be curved or bent into a U shape. The gut loop is only loosely attached to the body wall and partly covers the gonad on the left. In the present specimen the right gonad is single but biramous from halfway along its length.

Remarks. This species is comparatively rare. It is also remarkably constant in all characters except the number of gonads, which vary only between 1 and 2 on one side of the body only.

Styela serpentina Sluiter

Text fig. 164

Tethyum serpentina Sluiter, 1912, p. 456.
Styela serpentina Sluiter, 1914, p. 20.—Van Name, 1945, p. 305.
? *Styela subpinguis* Herdman, 1923, p. 24.

New Records. None.

Previous Records.

Antarctic: South Shetland Is., 75 meters [Sluiter, 1912]; Adélie Coast, Queen Mary Coast ?, 645 meters [Herdman, 1923].

Distribution. Thirteen specimens were taken together from the South Shetland Islands and single specimens only taken from eastern Antarctica. Depth range is from 75 to 645 meters.

Description. Up to 4.5 cm long, 1.5 to 1.7 cm wide. Siphons short, directed anteriorly, 1 cm apart. Surface smooth, with only weak longitudinal furrows. Whitish in alcohol. Body wall muscular. Branchial tentacles 14, of about the same size. Dorsal tubercle rounded, aperture with incurved horns. Dorsal lamina narrow and smooth. Branchial sac with 4 large folds, 12 to 20 internal longitudinal vessels on the

folds and 7 to 10 between them; 3 or 4 stigmata per mesh. Stomach long, narrow, with 18 folds. Intestine bent into 2 to 3 spirals. Two gonads on each side, each consisting of a straight tube with pinnate branches.

Remarks. S. *subpinguis* Herdman [1923] has a similar test and convoluted intestine, and possibly is a younger specimen of this species, before side branches of the gonads have developed (e.g. as in the left gonad of a specimen of S. *pfefferi* [> S. *paessleri*; Vinogradova, 1962]. The gonad branches of the present species are not indented at the tip to become biramous, thus distinguishing it from S. *pfefferi*. S. *pfefferi* does, however, have a rather long intestine and the species are probably closely related.

Styela pfefferi Michaelsen

Text figs. 165, 166

Styela pfefferi Michaelsen, 1898, p. 367; 1900, p. 77; 1907, p. 75.
Styela paessleri; Kott, 1954, p. 144.—Vinogradova, 1962, p. 201.
Cnemidocarpa pfefferi; Millar, 1960, p. 100.

New Records. Antarctic Peninsula: *Edisto* Sta. 180[17] (156–193 meters).

Previous Records.
Antarctic: South Georgia, South Shetland Is. [Michaelsen, 1898; Millar, 1960]; Davis Sea [Vinogradova, 1962]; Kerguelen Is. [Kott, 1954].

Distribution. Probably circum-antarctic in waters up to 383 meters. The 150-meter record from Kerguelen Islands may be indicative of a far wider range in the subantarctic area.

Description. Body generally upright with 2 prominent siphons anteriorly. From 2.2 to 5.2 cm high and 2.2 to 2.5 cm wide. Surface divided into irregular areas by shallow furrows. Specimens pale gray to white in preservative. Michaelsen's specimen was stalked. The test is thin and tough but not leathery. Body wall with longitudinal and circular muscles anteriorly and an irregular network posteriorly. The body wall is adherent to the test. The dorsal tubercle has a C-shaped slit with inrolled horns, the opening directed anteriorly. There are 10 to 32 branchial tentacles according to the size of the individual. Four distinct branchial folds on each side of the body have longitudinal vessels densely on the folds but only sparsely distributed between the folds.

---

[17] U.S. Navy Antarctic Expedition, 1947–1948.

There are 19 to 26 internal longitudinal vessels on the folds and 1 to 5 between them. In specimens in the present collection the longitudinal vessels are folded and convoluted, especially in the dorsal part of the sac. This is perhaps due to contraction. There are 4 to 6 stigmata per mesh. The gut loop is wide and simple; the stomach a rather short ellipse with 24 to 31 long folds. The anal border has up to 12 round irregular lobes. There are numerous endocarps on the body wall. The gonads, usually 2 on each side of the body, have testis follicles associated with the indented tips of more or less pinnate branches of the tubular ovary. The terminal indentation of these branches accommodates the testis ducts as they curve around the ovary to join the vas deferens on the mesial surface of the ovary [Millar, 1960]. Three of the gonads in the Kerguelen Islands specimen are biramous, and a single gonad in the *Ob* specimens from the Davis Sea may not be branched at all [Vinogradova, 1962]. The biramous branches of ovaries in the present specimen from the Antarctic Peninsula are quite long, but their origin and nature is apparent from an examination of the lateral aspect of the gonads. The testis ducts here pass through the fork of the branch and extend across and under the ovary to the testis lobes present along the outer edge of each branch.

Remarks. It has been found to be impossible to separate from this species Kott's [1954] specimen from Kerguelen Islands. For the present therefore, it seems safer to assume a wider distribution than to create a new species from Kerguelen Islands. The gonads are characteristic and interesting [Millar, 1960]. They appear to have developed by the extension outward of pinnate branches from the ovary; carrying out on the ends of these branches the testis lobes usually lining the parietal borders of the ovary. Apparently, as this occurs, the testis ducts, usually curving around the sides of the ovary to the mesial surface, do not appreciably lengthen but are pulled across the tip of the extension causing it to indent, forming the biramous branches through which they curve to the vas deferens on the mesial surface. The species is closely related to *S. paessleri* (see below).

Styela paessleri Michaelsen

Text fig. 167

Styela paessleri Michaelsen, 1898, p. 368; 1900, p. 69; 1907, p. 75.—Van Name, 1945, p. 301 [part].—Millar, 1960, p. 115 [not *Styela paessleri*; Kott, 1954, p. 144.—Van Name, 1945 p. 301 [part].—

Vinogradova, 1962 p. 201 (< *Styela pfefferi* Michaelsen, 1898, p. 367)].

? *Styela paessleri;* Herdman, 1912, p. 312; 1915, p. 94.

New Records. None.

Previous Records.

Subantarctic: Falkland Is. [Herdman, 1912; Millar, 1960]; Patagonian Shelf [Millar, 1960]; Tierra del Fuego [Michaelsen, 1898].

Distribution. This species, often in clusters, grows attached to stones, kelp, etc. It is limited to the Magellanic area and occurs in waters up to 121 meters on the Patagonian Shelf, although other records are in water of 2 to 10 meters.

Description. From dome-shaped to tall columnar individuals up to 4 cm high and 2.2 cm wide. Both apertures are close together anteriorly on short siphons. Test is wrinkled and leathery and generally brown to yellow in preservative. The body wall is not too closely adherent to the test, with continuous sheets of outer circular and inner longitudinal muscle fibers. Branchial tentacles from 35 to 60. The dorsal tubercle aperture is horizontal and straight; or S-shaped or C-shaped with the open interval directed posteriorly. The branchial sac has 4 low rounded folds with 12 to 20 internal longitudinal vessels per fold and 6 to 8 between the folds. There are wide intervals between the folds with 5 to 8 or more stigmata per mesh. The stomach is long and cylindrical, with 16 to 20 longitudinal folds. The gut loop is narrow. The anal opening is lobed. There are 2 gonads per side, each consisting of a branched ovary with pear-shaped testis follicles grouped around the ends of the ovarian branches. When well developed, the testis follicles become densely crowded together to form large irregular masses pressed against the side of the ovary and to some extent overlapping it.

Remarks. The species has much longer branches of the ovarian tube than have been described for *S. pfefferi.* However, these branches are biramous, and it is possible that the differences between *S. paessleri* and *S. pfefferi* are due to a smaller number of ovarian branches in the former and the development of the ends of these ovarian branches into secondary biramous branches rather than bidentate tips in the latter species. There is also a relative increase in the length of the testis ducts, and the testis follicles expand away from the sides of the ovary on to the body wall, as in *S. nordenskjoldi.* The branching ovary and leathery test distinguish the species from closely related *S. nordenskjoldi.*

Styela ohlini Michaelsen

Styela ohlini Michaelsen, 1898, p. 366; 1900, p. 8; 1907, p. 75.
Tethyum ohlini; Hartmeyer, 1909–1911, p. 1359.
Cnemidocarpa ohlini; Van Name, 1945, p. 268.

New Records. None.

Previous Records.

Subantarctic: Strait of Magellan, 27 meters [Michaelsen, 1898].

Description. Body elliptical, 2.6 cm long, 1.8 cm wide, and 1.6 cm high; attached ventrally. Both apertures 4-lobed, the branchial near the anterior end of the upper part of the body and the atrial aperture mid-dorsal. Test thin, hard, and tough; whitish with flesh tint and pearly luster. Body wall with diffuse musculature. Branchial tentacles about 32 of various sizes. Dorsal tubercle small, the slit with horns curved in to meet anteriorly. Dorsal lamina wide, not ribbed but with the margin uneven. Four branchial folds per side with about 30 internal longitudinal vessels on the highest dorsal folds and only about 10 on the ventral folds. Up to 8 longitudinal vessels between the folds. Parastigmatic vessels present. There are about 6 stigmata per mesh. Stomach is pear-shaped with about 20 longitudinal folds. Seven sausage-shaped gonads on the left and 10 on the right consist of the testis follicles in double rows beneath the tubular ovaries.

Remarks. This species is unusual in the large number of gonads present. Unfortunately, only one specimen has been taken, so that the extent of variation is not known. However, no antarctic species of this genus could be confused with the present species, which has distinctively high branchial folds and wide intervals between the folds, in addition to the large number of gonads.

Styela sericata Herdman

Text fig. 168

Styela sericata Herdman, 1888, p. 153.—Millar, 1959, p. 196.
Cnemidocarpa platybranchia Millar, 1955a, p. 226.

New Records. Southeast Pacific Basin: *Eltanin* Sta. 14, Cruise 17 (4192–4197 meters).

Previous Records.

Elsewhere: Southeast Pacific Basin [Herdman, 1888]; northwestern Atlantic Basin [Millar, 1955a]; Indian Ocean, Tasman Sea, Kermadec Trench [Millar, 1959].

Distribution. Records of this species from such geographically isolated localities suggest that the species has a wide cosmopolitan distribution through the oceans of the world in their deepest basins. The depth range is from 398 to 4820 meters.

Description. Rounded body from 0.6 to 1.5 cm in diameter. The body is covered by long branching hairs, which in the present specimens are especially long on the upper half of the body. In Millar's [1955a] specimens the hairs are longest around the middle of the body. The apertures, almost sessile on the upper surface, are here obscured by the long hairs. The test is thin and semitransparent. There are about 20 simple branchial tentacles. The dorsal tubercle has a simple slit-like opening. The dorsal lamina is a simple plain-edged membrane. The body wall is thin with weak musculature and is fairly closely adherent to the test.

The branchial sac has in smaller specimens [Millar, 1955a] 20 to 30 inner longitudinal vessels on each side of the branchial sac, but the largest specimen in the present collection (1.5 cm) has about 60 inner longitudinal vessels on each side. The branchial sac is not gathered into folds at all. There are small oval to rectangular stigmata arranged in transverse rows between the transverse vessels, 2 or 3 stigmata to each inner longitudinal vessel. The stigmata are crossed by parastigmatic vessels.

The gut forms a simple short tight loop across the posterior end of the body. The stomach is fairly short, almost spherical, with 8 to 10 longitudinal folds. The anus is lobed. Anterior and parallel to the gut loop on the left, and in a corresponding position in the middle of the body wall on the right are single long gonads of typical form. The tubular ovary terminates in a short oviduct directed toward the atrial opening. Numerous lobed testis follicles are present on the body wall beneath and along the sides of the ovary and their ducts pass around on to the mesial surface of the ovary, where they join a common vas deferens opening on top of the oviduct.

Remarks. The major difference between these specimens and those described by Millar [1955a] from the North Atlantic is the discrepancy in the number of internal longitudinal vessels in the branchial sac. However, there is considerable variation in the number of these vessels in the individuals in Millar's collection, and it is most possible that the discrepancy is due to size and age difference. The testis lobes

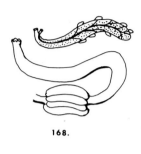

168.

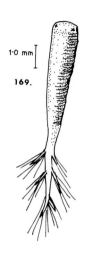

1·0 mm

169.

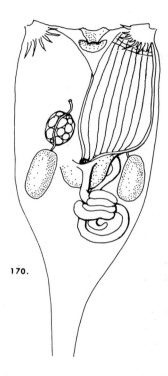

170.

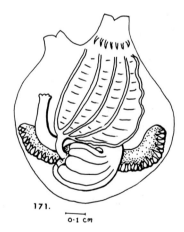

171.
0·1 cm

172.

173.

Styela sericata
168. Gut and gonad on left body wall.

Minostyela clavata
169. External appearance.
170. Inner body wall; right side of branchial sac removed.

Styelopsis tricostata
171. Gut and gonad [after Millar, 1960].

Bathyoncus enderbyanus
172. Portion of branchial sac [after Millar, 1959].
173. Gonad.

are not submerged in the ovary but form a discrete layer on the body wall and, depending on the extent of their proliferation, extend out from the ovary. There seems to be no justification for separating the species from *Styela* spp. with similar gonads. Loss of branchial folds in the branchial sac in this genus is not unprecedented; the loss occurs in *S. insinuosa*. The large numbers of inner longitudinal vessels in the branchial sac suggest that loss of folds is the only modification that has occurred to distinguish this abyssal form from other species of the genus.

Styela sp. ?, juvenile

Record. Southeast Pacific Basin: *Eltanin* Sta. 1248 (3386–3477 meters).

Genus *Styelopsis* Traustedt, 1883

Type species: *Ascidia grossularia* Van Beneden, 1846

Single long gonad on the right with one series of testis follicles on parietal surface of ovary against body wall. Sperm ducts with several openings along mesial surface of the ovary. Reduced branchial sac.

This genus was previously thought to be confined to the arctic and northern regions, as a subgenus of *Dendrodoa* MacLeay, 1825. However, the form of the gonad and extent of branchial sac reduction probably justify generic status.

Styelopsis tricostata (Millar)

Text fig. 171

Cnemidocarpa tricostata Millar, 1960, p. 106.

New Records. None.

Previous Records.

Antarctic: South Georgia, 110 meters [Millar, 1960].

Description. Pear-shaped body, narrowing anteriorly to adjacent short tubular siphons with 4-lobed openings. A specimen 1.2 cm high is 0.9 cm across at the widest point. Posteriorly, a thick coat of hairs, arising in groups of 2 or 3 or singly; anteriorly, rounded wartlike swellings, yellowish-gray in color. Test is thin and tough. Body wall with weak circular muscles externally around strong longitudinal muscles. Twenty-two branchial tentacles present. Dorsal tubercle small with oval transverse slit. Dorsal lamina plain, wider posteriorly. Branchial sac without folds, with only 3 tall internal longitudinal vessels. Meshes are consequently long with up to 30 stigmata. Parastigmatic vessels present. Gut loop is short and horizontal. Stomach ovoid with about 13 long folds and a small pyloric caecum. Rectum extends anteriorly

and terminates halfway up branchial sac in an anus bordered by 12 shallow lobes. A single gonad from the right side of the endostyle curves across the posterior part of the body between the gut loop and the body wall. Long narrow testis follicles arranged in a single series. No oviduct seen; 2 testis ducts open along mesial surface of the ovary into the peribranchial cavity. (After Millar.)

Biology. Although larvae have not been taken in the peribranchial cavity, the condition of the gonoducts suggests that the species is viviparous.

Remarks. The species is distinguished from known northern forms by the further reduction of the branchial sac and by the apparent absence of oviduct. From Millar's [1960] text fig. 40C the gonad appears to be on the left side of the body. The gut loop is, however, displaced posteriorly between the gonad and the endostyle. The actual position of the gonad is, as in other species of the genus, beneath the endostyle.

Genus *Minostyela* new genus

Solitary styelid; no folds; 7 internal longitudinal vessels on each side of the body; gonad consists of single follicle testis posterior to a circular ovary present on both sides of the body.

The genus is taken from 3587–3817 meters in the Southwest Pacific Basin. However, apart from its rooted form, there are no apparent modifications for its deep-water environment. Type species *Minostyela clavata* new species.

Minostyela clavata new species

Text figs. 169, 170

Type Locality. Southwest Pacific Basin: *Eltanin* Sta. 1209 (3587–3817 meters). Holotype, USNM 11964; paratype, 1 specimen, USNM 11965.

Distribution. The species is small and inconspicuous. Its range may be wider than this single record suggests.

Description. Body small, club-shaped, narrowing basally to a thick central root from which tufts of hairlike processes and sometimes thicker secondary roots branch. The body is 0.5 cm long and the root is 0.3 cm long. The apertures are sessile and anterior on either side of the flattened upper surface. The test is thin but tough and externally is marked by fine transverse wrinkles. The body wall is closely adherent to the test with an outer layer of circular muscles confined to the upper and wider part of the individual. An inner layer of longitudinal muscles extends posteriorly to the circular layer and down into the root. There are about 15 simple branchial tentacles. The dorsal lamina is simple. Inside the atrial opening there is a pronounced atrial velum. There are 7 internal longitudinal vessels in the branchial sac, and in the present specimens they pursue a very tortuous course because of contraction. There are 3 or 4 rectangular stigmata in each mesh and numerous transverse vessels. The stomach is fairly short, with 10 folds and a caecum curved in the loop of the gut. In the present specimen the contracted branchial sac is drawn anteriorly, leaving the gut loop and a large part of the gonads posterior to it. However, in a relaxed state the branchial sac would extend posteriorly, the gut loop lying to the left and loosely attached to the body wall. The gut forms a double loop and the rectum extends anteriorly toward the atrial opening. Gonads are present on both sides of the body. The testes are undivided and oval, inclined more or less longitudinally and on the left in the secondary gut loop. The vas deferens extends from the anterior end of the testis across a circular ovary of 8 to 10 eggs. The oviduct appears to open on the lateral aspect of the ovary, close to the point where it is attached to the body wall. It is therefore considerably overlapped by the ovary.

Biology. The short oviduct suggests viviparity.

Remarks. The gut, branchial sac, and body wall all bear a strong resemblance to *Dicarpa simplex* Millar, 1955a, and *D. pacifica* Millar, 1964. *D. pacifica* has 4 instead of 7 longitudinal vessels and the gonads are typically polycarps with testis follicles surrounding the ovary. In the present species the testis apparently consists of a single large follicle from which a single duct extends across the ovary. The relative position and form of the gonads and their ducts suggest a relationship with the polyzoinid *Symplegma*.

Genus *Bathyoncus* Herdman, 1882

Type species: *Bathyoncus mirabilis* Herdman, 1882
Branchial sac without folds, or with rudimentary folds. Stigmata absent.

Bathystyeloides Seeliger, 1905, p. 1120, was erected to accommodate *Bathyoncus enderbyanus* Michaelsen. It is not sufficiently distinct from the other species of *Bathyoncus* to justify a new genus. Huus [1937] also considers *Bathystyeloides* a synonym of the genus *Bathyoncus*.

Two other North Pacific species of this genus, *B. discoideus* (4140 meters) and *B. minutus* (5625 meters) both of Herdman [1886] are clearly distinguished from the species in the southern oceans.

KEY TO ANTARCTIC SPECIES OF *Bathyoncus*

1. Transversely elongated meshes in branchial sac.........
.... **enderbyanus,** p. 125
    (Atlantic, Pacific, Indian oceans and Enderby Land)
  Square meshes in the branchial sac.................... 2
2. 1 to 3 internal longitudinal vessels between the folds....
.... **herdmani,** p. 126
    (Enderby Land)
  No internal longitudinal vessels between the folds.......
......................................*mirabilis,* p. 126
    (Kerguelen Is.)

Bathyoncus enderbyanus Michaelsen

Text figs. 172, 173

Bathyoncus enderbyanus Michaelsen, 1904, p. 226.
Bathystyeloides enderbyanus; Hartmeyer, 1912, p. 258.—Millar, 1955a, p. 230; 1959, p. 197.
Bathystyeloides atlantica Millar, 1955a, p. 229.

New Records. None.

Previous Records.

Antarctic: North of Enderby Land, 4636 meters [Michaelsen, 1904].

Elsewhere: Tasman Sea, Indian Ocean, Atlantic Ocean, 2550 to 5300 meters [Millar, 1955a; 1959].

Distribution. The species is present in the deep waters of the southern Atlantic, Indian, and Pacific oceans. It has also been taken farther north in the tropical Atlantic. The depth range is from 2550 to 5300 meters.

Description. Body egg-shaped. Branchial opening 4-lobed on rather thick, short siphon near anterior end of the body. Atrial siphon wartlike, more than half-way along dorsal surface, aperture not distinctly lobed. Outer surface even but rough, with wartlike to fingerlike papillae, basal half with filamentous processes [Millar, 1959]. Body 11.5 mm high, 8 mm broad. Test very thin but tough. Body wall closely adherent to test. Musculature strong, forming an irregular mesh. Branchial tentacles 31, simple, of varying sizes. Dorsal tubercle simple, with a large elliptical opening set obliquely. Branchial sac without true folds, but internal longitudinal vessels on each side near the dorsal line are crowded together posteriorly. The rest of the internal longitudinal vessels are evenly distributed over the branchial wall. There are about 60 to 135 internal longitudinal vessels on each side of the body. Closely placed, simply branching transverse vessels below the internal longitudinal vessels form transversely elongated meshes that are lined by cilia and replace the stig-mata. The gut is on the left posteriorly and forms a simple short loop. Stomach is oval with 13 well defined folds. A small pyloric caecum is present. The anus is bordered by 12 rounded lobes. Herma-phrodite gonad on each side of the body comprises a thick tubular ovary with irregularly arranged testis follicles sometimes accumulating into flat cushion-like to lumpy masses along the sides of the ovary. Seminal ducts from the testis lobes join as a vas deferens near the distal end of the ovary. There is a large endocarp on each side of the body wall.

Remarks. The species is distinguished from *B. herd-mani* Michaelsen and *B. mirabilis* Herdman by the form of the transverse vessels and shape of the cilia-lined meshes.

Bathyoncus herdmani Michaelsen

Bathyoncus herdmani Michaelsen, 1904, p. 228.

New Records. None.

Previous Records.

Antarctic: North of Enderby Land, 4636 meters [Michaelsen, 1904].

Description. Body large narrow, laterally flattened with a large stalk, forming a more or less equilateral triangle. Stalk from the lower angle of the triangle and apertures on short cushion-like siphons on the upper corners. Branchial opening with 2 distinct posterior lips and 2 or 3 indistinct anterior lips. The atrial opening 4-lobed. The thin stalk is two-thirds as long as the rest of the body. Body 1.8 cm in length and height, stalk 1.0 cm. Surface of the test is even, smooth antero-ventrally but elsewhere there is a net-work of furrows to form cushion-like mounds. Color yellowish gray. Test very thin, but tough and leathery. Body wall tough, strongly adherent to test, and extending down into the stalk. Fine muscles form a network. Pear-shaped papillae present on inner surface of branchial siphon. Branchial tentacles about 30, simple, of varying length. The dorsal tubercle is a flattened cone anteriorly directed with a longitudinal deep groove on the left, so that the upper surface appears kidney shaped. The opening on the upper surface forms a semicircle parallel to the right border of the upper surface. The bran-chial sac has a rather large fold near the dorsal lamina on each side with numerous internal longi-tudinal vessels. Ventral to these are 3 more or less distinct rudimentary folds of 3 closely placed internal longitudinal vessels. Between the folds there are 1 to 3

vessels. The transverse vessels form square meshes with the internal longitudinal vessels. There are no true stigmata present. The gut is on the left side of the branchial sac. The stomach is large and sac-like with 30 sharply defined folds, not all running the whole length of the stomach. There is a small pyloric caecum. The intestine forms a short narrow closed loop with the stomach. The anal border has lobes of varying size. A hermaphrodite gonad present on each side of the body consists of tubular ovary and testis follicles beneath the ovary on the body wall, their ducts curving around onto the mesial surface.

Remarks. Michaelsen took this species together with *Bathyoncus enderbyanus.* They are distinguished mainly by the absence of the stalk in *B. enderbyanus* and the difference in shape of the branchial meshes, which is due to the smaller number of internal longitudinal vessels in the present species.

Bathyoncus mirabilis Herdman

Bathyoncus mirabilis Herdman, 1882, p. 165.

New Records. None.

Previous Records.

Subantarctic: Between Cape of Good Hope and Kerguelen Is., 2926 meters [Herdman, 1882].

Description. Body ovate to discoidal, laterally com-pressed. Anteriorly wide and slightly convex, pos-teriorly narrower and produced slightly into stout stalk for attachment. Apertures almost sessile, both anterior. Surface even and smooth with sand ad-hering posteriorly only. Test otherwise thin, mem-branous and rather transparent. Color is pale yellowish-gray. There are 20 to 25 uniform simple stout tentacles. The dorsal tubercle is small with a simple C-shaped aperture. The dorsal lamina is smooth and undulating. The body wall is thin, with numerous, closely placed but very fine muscle bands. Branchial sac with a single prominent fold on left near dorsal lamina and other rudimentary folds formed by the closer approximation of three internal longitudinal vessels. There are no internal longitudinal vessels between folds. Transverse vessels form large square meshes between the folds. On the folds, however, there are intermediate transverse vessels and the meshes are smaller. The gut is con-fined to the dorsal edge of the left side and there is no apparent stomach enlargement. Gonads, one on each side, are elongate, undulating bodies curving toward the atrial opening. Ovary is tubular. Testis follicles are probably between the ovary and the body wall, although Herdman has not described them. (After Herdman.)

Remarks. The species is known from a single specimen only. However, it is distinguished from others by the undifferentiated gut and the absence of internal longitudinal vessels between the rudimentary folds.

Family PYURIDAE Hartmeyer

Represented in Antarctica by several common, well characterized, and stable species with a wide range. The family is also successful in abyssal waters, where the specialized genera *Bathypera* and *Culeolus* are common. *Bathypera* is endemic in the Antarctic, but *Culeolus* occurs over a wide range in the Indian, Pacific, and Atlantic oceans.

KEY TO GENERA OF PYURIDAE

1. Stigmata always present 2
   Stigmata absent ....*Culeolus,* p. 142
2. Stigmata curved or irregular 3
   Stigmata straight 4
3. Tubular ovary ....*Bathypera,* p. 139
   Ovary not tubular....................... *Ctenyura*
4. Stigmata longitudinal........................... 5
   Stigmata transverse...................... *Boltenia*
5. Dorsal lamina with languets...................... 6
   Dorsal lamina smooth.................. *Microcosmus*
6. With barbed spines .... *Herdmania*
   Without barbed spines.......................... 7
7. Tubular ovaries numerous; testes separate.............
   ....*Halocynthia*
   1 or 2 hermaphrodite gonads on each side of the body...
   ....*Pyura,* p. 127

* These genera reported from Antarctica.

Genus *Pyura* Molina, 1782

Type species: *Pyura chilensis* Molina, 1782
Dorsal lamina with languets. Branchial sac folded. Stigmata regular and longitudinal. Gonads on both sides of the body consisting of 1 or 2 hermaphrodite glands often broken up into single or double series of blocks joined by ducts.

KEY TO ANTARCTIC SPECIES OF *Pyura*

1. Test covered with long flexible hairs or bristles......... 2
   Test not covered with long flexible hairs or bristles...... 3
2. Test covered with pointed flexible bristles...*setosa,* p. 127
   (circum-antarctic, Scotia Ridge to Patagonian Shelf)
   Test covered with branched hairs.........*tunica,* p. 137
3. Outer test modified into polygonal horny scales........
   ....*squamata,* p. 135
   (Enderby quadrant, Antarctic Peninsula,
   South Australian Basin)
   Outer test not modified into horny polygonal scales...... 4
4. Supported by narrow stalk........................ 5
   Not supported by narrow stalk.................... 6

5. Atrial organs present..................*legumen,* p. 133
   (Falkland Is., Magellanic area, Patagonian Shelf)
   No atrial organs.....................*georgiana,* p. 130
   (circum-antarctic, Scotia Ridge to South Georgia,
   Bouvet I.)
6. Gonad not divided into sac-like lobes.....*paessleri,* p. 129
   (Drake Passage, Falkland Is., Burdwood Bank)
   Gonad divided into sac-like lobes.................. 7
7. Test cartilaginous........................*obesa,* p. 138
   (South Shetland Is.)
   Test tough, leathery, wrinkled.................... 8
8. No needle-like spines line siphons.....*discoveryi,* p. 136
   (circum-antarctic to South Georgia)
   Needle-like spines line siphons...........*vittata,* p. 138
   (Kerguelen Is., Macquarie I., Marion I.,
   and elsewhere to the north)

Pyura setosa (Sluiter)
Text figs. 174–176

? *Cynthia stubenrauchi* Michaelsen, 1900, p. 102.
Halocynthia setosa Sluiter, 1905b, p. 472; 1906, p. 40; 1906a, p. 554.—Herdman, 1910, p. 7; 1912, p. 309; 1915, p. 91; 1923, p. 22.
? *Halocynthia stubenrauchi* Michaelsen, 1907, p. 79.
Pyura setosa; Hartmeyer, 1911, p. 442.—Sluiter, 1914, p. 10.—Van Name, 1945, p. 331.—Kott, 1954, p. 126.—Millar, 1960, p. 117.
? *Pyuropsis stubenrauchi* Michaelsen, 1912, p. 112.
Pyura echinops Ärnbäck, 1938, p. 25.—Millar, 1960, p. 117.
? *Pyura stubenrauchi* Ärnbäck, 1938, p. 27.—Van Name, 1945, p. 330.—Millar, 1960, p. 117.

New Records. Antarctic Peninsula: *Edisto* Sta. 189[18] (64 meters), Sta. 230[18] (74 meters), Sta. 35, TR 18 (154 meters); *Staten Island* Sta. 32/63 (46 meters), Sta. 37/63 (49 meters). South Shetland Is.: *Staten Island* Sta. 64/63 (86 meters), Sta. 75/63 (40 meters); *Eltanin* Sta. 410 (240 meters), Sta. 436 (73 meters). South Orkney Is.: *Eltanin* Sta. 1082 (298–302 meters). Ross Sea: *Northwind* Sta. 2 (203 meters).

Previous Records.

Antarctic: Antarctic Peninsula [Sluiter, 1905b]; South Shetland Is. [Millar, 1960]; South Orkney Is. [Herdman, 1912]; Enderby Land, Mac. Robertson Land [Kott, 1954]; Wilhelm II Coast [Hartmeyer, 1911]; McMurdo Sound [Herdman, 1910]; Adélie Coast [Herdman, 1923].

Subantarctic: ? Argentina [Ärnbäck, 1938]; ? Magellanic area [Michaelsen, 1900].

Distribution. Circum-antarctic in shallow shelf waters from 18 to 400 meters. Extension into the Magellanic

[18] U.S. Navy Antarctic Expedition, 1947–1948.

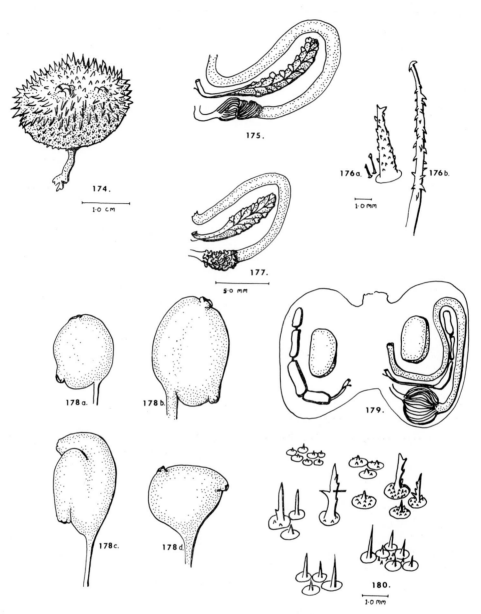

Pyura setosa
174. External appearance, small stalked specimen.
175. Gut with liver lobes; gonads.
176. Spines from test: (*a*) Specimen 2 cm in diameter;
     (*b*) specimen 5 cm in diameter.

Pyura paessleri
177. Gonads and gut.

Pyura georgiana
178. Effect of differential growth on shape and orientation of head on stalk.
179. Inner body wall showing gut, gonads, and pariental organs.
180. Spines from outer test of various specimens.

area and on to the Patagonian Shelf up to 37°50′S is suggested by records of *P. stubenrauchi*, a possible synonym of the present species.

Description. Ovoid, up to 7.5 cm long, slightly dorso-ventrally flattened. Smaller specimens 2 cm long with a short narrow stalk from midventral surface, but the stalk is absent in larger specimens, which rest by the whole ventral surface. Usually completely covered, except for a small area ventrally, with pointed flexible bristles up to 2 cm long, with small hooks or thorns along their length. Smaller specimens of 2 cm have shorter, thicker, less flexible bristles 3 mm long. Bristles especially long anteriorly, protecting and concealing the almost sessile apertures, although the bristles on the lobes and immediately surrounding the apertures are shorter. Long, thin spines line the siphons internally. Test fairly thin and flexible. Body wall only weakly connected to test, with longitudinal muscle bands radiating from the siphons; an outer thinner layer of circular muscles. In smaller stalked specimens (*Eltanin* Sta. 410) the longitudinal bands extend down into the stalk. Larger specimens with vestigial stalk have longitudinal muscles on both sides of the body extending on to the ventral surface. In the specimens in which the stalk is completely absent longitudinal muscles on the left extend only as far as the gut loop, slightly farther on the right but never on to the ventral surface. About 20 to 35 branchial tentacles of three orders with long primary branches and short secondary branches. Dorsal tubercle large, both horns spiral inward, the open interval facing forward and to the right. Dorsal lamina a narrow membrane with very long pointed tongues closely packed and sometimes forked; anteriorly the languets are shorter, the membrane wider, or it may be reduced to a wide toothed membrane here. Up to 6 branchial folds on each side of the body (4 in subantarctic specimens). A maximum of 15 to 31 internal longitudinal vessels on the folds and a maximum of 2 to 4 between them.

The most dorsal fold is often, but not always, the largest fold. Typical arrangement of internal longitudinal vessels: E3(21)4(28)4(31)3(25)3(15)3(28) 1 DL. Up to 12 stigmata per mesh. Gut loop long and straight, enclosing the left gonad. Stomach finely pleated internally. Anal border with 12 rounded lobes. Liver of characteristic form, consisting of series of apparently flat lamellae closely packed around the pyloric end of the stomach, their flat surfaces at right angles to the plane of the body wall. Gonads are single tubular ovaries surrounded by testis follicles and present on each side of the body.

Remarks. The stalk of this interesting species deserves special notice. Largest individuals with longitudinal body musculature extending only part of the way down the dorsal surface do not have any sign of a stalk; individuals in which a vestigial stalk is present differ only in the extension of body musculature on to the ventral surface, whereas specimens with a distinct stalk are small with shorter, thicker test bristles and longitudinal muscles extending down into an apparently functional stalk. There is some indication therefore that the stalk, when present, is lost as the animal increases in size while the bristles increase in length and flexibility. Both Michaelsen [1900] and Ärnbäck [1938] describe small individuals 1.5 and 2.5 cm, respectively, with no sign of a stalk and body musculature absent from the ventral surface. These records, the only ones of this species from the subantarctic area, are of single individuals with only 4 branchial folds on each side.

The synonymy of *P. stubenrauchi* (Michaelsen) (> *P. echinops* Ärnbäck), from the Subantarctic, with the present antarctic species was first suggested by Van Name [1945]. *Pyura stubenrauchi* is known only from two small specimens, 1.5 and 2.5 cm long, and is distinguished from *P. setosa* by the unique branchial sac with only 4 folds on each side, the dorsal lamina, which is smooth anteriorly and toothed posteriorly, and the shorter, thicker, and less flexible bristles. In *P. setosa* similar bristles do occur in smaller specimens (*Eltanin* Sta. 410, from the South Shetland Islands) and the dorsal lamina has longer languets posteriorly and is often merely toothed anteriorly. Therefore, the condition of the bristles and of the dorsal lamina is more likely associated with growth and the size of the individuals concerned, rather than representing a specific distinction. Ärnbäck's and Michaelsen's specimens may either belong to a distinct subantarctic species, isolated from related *P. setosa* in the Antarctic and characterized by the condition of the branchial sac, or be aberrant specimens of *P. setosa* at the northern limits of its geographic range, in which growth is interrupted resulting in a reduced branchial sac. Further records of specimens from the Subantarctic should clarify the situation.

Pyura paessleri (Michaelsen)

Text fig. 177

Cynthia paessleri Michaelsen, 1900, p. 106.
Halocynthia paessleri Michaelsen, 1907, p. 79.

Pyura [*Halocynthia*] *paessleri* Michaelsen, 1908, p. 231.—Hartmeyer, 1909–1911, p. 1340.—Van Name, 1945, p. 329.

Paracynthia distincta Ärnbäck, 1938, p. 22.

New Records. Drake Passage: *Eltanin* Sta. 219 (115 meters). Scotia Sea: *Eltanin* Sta. 370 (115 meters).

Previous Records.

Subantarctic: Falkland Is. [Michaelsen, 1900; Ärnbäck, 1938].

Distribution. Known only from the Falkland Islands-Magellanic area in 2 to 280 meters.

Description. Body spherical or elliptical, up to 3.4 cm long, 2.8 cm high, and 1.8 cm across. Both apertures on not very prominent siphons separated from one another by one-third of body circumference. In spherical specimens the branchial aperture terminal; in elliptical specimens both apertures on dorsal surface. Test tough and leathery, but not very thick, with adherent shell particles and sand. Smaller specimens with semitransparent test. There are minute spines 0.03 to 0.05 mm long lining the outer part of the siphons. Body wall with fine muscle bands radiating from siphons and finer outer circular muscle bands. Both circular and longitudinal muscles extend around the whole extent of the body. The body wall is usually whitish. From 12 to 18 branchial tentacles simply pinnate or barely twice pinnate with rudimentary tentacles between them. Dorsal tubercle, a simple slit deep in the peritubercular area. The dorsal ganglion is elongate. Curved languets on the dorsal lamina. Six well developed folds on each side of the body with 1 to 5 internal longitudinal vessels between and 10 to 20 on the folds. There are 2 or 3 stigmata per mesh in smaller specimens but in larger (3 cm) specimens up to 8 stigmata per mesh on the flat part of the branchial sac. Stigmata are often divided into two across their length. The gut loop is wide and fairly open with arborescent sac-like liver lobes obscuring the long narrow stomach. Anal border fringed by about 12 minute lobes. There are 1 or 2 gonads on each side of the body, the most posterior on the left enclosed in the gut loop. The tubular ovary may be sinuous or slightly branched with pyriform testis follicles scattered around the border. Seminal ducts extend across the mesial surface of the ovary and join the median vas deferens.

Remarks. This species shares with *Pyura setosa* and *Pyura millari* Rodrigues, 1966, the unusually styelid-type gonads but is distinguished from both these species by the absence of long spines lining the siphons. It is one of the few species with such a limited distribution, confined to the Falkland Islands area. However, it is a small sandy species and accordingly inconspicuous and could conceivably have been overlooked.

Pyura georgiana (Michaelsen)

Text figs. 178–180

Boltenia georgiana Michaelsen, 1898, p. 364; 1900, p. 118; 1907, p. 80.

Boltenia bouvetensis Michaelsen, 1904, p. 216.

Boltenia salebrosa Sluiter, 1905b, p. 474; 1906, p. 45; 1906a, p. 554.

Boltenia turqueti Sluiter, 1905b, p. 474; 1906, p. 43; 1906a, p. 554.

Pyura georgiana; Hartmeyer, 1909–1911, p. 1340.—Ärnbäck, 1938, p. 35.—Van Name, 1945, p. 328.—Millar, 1960, p. 121.

Pyura turqueti; Hartmeyer, 1909–1911, p. 1342.—Ärnbäck, 1938, p. 37.—Van Name, 1945, p. 331.

Pyura (Boltenia) turqueti Sluiter, 1914, p. 11.

Boltenia scotti Herdman, 1910, p. 10.

Boltenia antarctica Van Beneden and Selys Longchamps, 1913, p. 23.—Herdman, 1923, p. 17.

Pyura legumen; Kott, 1954, p. 124.—Vinogradova, 1962, p. 204.

New Records. Ross Sea: *Edisto* Sta. ?, Deep Freeze I (depth ?). Antarctic Peninsula: *Edisto* Sta. 36, TR 19 (307 meters); *Staten Island* Sta. 14/63 (45–76 meters); *Eltanin* Sta. 291 (370 meters). South Shetland Is.: *Staten Island* Sta. 64/63 (86 meters); *Eltanin* Sta. 406 (287 meters), Sta. 410 (240 meters), Sta. 426 (809–1116 meters), Sta. 428 (662–1120 meters), Sta. 430 (681–1409 meters), Sta. 432 (935 meters), Sta. 437 (311 meters), Sta. 441 (253 meters). South Orkney Is.: *Eltanin* Sta. 496 (234 meters), Sta. 499 (485 meters), Sta. 1082 (298–302 meters), Sta. 1083 (284 meters), Sta. 1084 (298–403 meters). Weddell Sea: *Staten Island* Sta. ?, Deep Freeze II (552 meters); *Westwind* Sta. 3 (210 meters); *Edisto* Sta. 17, TR 3 (1454 meters), Sta. 18, TR 4 (1555 meters).

Previous Records.

Antarctic: Antarctic Peninsula, South Shetland Is. [Michaelsen, 1904; Sluiter, 1905b, 1914; Ärnbäck, 1938; Millar, 1960]; Davis Sea, Enderby Land, Mac. Robertson Land [Kott, 1954; Vinogradova, 1962]; Victoria Land [Herdman, 1910]; South

Georgia [Michaelsen, 1898; Ärnbäck, 1938; Millar, 1960]; Bouvet I. [Michaelsen, 1904].

Subantarctic: Argentine coast [Ärnbäck, 1938].

Distribution. Probably circum-antarctic and extending northward along the Scotia Ridge to the South Orkney Islands, South Georgia, and to Bouvet Island on the Atlantic-Indian Ridge. From 100 meters and over the edge of the continental shelf to depths of 1555 meters. The single record of two specimens from the Argentine coast is puzzling [see Millar, 1960].

Description. Stalked body oval to triangular, up to 5 cm long and 2 cm high. The stalk ranges from slightly more than the length of the body to as much as 35 cm. It is narrow and wiry, becoming increasingly narrow toward the base, where it widens into a basal membrane or branched roots attached to the substrate. The surface of the stalk is always leathery.

As is often the case for stalked species of Stolidobranchia, the animal stands 'upside down' and in small specimens the stalk rises from the anterior end of the oval body. The atrial aperture is almost sessile from the postero-dorsal or uppermost corner, directed upward and away from the body. The branchial aperture from the anterior one-third of the dorsal border is produced from its posterior margin, so that the opening is directed anteriorly toward the ground.

In larger specimens the orientation of the body on the stalk changes and it appears to rotate through 90°, so that the stalk originates from the ventral aspect. The body consequently becomes more triangular with apertures at either end of the dorsal surface forming the upper corners of the triangle and the ventral border narrowing toward the stalk to form the apex. This rotation may be due to differential growth of the antero-dorsal corner of the body in the region of the stalk. The apertures at first maintain their orientation in relation to the body of the individual, and consequently the branchial aperture is directed horizontally, while the atrial aperture is directed vertically above the body. Further growth tends to compensate for the rotation of the body with regard to the apertures. This is achieved as follows:

1. Further differential growth of the posterior margin of the branchial siphon in the opposite direction to the rotation of the body, so that the siphon is curved around to face the ground. A similar development of the anterior margin of the atrial siphon turns it farther in the same direction as the rotation of the body, so that the opening is directed farther posteriorly and not immediately above the body.

2. A simple bending of the body on the stalk back to the primary position where the dorsal border is again vertical. This apparently occurs by differential growth of the ventro-posterior border of the body, where it joins the stalk.

The test is thin and very tough, from semitransparent to opaque and leathery. The surface is covered by rounded projections or scale-like areas (thickenings) with a small pointed spine in the center. This spine may be minute, conical, or long and needle-like up to 2.0 mm and often has secondary points or branches. Secondary points may also project from the surface of the basal mound or plate or from the test between. All variations in the form of the test spines occur in individuals from the same location, the same collection and sometimes on the one individual. Toward the siphons the basal mounds or scales decrease in size and the spines are closer together, changing gradually to the denser lining of outwardly directed thorns on the distal third of the siphonal lining.

The body wall is not thick. Well spaced longitudinal muscle bands radiate from both siphons, toward the ventral surface, where they break up into finer more diffuse fibers crossing the ventral line. Because the siphons are so far apart, only a few of the longitudinal bands cross one another well toward the ventral border. Outer circular muscles in less well defined bands surround the siphons and the body. A number of fibers from the branchial siphon extend deep to the dorsal ganglion along the base of the dorsal lamina. A thin muscle-free prolongation of the body wall extends down into the stalk. Up to 15 long, broad, and flat branchial tentacles have short primary branches with secondary branches. Smaller tentacles are present between these. The peritubercular area is deep, and the dorsal tubercle is large with a pronounced slit, horns rolled in or out. The dorsal ganglion, very apparent through the body wall, is long and occupies the middle half of the dorsal surface with paired anterior and posterior nerves circling the base of the branchial and atrial siphons, respectively. The dorsal lamina is a broad membrane with fine-pointed languets close together along the free edge. Seven branchial folds are present on the right and 8 on the left with a maximum of 24 internal longitudinal vessels on the folds and 3 between them. The stomach, with about 20 longitudinal folds, is short, spherical, or pear-shaped; the simple long and narrow gut loop, enclosing the left gonad, extends around the ventral aspect of the left side of the body and terminates at the base of the atrial opening, adjacent to the esophagus. Only small tufts of liver lobes are present. A single gonad on each side of the body, consists of a central tubular ovary with a single series of 4 or 5 testis blocks, sometimes confluent, around the sides and mesial surface of the ovary, and sometimes spreading across the intestine. Testis lobes joined by a median duct that opens near the oviduct at the base of the atrial siphon. Openings of the gonoducts are sometimes multiple. A single large, cushion-like, oval parietal organ present on each side of the body. The parietal organs are composed of vesicular cells with spaces between, which may be blood sinuses. They are highly vascular and their sole blood supply, as far as could be ascertained, is from the large trabecular vessels from the middle two enlarged transverse vessels across the branchial sac. Occasionally, a parietal organ may be absent from one or both sides of the body, or may be reduced to an empty membranous sac on the surface of which small ramifying blood sinuses are very apparent [Ärnbäck, 1938 and specimens from *Eltanin* Sta. 428].

Behind the branchial sac 4 transverse vessels are immensely enlarged. Trabecular vessels from the most posterior transverse vessel enter gut and gonads; enlarged trabecular vessels from the middle two transverse vessels enter the parietal organ; other trabeculae from all the transverse vessels enter the body wall; the anterior transverse vessel enters the body wall dorsally at the posterior end of the dorsal ganglion.

Biology. With increasing age the length of stalk, size of the body, opacity of the test, and length of both branchial and atrial siphons may all increase.

Millar [1960] suggests that the thin long stalk lacks sufficient rigidity to support the body in an upright position. However, both the test and body wall are thin, the branchial sac is delicate, and the living animal, when distended with and supported by water, would probably act as a float keeping the stalk upright. Further, species characterized by the presence of a stalk invariably are supported 'upside down' with the stalk originating from the anterior surface, the branchial aperture directed toward the substrate, and the effluent current directed away from

the animal into the water above, thus dispersing waste and genital products. There seems no reason to suppose the situation differs here. If the head of the zooid were to rest on the bottom, the atrial aperture would be so oriented that waste and genital products would be projected toward the substrate, which seems unlikely. Further, the differential growth of the siphonal margins following rotation of the body on the stalk seems designed to ensure that the branchial opening is directed downward and the atrial opening directed up and away from the body.[19] It is probable that this species sometimes hangs from under surfaces.

The function of the parietal organs has always been puzzling. Ärnbäck [1938] suggests their function as 'Schwellkörper' or turgid organs helping to maintain the proper relationships of the body during muscular activity. Although other ascidians do not require such organs, they may be important here, where the body is balanced on the long stalk. However, the species is taken from comparatively shallow shelf waters, which, although sufficiently deep to avoid salinity variations during the antarctic summer, do show some seasonal variation associated with melting ice [Ostapoff, 1965]. The plentiful blood supply of parietal organs, directly from the branchial sac and the vesicular structure of the cells, suggest that perhaps their function may be associated with salinity regulation in the body (see also below, *P. legumen*).

Remarks. This species is separated from *P. legumen* only by the atrial organs, which are never present in *P. georgiana*, which is distributed around the Antarctic, extending to Bouvet Island and South Georgia, although *P. legumen* is confined to the Magellanic area.

Although Millar [1960] used the form of the spines to distinguish three species, *P. legumen*, *P. bouvetensis* (South Shetland Islands and Palmer Archipelago), and *P. georgiana*, all types of spines may at times be found on one individual, whereas branched or unbranched spines up to 2 mm are found on specimens from the high Antarctic as well as on specimens from South Georgia. This variability is set forth in the following recapitulation of the distribu-

---

[19] Underwater photographs (Pl. I, figs. 1 and 3) of the sea bed at from 371 to 607 meters showing living specimens of *Pyura georgiana* became available as this volume went to press [1968]. Individuals are seen with straight stalks supporting the body well above the substrate in which they are rooted. Branchial apertures are directed toward the substrate, and atrial apertures are directed upward as inferred above by the author.

Pyura georgiana

Occurrence	Depth, meters	Month	Spines of Test		Author or Station
			Primary Branches	Secondary Branches	
South Georgia	20–26	. . .	Short needles	. . .	Michaelsen [1900]
	26–247	Dec. to April	Long needles	Absent	Millar [1960]
	75–25	May	Conical	?	Ärnbäck [1938]
South Orkney Is.	234	Feb.	Short needles	Present	*Eltanin* Sta. 496
	485	Feb.	Short needles	At base only	*Eltanin* Sta. 499
	298–302	April	Conical or needles	Sparse at base	*Eltanin* Sta. 1082
	284	April	Minute needles	At base only	*Eltanin* Sta. 1033
	298–403	April	Short or long needles	At base only	*Eltanin* Sta. 1084
South Shetland Is.	253	Jan.	Short or long needles	Absent	*Eltanin* Sta. 441
	93–527	Jan. to March	Conical	Absent	Millar [1960]
	240–1409	Dec. to Jan.	Conical	Absent	*Eltanin* Sta. 406, 410, 426, 428, 430
	935	Jan.	Long or short needles	Present or absent	*Eltanin* Sta. 432
	311	Jan.	Short needles	Absent	*Eltanin* Sta. 437
Antarctic Peninsula	370	Oct.	Short needles Conical	Present or absent	*Eltanin* Sta. 291
	307	April	Short needles	Absent	*Edisto* Sta. 36, TR 19
	100–400	Jan. to Feb.	Conical	?	Ärnbäck [1938]
	45–76	Jan.	Short needles	At base only	*Staten Island* Sta. 14/63
Weddell Sea	210	Jan.	Short needles	Absent	*Westwind* Sta. 3
	552	Jan.	Short needles	Present or absent	*Staten Island* Sta. ?, Deep Freeze II
	1454	Jan.	Short needles	Present or absent	*Edisto* Sta. 17, TR 3
	1555	Jan.	Short needles	Present or absent	*Edisto* Sta. 18, TR 4
Mac. Robertson Land	437	Dec.	Long or short needles	Present or absent	Kott [1954]
Enderby Land	300–193	Jan.	Long or short needles	Absent	Kott [1954]
Prydz Bay	580	Oct.	Minute needles	Absent	Van Beneden and Selys Longchamps [1913]
McMurdo Sound	Winter quarters	?	Conical	?	Herdman [1910]
Ross Sea	?	Jan.	Short needles	At base only	*Edisto* Sta. ?, Deep Freeze I
Bouvet I.	567	Nov.	Long needles	?	Michaelsen [1904]

tion and spination of the identified and recorded specimens of *Pyura georgiana*.

Pyura legumen (Lesson)

Text figs. 181–183

Boltenia legumen Lesson, 1830, p. 433; 1830a, p. 149. —Cunningham, 1871, pp. 111, 263 [listed generically]; 1871a, p. 489.—Herdman, 1881, p. 81; 1882, p. 88; 1912, p. 308; 1915, p. 90.—Michaelsen, 1898, p. 363; 1900, p. 109, p. 110 [listed as f. *typica*]; 1907, p. 79 [listed as f. *typica*].
Boltenia legumen f. *delfini* Michaelsen, 1898, p. 364; 1900, p. 113; 1907, p. 80.
Boltenia legumen f. *ohlini* Michaelsen, 1898, p. 364; 1900, p. 116; 1907, p. 80; 1912, p. 180.
Boltenia legumen f. *cunninghami* Michaelsen 1898, p. 364, 1900, p. 117; 1907, p. 80.

Pyura legumen; Hartmeyer, 1909–1911, p. 1340.— Van Name, 1921, p. 488; 1945, p. 326.—Ärnbäck, 1938, p. 33.—Millar, 1960, p. 119.

New Records. Scotia Sea: *Eltanin* Sta. 370 (115 meters). Off Tierra del Fuego: *Eltanin* Sta. 981 (40–49 meters).

Previous Records.

Subantarctic: Falkland Is., Magellanic area [Michaelsen, 1898; Ärnbäck, 1938; Herdman, 1881, 1912; Millar, 1960]; Patagonian Shelf [Ärnbäck, 1938; Millar, 1960].

Distribution. Falkland Islands-Patagonian Shelf region of the subantarctic area. Depth range is from 0 to 115 meters.

Description. Specimen with a short stalk. Body elongate antero-posteriorly, up to 8 cm long. Surface

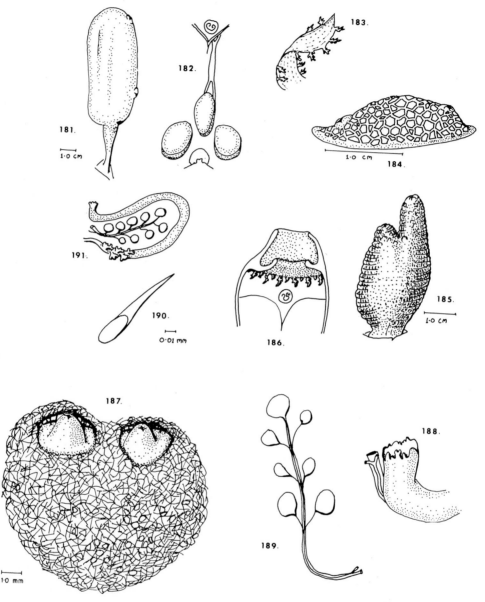

Pyura legumen
181. Outer appearance.
182. Dorsal tubercle, atrial organs, and long dorsal ganglion anterior to atrial opening.
183. Branchial tentacle.

Pyura squamata
184. External appearance.

Pyura discoveryi
185. External appearance.
186. Siphonal velum and sphincter: portion showing branchial tentacles from base of velum.

Pyura tunica
187. External appearance.

Pyura obesa
188. Distal portion of rectum partly covering gonoducts.
189. Immature gonad from right side of body.

Pyura vittata
190. Siphonal spine.
191. Gut loop and gonads.

of test longitudinally furrowed and covered by scale-like thickenings, each of which has a pointed spine from the center and often secondary minute spines from the basal scale. The largest spines are 2 mm and may have branches along the length as in *Pyura georgiana*.

The stalk arises from the anterior or antero-ventral aspect of the body. Both apertures are far apart on the dorsal surface and are almost sessile.

In the siphonal lining test spines change to outwardly directed flattened thorns as in *P. georgiana*. Branchial tentacles, dorsal tubercle, dorsal ganglion, branchial sac, gut, and gonads are all similar to those of *Pyura georgiana*. The dorsal lamina usually has closely placed pointed languets but may be toothed [Ärnbäck, 1938]. In the middle of the body wall on both sides there may be a large parietal organ, as in *P. georgiana*, although these parietal organs are not always present. There are invariably 3 large pad-like, highly vascular atrial organs at the base of the atrial siphon: one median and dorsal between the posterior paired nerves from the dorsal ganglion and a dorso-lateral pair, outside the nerves and slightly posterior to the median pad. The median atrial organ receives its blood supply from the dorsal vessel, and the lateral organs from trabecular sinuses from the posterior transverse vessels of the branchial sac.

Biology. The species has been taken throughout the year, always from very shallow water, where the variations in both salinity and temperature are marked. If the parietal organs are a mechanism for water regulation in varying salinity, as suggested above for *P. georgiana*, it is surprising that they have not always been found in this species. It is possible, however, that the atrial organs have a similar function and that, where they are present, the function of the parietal organs is supplementary. As with parietal organs, large blood vessels from the transverse sinuses of the branchial sac enter the atrial organs.

Remarks. Millar has indicated the close relationships between this species and *Pyura georgiana*. They are distinguished by the length of the body, the short stalk, and particularly the presence of the atrial organs in *Pyura legumen* and their absence in *P. georgiana*. The known distribution, the spination of the test, and the atrial and parietal organs of *Pyura legumen*, based on published accounts and a single specimen taken by the *Eltanin* in the Scotia Sea and the Strait of Magellan, are noted in the following table.

Pyura squamata Hartmeyer

Text fig. 184

Pyura squamata Hartmeyer, 1909–1911, p. 1337; 1911, p. 439.—Sluiter 1914, p. 8.—Pérès, 1949, p. 194.—Millar, 1960, p. 119.

? *Pyura lepidoderma* Tokioka, 1949, p. 10; 1953a, p. 19; 1953b, p. 28; 1954, p. 91; 1959, p. 231; 1960, p. 215.—Kott, 1966, p. 299.

New Records. South Orkney Is.: *Eltanin* Sta. 494 (1226 meters).

Pyura legumen

Occurrence	Month	Depth, meters	Spines of Test	Atrial organs	Parietal organs	Author or Station
Falkland Is.	Feb. March	0–80	Long branched or conical	Present	. . .	Millar, 1960
Magellanic area	April July Aug. Sept.	0–40	Short stiff hairs branched ?	Present	Sometimes present	Ärnbäck, 1938
	Jan. Feb. March July Oct.	2–46	Long spines and bristles	Present	Sometimes present	Michaelsen, 1900
	Dec.	115	Short spines very short to short; branched secondary spines on base	Present	Present (1 empty)	*Eltanin* Sta. 370
	Feb.	40–49	Long branched	Present	Absent	*Eltanin* Sta. 981
Patagonian Shelf	Dec. Jan. Feb. March April	27–29	Long branched or conical	Present	. . .	Millar, 1960

Previous Records.

Antarctic: Wilhelm II Coast [Hartmeyer, 1911]; Charcot Island [Sluiter, 1914]; Antarctic Peninsula [Millar, 1960].

Elsewhere: ? Senegal, Africa [Pérès, 1949]; Japan, N.W. Australia [Tokioka, 1949, 1953a, 1953b, 1954, 1959, 1960; Kott, 1966].

Distribution. Records are isolated and are usually of a very few specimens. However, a circum-antarctic distribution is indicated for depths ranging from 259 to 1226 meters. The species is present on the continental slope only at its northern limits. It is remarkable that from all stations this species has been taken with *Styela nordenskjoldi* (above, p. 112). Records from tropical regions in shelf waters are probably of a different, though related, species representing a relict population. (See Remarks below and chapter 9, Zoogeographic Discussion).

Description. Dorso-ventrally flattened, from 1.5 to 2 cm long, 1 cm broad and up to 0.5 cm high. The surface is hardened into close fitting horny polygonal scales of varying sizes. The surface of the scales is marked by concentric rings presumably indicating growth. The whole basal surface is fixed to the substrate. The apertures are inconspicuous, widely separated on the upper surface. The body wall has strong muscle bands on the upper surface radiating from the siphonal region, but they do not extend on to the basal half of the body. There are about 16 branchial tentacles with only very thin, short primary branches alternating with rudimentary unbranched tentacles. The dorsal tubercle has a C-shaped opening with the open interval inclined to the right or anteriorly. Dorsal lamina with pointed languets. The branchial sac has 5 or 6 folds on each side, one of which is usually incomplete or rudimentary. There are a maximum of 15 internal longitudinal vessels on the folds and 6 between the folds. Transverse vessels and parastigmatic vessels are present and, there are about 4 stigmata per mesh. The stomach is obscured by fingerlike liver lobes, the gut forms a simple loop enclosing the left gonad, and the rectum terminates in an 8- to 12-lobed anus. Gonads consist of separate hermaphrodite sacs arranged along either side of central ducts. Hartmeyer's two specimens had up to 19 gonadial sacs on either side of the body. In the present damaged specimens a maximum of 4 or 5 sacs only were detected from any one side of the body.

Biology. Unlike *Styela nordenskjoldi* (with which the present species has always been taken), which is able to adapt its test to ensure anchorage on any substrate, the present species has been taken only where larger pebbles, shells, and rocks provide a flat surface to accommodate the flattened base. The shape of specimens, similar to the dorso-ventrally flattened *S. nordenskjoldi,* together with analogus scale-like test modification in both species, suggests convergent evolution in the type of environment favored by *Pyura squamata.*

Remarks. Owing to their strong adherence to the substrate, specimens of this species are often damaged during collection (unless the rock to which they are attached is small enough to be preserved with the intact specimen). The gonads are similar to those of *P. discoveryi* and *P. vittata.* There is apparently great variation in the number of hermaphrodite gonadial sacs that are present. This variation occurs also in specimens of *P. lepidoderma* Tokioka [Kott, 1966] from Japan and Australia, where from 3 to 10 separate sacs occur in specimens from one area in northeast Australia. *P. lepidoderma* species is morphologically indistinguishable from the antarctic *P. squamata.* The *Pyura squamata* of Pérès from Senegal is also indistinguishable from the present species. *Pyura mariscata* Rodrigues, 1966, taken from 140 meters off Ilha de São Sebastião, Brazil, is a similar species. However, the scale-like, or tessellated, structure of the test is apparent only around the apertures, and the remainder of the test is obscured by adherent sand and shell. Rodrigues has characterized the species by the absence of hermaphrodite gonad sacs from one side of the common duct. However, they are absent in some specimens of *P. lepidoderma* [Kott, 1966] from Australia and cannot be considered a specific character.

Pyura discoveryi (Herdman)

Text figs. 185, 186

Halocynthia discoveryi Herdman, 1910, p. 9; 1923; p. 19.

Pyura discoveryi; Hartmeyer, 1911, p. 436.—Ärnbäck, 1938, p. 29.—Van Name, 1945, p. 332.—Kott, 1954, p. 126.—Millar, 1960, p. 117.—Vinogradova, 1962, p. 205.

Pyura discoveryi var. *septemplicata* Sluiter, 1914, p. 8.

New Records. Ross Sea: *Edisto* Sta. ?, Deep Freeze I (depth ?). Weddell Sea: *Edisto* Sta. 20, TR 5 (384 meters), Sta. 20, TR 6 (394 meters), Sta. 21, TR 7 (412 meters), Sta. 21, TR 8 (413 meters); *Staten Island* Sta. 25, OP 10 (331 meters); *Westwind* Sta. 3 (210 meters). Antarctic Peninsula:

Edisto Sta. 189[20] (64 meters), Sta. 35, TR 18 (154 meters); *Staten Island* Sta. 32/63 (46 meters). South Shetland Is.: *Staten Island* Sta. 64/63 (86 meters). South Orkney Is.: *Eltanin* Sta. 1082 (298–302 meters), Sta. 1083 (284 meters), Sta. 1084 (298–403 meters).

Previous Records.

Antarctic: McMurdo Sound [Herdman, 1910]; Wilkes Land [Herdman, 1923]; Wilhelm II Coast [Hartmeyer, 1911]; Knox Coast, Davis Sea [Vinogradova, 1962]; Mac. Robertson Land, Enderby Land [Kott, 1954]; South Shetland Is. [Sluiter, 1914]; Antarctic Peninsula [Ärnbäck, 1938; Sluiter, 1914, Millar, 1960]; South Georgia [Ärnbäck, 1938; Millar, 1960].

Distribution. The present specimens complete the records for circumpolar distribution of this species in waters ranging from 75 to 680 meters.

Description. Body low, dorso-ventrally elongate, or upright. Maximum body length 6 cm, although generally smaller. The apertures on long widely separated siphons from the upper surface. The siphons are often bent or curved. The test is thin, but very tough and leathery and sharply wrinkled, especially transversely and around the siphons. There may or may not be sand and shell adhering to the test, and specimens are often found in aggregates of numerous individuals. The body wall is tough and muscular. At the base of each siphon, there is a membrane projecting into the lumen with a strong ring of muscle around the free edge, presumably a sphincter to close the apertures and perhaps a safety mechanism in view of the length of the siphon. Beneath this membrane, where it joins with the body wall, the branchial tentacles are present. There are from 16 to 30 comparatively short branchial tentacles, the number possibly increasing with the size of the individual. These tentacles have narrow primary branches and only rudimentary secondary branches. The dorsal tubercle is fairly large, sometimes having a more complicated aperture but generally having a U-shaped slit directed anteriorly with the horns sinuous or coiled in or out. The dorsal lamina consists of a series of long pointed languets. The branchial sac has 7 low narrow folds on each side, although the most ventral fold, well developed anteriorly with 8 or 9 longitudinal vessels, is posteriorly reduced to an accumulation of only 2 or 3 vessels, and consequently has often been over-

looked. There is a maximum of 24 internal longitudinal vessels on the folds and 2 or 2 between them. The stomach is elongate with a large arborescent digestive gland. The gut loop is horizontal, long, and wide, enclosing the left gonad. The rectum extends forward for a short distance and terminates in an anus with a few blunt lobes around the border. Hermaphrodite gonads composed of polycarp-like lobes present along either side of central oviduct and vas deferens. There are usually more on the right (27 to 54) than on the left (24 to 52). The testis follicles cover the ovaries on the mesial side. The vas deferens opens on top of the oviduct near the base of the atrial siphon. One specimen [Millar, 1960] has been taken with a branched gonad.

Remarks. This species shows a striking resemblance to *Pyura haustor* from the arctic regions in both external and internal characters, including the occluding membrane at the base of the siphons. The two species may be a valid example of bipolarity. The separate gonadial sacs are similar to those of *P. squamata* and *P. vittata*.

Pyura tunica new species

Text fig. 187

Type Locality. Knox Coast: *Edisto* Sta. 44[21] (184 meters). Holotype, USNM 11962; paratypes, 27 specimens, USNM 11963.

Description. Rounded individuals, maximum of 1 cm in diameter. The body is surrounded by a feltwork of branching and anastomosing hairs and sand, leaving a space between the test and this outer coat, which is traversed only by the basal stalk of the hairs. This space is open to the exterior around the siphons, which extend as short white opaque projections a small distance apart on the upper surface. The test is very thin, translucent, and tough, beneath its outer coat. There are 15 branchial tentacles with short simple pinnate branches. The dorsal tubercle has a simple U-shaped slit with one horn turned in. The dorsal lamina has sharply pointed languets. The body wall is closely adherent to the test. Strong longitudinal muscle bands radiate from the siphons and cross one another on the sides of the body. Circular muscles are present outside these longitudinal muscles. There are 7 folds on each side of the body with internal longitudinal vessels arranged according to the following formula: DL I(14)I(13)I(15)I(17)I(12)I(9)I(5)IE. There are 4 oval stigmata in each mesh.

[20] U.S. Navy Antarctic Expedition, 1947–1948.

[21] U.S. Navy Antarctic Expedition, 1947–1948.

The gut forms a narrow loop enclosing the gonad on the left side of the body. There are liver lobes in the region of the stomach. The anal border has 10 lobes. There is a single gonad on each side of the body, consisting of about 7 pairs of polycarp-like sacs on either side of central ducts.

Remarks. In the nature of the secondary coat formed around and separated from the test this species most resembles *Pyura cancellata* Brewin from the North and South Islands of New Zealand and from Chathman Island [Brewin 1946, 1948, 1951, 1956a, 1957, 1958], although the outer layer in *P. cancellata* forms a more dense coat than in the present species (personal observation). The New Zealand species is also very much larger than specimens from Antarctica, and the larger numbers of branchial vessels and gonad lobes may be related to this size difference. The only definitive difference that can be used to distinguish the two species is the wide loop of the gut in *P. cancellata*, which distinguishes it from the present species, which has narrow gut loop. The species is highly modified for a free existence on a sandy open substrate.

Pyura obesa Sluiter

Text figs. 188, 189

Pyura obesa Sluiter 1912, p. 454; 1914, p. 14 [not *Pyura obesa* Hartmeyer 1919, p. 14].

New Records. Between South Shetland Is. and South Orkney Is.: *Eltanin* Sta. 1003 (210–220 meters).

Previous Records.

Antarctic: South Shetland Is., King George I., 75 meters [Sluiter, 1912, 1914].

Distribution. Previously only a single damaged specimen of this very large species was taken. It may be rare and distributed sparsely. However, in view of the fact that the two present specimens have been taken from an area adjacent to the type location it is more likely that the species has a limited distribution in the southern extent of the Scotia Ridge and is absent altogether from the heavily sampled area of the Antarctic Peninsula to the south and the Falkland Islands and Patagonian Shelf to the north.

Description. The species is large, up to 17 cm long, 13 cm wide, and 10 cm thick. From the basal part of the test there is a small flattened tongue-like extension or degenerate stalk 5 cm long and 3 cm wide. This extension may help to anchor the individual. The apertures are close together, a short distance down the dorsal surface. The atrial opening is sessile and just above the branchial opening, which is directed downward by the downward extension of its upper border. The test is thick and fleshy with longitudinal grooves. There are few foreign particles adhering to the surface, which is rather tough and leathery. The body wall is not especially thick and has muscle bands crossing and anastomosing irregularly over both sides of the body. There are about 20 branchial tentacles with primary, secondary, and sometimes tertiary branches. The branches are not long, however, and the tentacles are not bushy. The dorsal tubercle is a double cone and the horns of the slit spiral around each cone in a convoluted course. The dorsal lamina is very short with a double row of short pointed languets. There are 6 branchial folds on each side of the body. Either side of the dorsal lamina a stretch of membrane extends to the base of the dorsal fold on each side of the body pierced only by occasional reduced stigmata. There are 2 internal longitudinal vessels extending along this membrane. Other internal longitudinal vessels in the branchial sac are arranged according to the following formula: DL2(32)8(31)7(34)4(31)5(25)4(22)12E. There are about 8 stigmata per mesh. The gut forms a narrow loop extending two-thirds of the way anteriorly. The proximal part of the gut is covered with short dense liver lobes. The rectum is short and is turned up to terminate in large irregular lobes near the atrial opening. There are 2 gonads on the right parallel to one another and to the ventral curve of the body. On the left a single gonad is enclosed in the gut loop. Gonads consist of 4 or 5 polycarp-like sacs on either side of central ducts, which open near the atrial opening. The vas deferens may divide into two terminally. Both gonads and gut loop are more or less embedded in the body wall, which expands into fleshy endocarp-like swellings in the region of these organs.

Remarks. The species is remarkably large and solid. The downward-directed branchial opening and sessile atrial aperture just above it are distinctive.

Pyura vittata (Stimpson)

Text figs. 190, 191

Cynthia vittata Stimpson, 1852, p. 230.
Cynthia jacatrensis Sluiter, 1890, p. 331.
Halocynthia jacatrensis Sluiter, 1904, p. 47; 1913, p. 68.
Pyura jacatrensis; Hartmeyer, 1919, p. 8. — Kott, 1952, p. 273; 1954, p. 127.—Millar, 1960, p. 125.
Pyura vittata; Pérès, 1949, p. 195.—Tokioka, 1952,

p. 134; 1953, p. 273; 1967, p. 202.—Millar, 1960, p. 126.—Kott, 1964, p. 142; 1966, p. 300. For further synonymy and literature to the species in the Atlantic, West Indies, Japan, and Indonesia, see Van Name, 1945, p. 321.

New Records. West of Macquarie Island: *Eltanin* Sta. 1417 (79–93 meters), Sta. 1418 (86–101 meters).

Previous Records.

Subantarctic: Kerguelen Is., Macquarie I. [Kott, 1954]; Marion I. [Millar, 1960].

Elsewhere: Tasmania, southwestern Australia [Kott, 1952, 1954]; Arafura Sea, Indonesia, northeastern Australia [Tokioka, 1952; Kott, 1964, 1966; Sluiter, 1890, 1904, 1913; Van Name, 1945]; Palau Is. [Tokioka, 1967]; Japan [Tokioka, 1933; Van Name, 1945]; Atlantic Ocean, West Indies [Van Name, 1945; Pérès, 1949; Millar, 1960].

Distribution. Although there is some doubt about the relationships of this species, specimens from the subantarctic area appear to be identical with those from Australia, where it is usually taken in shallow waters, often attached to stones or shells, near the low water mark. The greatest depths recorded are from the Subantarctic: 99–113 meters, Marion Island [Millar, 1960] and 128–676 meters, Kerguelen Islands [Kott, 1954]. The species has not yet been recorded from South Africa.

Description. Body more or less oval, often slightly laterally flattened, up to 6.5 cm long. Apertures on siphons of varying length, about one-third of the body circumference apart. Siphons may be short and wart-like or longer tubes, which, when contracted may flatten into a depression on the dorsal surface surrounded by a thickened rim of test. The test is tough and fairly thick, externally wrinkled or covered by wart-like swellings, and may be rigid and stiff, with sand or shell adhering. The outer siphonal wall of the everted siphon is occupied by a continuation of the inner lining, carrying closely placed and overlapping layers of long spines from 0.1 to 0.2 mm. Shorter spines continue over most of the test but are often obscured by sand and other adherent matter. The inner siphonal lining is either red or green (subantarctic specimens are red). There are numerous longitudinal muscle bands radiating from the siphons and an outer layer of fine circular bands. Branchial tentacles, from 16 to 24, are simply pinnate or have very short secondary branches. The dorsal tubercle is comparatively simple, and the opening varies from a crescentic to a U-shaped slit with or without horns

turned in. The branchial sac has 6 well defined folds on each side of the body with from 15 to 30 internal longitudinal vessels on the folds and 3 to 6 between them. There may be 13 stigmata per mesh in parts of the branchial sac, although there are often only 3 to 5.

The gut loop is usually simple and fairly open, but it may be curved and narrower. The liver is arborescent. The anal border in all subantarctic specimens has about 30 minute rounded lobes (specimens from Kerguelen Islands and Macquarie Island [Kott, 1954]), although specimens from other regions have plain, bilabiate, or distinctly lobed margins. Gonads consist of double rows of numerous polycarp-like sacs joined to central ducts that open near the base of the atrial siphon.

Remarks. Specimens from Kerguelen, Macquarie and Marion islands, Tasmania, southwestern Australia, and northeastern Australia with long siphonal spines from 0.1 to 0.2 mm extending on to the outer surface of the test may represent a distinct species from the Atlantic Ocean-West Indies representative of *Pyura vittata* (Stimpson), which have spines of only 0.03 mm confined to the inner linings of the siphons. Specimens described from Japan (*P. vittata*; Tokioka, 1953), and from Indonesia and northwestern Australia (*P. jacatrensis* Sluiter, 1890, 1904, 1913; Hartmeyer, 1919) have small siphonal spines and may be identical with the Atlantic Ocean-West Indies species. However, specimens from the Palau Islands in the Pacific (*P. vittata*; Tokioka 1967) are intermediate between the two forms and have siphonal spines of an average length of 0.07 mm. The anal border varies from smooth bilabiate to lobed in all localities except those recorded from the Antarctic. This does not therefore provide a reliable taxonomic character. Further information on the variation in length and distribution of siphonal spines extending on to the outer layer of test may help to resolve the situation. *Pyura curvigona* Tokioka, 1950 and 1967, is also a closely related form with spines continuous over the outer test, but in this species the base of the spine is distinct and the anal border has long fingerlike lobes that at present distinguish it from other species from the Palau Islands. The gonads are unusual in the genus, but they also occur in *P. squamata* and *P. discoveryi*.

Genus *Bathypera* Michaelsen, 1904

Type species: *Bathypera splendens* Michaelsen, 1904
Body surface covered by papillae in a regular pat-

tern and filled with calcareous spicules. Branchial sac folded; stigmata curved or irregular. No large kidney present.

With the exception of *B. ovoida* from 3680 meters off California [Van Name, 1945], the only records of this genus are from the Antarctic.

KEY TO ANTARCTIC SPECIES OF *Bathypera*

Test papillae terminate in numerous pointed spines of similar
size .... ***splendens,*** p. 140
                                    (circum-antarctic to Antarctic Peninsula)
Test papillae terminate in central long spine surrounded by
5 or 6 shorter spines................***hastaefera,*** p. 140
                                    (Wilkes Land, Mac. Robertson Land)

Bathypera splendens Michaelsen

Text figs. 192, 193

Bathypera splendens Michaelsen, 1904, p. 192.—Hartmeyer, 1911, p. 426; 1912, pp. 374, 376.—Herdman, 1923, p. 11.—Kott, 1954, p. 129.—Millar, 1960, p. 127.—Vinogradova, 1962, p. 205.
Pyura liouvillia Sluiter, 1912, p. 453; 1914, p. 12.

New Records. Antarctic Peninsula, *Edisto* Sta. 193[22] (64 meters), Sta. 28, TD 4 (135 meters). South Shetland Is.: *Staten Island* Sta. 45/63 (55 meters). Weddell Sea: *Edisto* Sta. 21, TR 7 (412 meters). South Orkney Is.: *Eltanin* Sta. 494 (1226 meters).

Previous Records.

Antarctic: Antarctic Peninsula [Sluiter, 1912, 1914; Millar, 1960]; Enderby Land, Mac. Robertson Land, Davis Sea [Kott, 1954; Vinogradova, 1962]; Wilhelm II Coast [Michaelsen, 1904; Hartmeyer, 1911, 1912; Vinogradova, 1962]; Wilkes Land, Adélie Coast [Herdman, 1923; Vinogradova, 1962].

Distribution. Eurybathic and probably circum-antarctic in depths ranging from 75 to 1226 meters, although the species has not yet been recorded from the Ross Sea area.

Description. Spherical, with or without a short stalk, to dome-shaped, attached by a broad base. Maximum diameter 9.0 cm. Apertures about one-fourth body circumference apart, almost sessile, and both bilabiate. Test thin, brittle, and rather fragile, sometimes paperlike; surface covered by intersecting rows of small rather stout papillae produced into numerous spines on their expanded and flattened free ends. These spines vary in different individuals from minute to conical points. Minute calcareous spicules present in papillae causing their white color. Surface test with papillae turns inward to line the whole length of the

---

[22] U.S. Navy Antarctic Expedition, 1947–1948.

short siphons, terminating at the base of the tentacular ring. Body wall with strong but sparse muscle bands radiating from siphons. These muscle bands subdivide in the region of the gut and gonad and extend on to the ventral surface as very diffuse muscles only. Circular muscle bands present only in the region of the siphons. Branchial tentacles of at least 3 sizes: larger tentacles 10 to 14, but they alternate with smaller ones, which apparently increase in number with the size of the individual. Dorsal tubercle large, almost completely filling peritubercular area with horns of aperture curved in. Dorsal lamina sometimes with minute pointed languets; sometimes forked languets on the border of a continuous membrane anteriorly, although posteriorly the membrane is plain or the languets are broader. Branchial sac with 6 high folds on each side. From 12 to 24 internal longitudinal vessels on the folds and 5 or 6 between them. Stigmata in smaller individuals are very irregular punchhole to small crescentic perforations especially between the folds. On the folds longer rectangular stigmata are arranged more regularly, about 6 to 10 per mesh. In larger specimens extensive areas of unbroken membrane occur between the folds interrupted by irregular infundibula formed by crescent-shaped stigmata. Gut loop rather narrow, horizontal, in posterior part of body, enclosing the single left gonad. Stomach long and spindle-shaped with minute plications. Rectum extends anteriorly. One gonad only on each side of the body, consisting of a tubular ovary fringed by many-branched testis lobes. Gonad on the right is close to the endostyle separated from the gut loop only by the ventral blood sinus. The long oviduct extends almost as far anteriorly as the anal opening, whereas the vas deferens is shorter. No kidney present; however, there are rows of about 8 mushroom-shaped endocarps dorsal to the gonad on the right and gut loop on the left, respectively. These may have an excretory function.

Remarks. This species is closely related to *B. ovoida* Ritter from 3680 meters off California. It is probable that *B. ovoida* represents a case of tropical submergence of an antarctic species.

Bathypera hastaefera Vinogradova

Text fig. 194

Bathypera hastaefera Vinogradova, 1962, p .206.

New Records. None.

Previous Records.

Antarctic: Wilkes Land 320 meters, Mac. Robertson Land 540–2000 meters [Vinogradova, 1962].

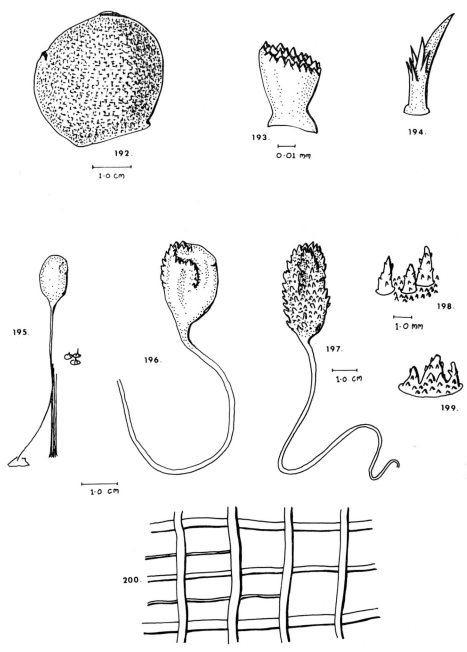

Bathypera splendens
192. External appearance.
193. Test spine.

Bathypera hastaefera
194. Test spine [after Vinogradova, 1962].

Culeolus murrayi
195. Specimen from *Eltanin* Sta. 469; test spines.

196. Specimen from *Eltanin* Sta. 135.
197. Specimen from *Eltanin* Sta. 451.
198. Test spines from specimen *Eltanin* Sta. 451.
199. Spines from enlarged arc, specimen from *Eltanin* Sta. 451.
200. Portion of branchial sac showing occasional accessory transverse vessels.

Description. Body hemispherical from 1 to 8 cm in diameter, fixed by a broad flat base. Apertures bilabiate, almost sessile, and both on the upper surface. Surface of the test with small longitudinal folds between the siphons and concentric folds lower down. Test thin, covered with intersecting rows of papillae produced into one long and 5 or 6 shorter spines terminally. Body wall closely attached to the test. Strong longitudinal muscle bands extend on to the ventral surface, and transverse circular fibers are particularly strong around the siphons. Muscles form a strong network. Nine longer branchial tentacles alternate with 2 or 3 smaller ones. Dorsal tubercle with horns turned in. Dorsal lamina a broad membrane with pointed languets anteriorly. Branchial sac with 6 folds on each side of the body. Crescentic stigmata between the folds anteriorly, and short, broader, less regular stigmata posteriorly, about 10 to 13 stigmata per mesh. Gut loop narrow. Stomach with 35 fine internal folds. Anal border with 6 to 8 indistinct lobes. Single gonads on each side of the body. The left gonad is in the gut loop. (After Vinogradova.)

Remarks. This species is known only from a single specimen from Mac. Robertson Land and two specimens from Wilkes Land, which were taken with three specimens of *B. splendens*, suggesting the possible identity of the two species. However, in addition to the differences of papillary spines, the ventral musculature persists in bands in *B. hastaefera*, whereas in *splendens* it is diffuse. Stronger musculature and the adherence of the body wall to the test may account for the folding of the test observed in *B. hastaefera*. Therefore, although other differences described [Vinogradova, 1962] fall within the range of variation recorded for *B. splendens*, and despite the fact that both species have been taken together, *B. hastaefera* appears to be distinct, occurring in a limited region in the eastern antarctic area.

Genus *Culeolus* Herdman 1881

Type species: *Culeolus murrayi* Herdman, 1881
Egg-shaped or pyramidal body on long slender stalk. Branchial sac reduced; longitudinal and transverse vessels but no folds and no stigmata.

The genus has a wide distribution in the deeper basins of all oceans. It shows modifications common to other abyssal species. A single cosmopolitan species occurs in Antarctica.

Culeolus murrayi Herdman
Text figs. 195–200
Culeolus murrayi Herdman, 1881 p. 83; 1882, p. 91.—Hartmeyer, 1911, p. 443.

Culeolus wyville-thomsoni Herdman, 1881, p. 84; 1882, p. 103.
Culeolus recumbens Herdman, 1881, p. 85; 1882, p. 107.
Culeolus perlucidum Herdman, 1881, p. 86; 1882 (*perlucidus*), p. 111.
Culeolus suhmi Herdman, 1881, p. 86.—Van Name, 1912, p. 540; 1945, p. 364.—Millar, 1955a, p. 232; 1959, p. 199.
Culeolus perlatus Herdman, 1882, p. 115.
Culeolus moseleyi Herdman, 1881, p. 87; 1882, p. 117.
Culeolus tanneri Verrill, 1885, p. 529; 1885a, p. 447.
Culeolus willemoesi Herdman, 1886, p. 403.
Culeolus herdmani Sluiter, 1904, p. 105.—Van Name, 1918, p. 83.—Tokioka, 1953, p. 289.
Culeolus pyramidalis Ritter, 1907, p. 16.—Van Name, 1945, p. 366.
Culeolus sluiteri Ritter, 1913, p. 463.—Van Name, 1945, p. 366.
Culeolus antarcticus Vinogradova, 1962, p. 207.

New Records. South Shetland Is.: *Eltanin* Sta. 135 (3752 meters). Antarctic Peninsula: *Eltanin* Sta. 268 (2818 meters). Scotia Sea.: *Eltanin* Sta. 469 (3714 meters). Drake Passage: *Eltanin* Sta. 451 (4026 meters). Southeast Pacific Basin: *Eltanin* Sta. 1140 (4731 meters), Sta. 1150 (4758–4804 meters), Sta. 1154 (4709 meters), Sta. 1161 (4447–4502 meters).

Previous Records.

Antarctic: Eastern antarctic area [Hartmeyer, 1911; Vinogradova, 1962]
Subantarctic: Crozet Is. [Herdman, 1882].
Elsewhere: Pacific Ocean north to Aleutian Is. and from Japan east to California [Herdman, 1881, 1882, 1886; Sluiter, 1904; Ritter, 1907, 1913; Van Name, 1918, 1945; Tokioka, 1953]; Atlantic Ocean [Herdman, 1881; Van Name, 1945; Millar, 1955a]; Indian Ocean, Tasman Sea [Millar, 1959].

Distribution. In waters deeper than 2000 meters this species is found in the Pacific, Atlantic, and Indian oceans. At its northernmost limit, however, it has been taken in only 518 meters off the Aleutian Islands.

Description. Oval to pyramidal head up to 6 cm long. Anterior end tapering or abruptly joined to a thin stalk up to 15 cm long, which gets thinner toward the base. Both apertures sessile, separated by most of the dorsal border. Branchial aperture is triradiate, apex directed posteriorly, and the atrial aperture is bilabiate, a transverse slit. The test may be thin and semitransparent in smaller specimens but is more often thicker and completely opaque. There is great variation in the external appearance of the heads, owing to varying development of test vascularization [see Herdman, 1882] and the consequent formation of surface test papillae. The most simple condition is found where the surface of the test is thrown up into low mounds or scales with a central papilla, hollow and more or less pointed (as in the specimen described as *C. perlucidus* Herdman). Usually the postero-ventral border of the body is marked by an arc of enlarged conical papillae, which curve anteriorly on either side of the atrial aperture. These papillae are especially enlarged mid-ventrally and may continue anteriorly down the ventral border. Although the general test papillae are not always branched, the enlarged papillae of the postero-ventral arc, especially in larger specimens [Van Name, 1945, and present specimens from *Eltanin* Sta. 469] have side branches. The smaller (0.8 cm) specimens (e.g. *C. suhmi* of Herdman in synonymy above) sometimes have enlarged papillae with branches, however. Minute branches also develop on the general surface papillae (*C. recumbens* Herdman), and *C. murrayi* Herdman, 1881 and 1882, had several points, sometimes branched, rising from the same scale-like base. The central papillary spine may increase in size to become conical (*C. moselyi* Herdman and *C. suhmi* [Millar, 1955a] and specimens from *Eltanin* Sta. 451), and larger conical branched papillae, similar to those found often in the postero-ventral arc, may occur about 2 mm apart all over the body, with smaller conical papillae between (*Eltanin* Sta. 451). *Culeolus wyville-thompsoni* Herdman and *C. sluiteri* Ritter represent large specimens of this species, in which the test scales increase in size and form large mounds with central papillary spine, although smaller conical papillae persist between the spines. These variations of *C. murrayi* and its synonyms, as will be seen by the table below, cannot be correlated with size, depth, or horizontal distribution. Communities of individuals collected together often show the same condition of the test, which therefore may reflect some local condition of nutrition or aeration. Even with the limited numbers of specimens described, it is impossible to use the surface test as a specific character. Increases in size or branching of the general surface papillae are always accompanied by even greater complications of the larger papillae of the postero-ventral arc, when it is present. In larger, older specimens the tip of the papillae may be hardened and is often brown. The upper part of the stalk may have branched papillae and hairs are also often present along the length of the stalk, which is thin and wiry. The body wall has longitudinal muscles crossing to form a rather open meshwork. Circular

muscles present in the siphonal region. From 20 to 30 branchial tentacles have long primary branches and minute secondary branches and are irregular in length and arrangement. The dorsal tubercle has a simple U-shaped slit with horns turned in or out. The dorsal lamina has up to 16 characteristic leaf-shaped lobes, antero-posteriorly flattened. The branchial sac is formed into 6 folds with a maximum of 6 to 15 internal longitudinal vessels on the folds and 1 to 3 between them. There are no stigmata. In smaller specimens transverse vessels are all one size, although later, parastigmatic vessels occur and in even larger specimens a third order of transverse vessels (often incomplete) develops, especially anteriorly, to form smaller, transversely elongate meshes (*C. wyville-thomsoni*, *Eltanin* Sta. 451). Longitudinal connectives (*C. recumbens* Herdman, *C. perlucidus* Herdman) are present occasionally in smaller specimens in which number of longitudinal vessels are also small.

The gut loop is simple with rounded terminal lobes of the arborescent liver in the region of the stomach. The anal border of the specimens in the present collection is broken into 20 to 30 lobes, although previous authors [Herdman, 1882; Van Name, 1945] have sometimes observed a sinuous anal border. There are 1, 2, or 3 tubular ovaries on each side of the body directed toward the atrial opening with 4 to 7 testis lobes developed along the mesial surface of the ovary. Mushroom-shaped endocarp-like material forms over the ovary and the testis lobes appear to develop into this. The most posterior gonad on the left is in the gut loop.

Biology. As with other specimens with a thin wiry stalk, it has been suggested that the stalk of the present species is not sufficiently strong to support the head (see *P. georgiana* above). In the present collection there are two specimens from *Eltanin* Sta. 469 with large heads 4 cm long, in which the stalk is strengthened by a polyzoan 'prop' that adheres to and strengthens the stalk for about the middle two-thirds of its length and basally diverges away from the stalk: The ascidian appears to lean on the polyzoan and is fixed to it by hairs on the stalk. There is no sign that either has been bent over.

Remarks. It has been found impossible, by any criterion, to separate the individuals previously described as different species. They are remarkably similar internally and only specimens described as *C. sluiteri* Ritter, *C. wyville-thomsoni* Herdman, and the specimens from *Eltanin* Sta. 451 show differences in external appearance, which could represent a different spe-

Culeolus murrayi and synonyms

Species Name	Occurrence	Maximum Depth, meters	Size, cm	Test, Surface Projections	Arc of Enlarged Papillae	Spicules
C. perlucidus Herdman 1882	Crozet Is.	2516	2	Scale with single point	Absent	Present
C. willemoesi Herdman 1886	Japan	4636	2	Scale with single point	Ventrally only	Present
C. suhmi Herdman 1881	Off Long I., New York	3111	0.8	Scale with single point	Moderate	Present
C. perlatus Herdman 1882	Off Long I., New York	3111	0.8	Scale with single point	Moderate	Present
C. pyramidalis Ritter 1907	California	4134	2.5	Scale with single point	Moderate	?
C. suhmi Van Name 1945	Eastern U.S.A. (37° to 40°N), Spanish coast (47°23′N)	2943–5342 3926	1–6	Scale with single point	Moderate	Sometimes present
C. recumbens Herdman 1882	Crozet Is.	2516	2.5	Scale with single point	Moderate	Sometimes present
Eltanin Sta. 268	Antarctic Peninsula	2818	1.5	Scale with single point	Moderate	Absent
Eltanin Sta. 469	Scotia Sea	3714	4	Scale with single point	Moderate	Absent
Eltanin Sta. 135	South Shetland Is.	3752	2	Scale with single point	Moderate	Absent
Eltanin Sta. 1150	Southeast Pacific Basin	4804	3	Scale with single point	Moderate	Absent
Eltanin Sta. 1154	Southeast Pacific Basin	4709	2	Scale with single point	Moderate	Absent
C. antarcticus Vinogradova 1962	Knox Coast	3800	2	Scale with single point	Moderate	Present
C. murrayi Hartmeyer 1911	Wilhelm II Coast	3397	2	?	Moderate	Probably present
C. suhmi Millar 1959	Indian Ocean, Tasman Sea	3310–4820	2.5	Scale with single point	Moderate	Probably present
C. murrayi Herdman 1882	Japan	4206	5–6	Scale with single point	Well developed	Present
C. herdmani Van Name 1918	Philippine Is.	500	3.6	Minute conical	Small	Absent
C. herdmani Tokioka 1953	Japan	400	3	Minute conical	Moderate	Absent
C. herdmani Sluiter 1904	Indonesia	216	4	Minute conical	Moderate	Absent
Eltanin Sta. 1140	Southeast Pacific Basin	4731	1.2–4	Minute conical with single point	Moderate to well developed	Absent
C. moseleyi Herdman 1882	Pacific Ocean equator	4438	2	Larger single conical	Absent	Absent
C. suhmi Millar 1955a	Mid-Atlantic (40°33′N)	4600	. . .	Larger single conical	Well developed	Present
Eltanin Sta. 451	Drake Passage	4026	1.5–4	Conical with multiple points	Well developed	Absent
C. sluiteri Ritter 1913	North Pacific	518	6.5	Tubercular	Well developed	Present
C. wyville-thomsoni Herdman 1882	Kermadec Is.	1152	5	Tubercular	Well developed	Present

cies. These specimens are not, however, geographically separated from the location of more typical individuals. The condition of their test is possibly derived by increased vascularization and probably represents individual variation rather than distinct species. The species is abyssal and probably ancient. Sluiter's [1904] specimens of the genus from Malaya were taken from much shallower waters. They may not all be easily distinguished from the present species and are in any case closely related. A species of the genus has also been taken in shallow water off Tasmania [Kott, 1956]. The occurrences on the continental shelf may be considered as secondary invasions of this abyssal genus.

Family MOLGULIDAE Lacaze-Duthiers

Successful in the Antarctic with many diverse and widespread species. Species are well established with few intraspecific variations. Certain species become especially large, representing the largest members of the class Ascidiacea, and suggest a special longevity. Members of this family are also particularly widely distributed and not limited by usual zoogeographic boundaries. They extend from the antarctic area into the subantarctic area and often farther north. Many species also have special mechanisms to ensure viviparity, a fact that may be associated with their age and success in the area.

KEY TO GENERA OF MOLGULIDAE

1. Branchial sac reduced to paired pouches expanded from pharyngeal wall..................*Oligotrema, p. 168
   Branchial sac formed by usual perforation of pharyngeal wall to form stigmata........................ 2
2. With folds in the branchial sac.................. 3
   Without folds in the branchial sac.................. 6
3. Branchial sac without stigmata........*Fungulus, p. 166
   Branchial sac with stigmata........................ 4
4. Gonads on both sides of the body.................. 5
   Gonad on only one side of the body.................. 9
5. The left gonad anterior to primary intestinal loop.......
   ....*Molgula, p. 145
   The left gonad enclosed in primary intestinal loop.......
   ....*Molguloides, p. 156
6. Secondary infundibula enormously developed, irregularly distributed 7
   Regular primary infundibula beneath longitudinal vessels 8
7. Gonad on left only, in primary gut loop...............
   ....Bostrichobranchus
   Gonads on both sides of the body, on the left anterior to the gut loop....................*Paramolgula, p. 164
8. Gonads outside primary gut loop.*Pareugyrioides, p. 160
   Gonads at least partially within primary gut loop.......
   ....*Eugyra, p. 159
9. Gonad on right only.....................Anomopera
   Gonad on left only in primary intestinal loop..........
   ....Rhizomolgula

---

* These genera reported from Antarctica.

Genus *Molgula* Forbes, 1848

Type species: *Molgula oculata* Forbes, 1843
Stigmata spiral. Branchial sac folded. Single gonad on both sides of the body; left gonad outside gut loop.

KEY TO ANTARCTIC SPECIES OF *Molgula*

1. Numerous testis ducts open separately over surface of ovary 2
   Testis ducts unite into a single vas deferens........... 4
2. Tubular ovary long and narrow, continuous with oviduct. 3
   Ovary broader than long with oviduct from the middle of its long axis........................*euplicata*, p. 153
   (Victoria and Enderby quadrants, Antarctic Peninsula)
3. Right gonad parallel and adjacent to curved border of kidney ....*kerguelenensis*, p. 153
   (Kerguelen Is.)
   Right gonad not parallel or adjacent to curved border of kidney ....*gigantea*, p. 155
   (circum-antarctic, South Sandwich Is., South Georgia, Kerguelen Is.)
4. Tubular ovaries curve around anterior to the pole of the gut loop and kidney..............*malvinensis*, p. 149
   (circum-subantarctic and circum-antarctic)
   Gonad does not curve around anterior to pole of gut loop or kidney.. 5
5. Testis lobes around and sometimes on mesial surface of whole extent of oval or elongate ovary; ovary never flask-shaped 6
   Testis lobes confined to proximal end of oval to elongate ovary; or ovary flask-shaped........................ 7
6. Gonad parallel and adjacent to descending limb of intestinal loop............................*setigera*, p. 147
   (South Georgia, Falkland Is., Magellanic area)
   Gonad not parallel and adjacent to descending limb of intestinal loop....................*pedunculata*, p. 145
   (circum-antarctic, Kerguelen Is., Macquarie I.)
7. Concavity of kidney occupied by right gonad........... 8
   Concavity of kidney not occupied by right gonad........ 9
8. Oviduct long, curves ventrally.............*sluiteri*, p. 152
   (New Zealand, Macquarie I.)
   Oviduct short and wide, not curved......*confluxa*, p. 151
   (Antarctic Peninsula, South Shetland Is., Campbell I.)
9. Vas deferens very convoluted.............*pulchra*, p. 150
   (Victoria quadrant, South Georgia, Magellanic area, Kerguelen Is., Macquarie I.)
   Vas deferens not convoluted..........*pyriformis*, p. 149
   (Magellanic area, Patagonian Shelf)

Molgula pedunculata Herdman

Text fig. 201

Molgula pedunculata Herdman, 1881, p. 234; 1882, p. 74.—Sluiter, 1906, p. 48.—Ärnbäck, 1938, p. 11. —Van Name, 1945, p. 411.—Millar, 1960, p. 128.
Molgula maxima Sluiter, 1905b, p. 472; 1906, p. 47.
Caesira concomitans; Hartmeyer, 1909–1911, p. 1739.
Caesira hodgsoni; Hartmeyer, 1909–1911, p. 1739.
Caesira pedunculata; Hartmeyer, 1909–1911, p. 1739. —Sluiter, 1914, p. 3.

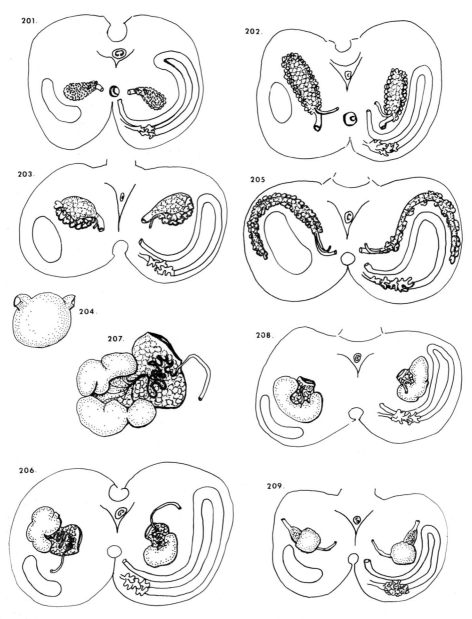

Molgula pedunculata
201. Inner body wall showing gut, gonads, and kidney.

Molgula setigera
202. Inner body wall showing gut, gonads, and kidney.

Molgula pyriformis
203. Inner body wall showing gut, gonads, and kidney.
204. Animal removed from test.

Molgula malvinensis
205. Inner body wall showing gut, gonads, and kidney.

Molgula pulchra
206. Inner body wall showing gut, gonads, and kidney.
207. Testes and ovary pulled apart to show course of vas deferens.

Molgula confluxa
208. Inner body wall showing gut, gonads, and kidney.

Molgula sluiteri
209. Inner body wall showing gut, gonads, and kidney.

Molgula hodgsoni Herdman, 1910, p. 11.

Molgula concomitans Herdman, 1910, p. 15; 1923, p. 14.

Caesira maxima; Hartmeyer, 1911, p. 417.

Molgula angulata Ärnbäck, 1938, p. 9.

Molgula setigera; Kott, 1954, p. 133.

Molgula sabulosa; Kott, 1954, p. 134.—Vinogradova, 1962, p. 210.

Molgula macquariensis Kott, 1954, p. 138.

New Records. Weddell Sea: *Edisto* Sta. 20, TR 5 (384 meters). South Orkney Is.: *Eltanin* Sta. 496 (234 meters), Sta. 1082 (298–302 meters), Sta. 1084 (298–403 meters). Antarctic Peninsula: *Staten Island* Sta. 32/63 (46 meters).

Previous Records.

Antarctic: Antarctic Peninsula, South Shetland Is. [Sluiter, 1905b, 1914; Ärnbäck, 1938; Millar, 1960]; South Georgia [Millar, 1960]; Enderby Land [Kott, 1954]; Wilhelm II Coast [Hartmeyer, 1911]; Knox Coast [Vinogradova, 1962]; Commonwealth Bay [Kott, 1954]; McMurdo Sound [Herdman, 1910].

Subantarctic: Kerguelen Is. [Herdman, 1881]; Macquarie I. [Kott, 1954].

Distribution. Circum-antarctic with a fairly limited depth range from 100 to 437 meters, but generally between 100 and 300 meters. Despite the fact that the species is large and conspicuous, the only known specimens from the subantarctic area are from Kerguelen and Macquarie islands. Specimens taken in over 300 meters are small [Kott, 1954; Vinogradova, 1962], and possibly the preference for shallower water tends to confine the species mainly to the antarctic continental shelf.

Description. Ovoid or rectangular, longer than wide, up to 18 cm long [Sluiter, 1906], although generally only 3 to 4 cm long. Smaller specimens may have a short wide stalk from the mid-ventral surface, although generally fixed by part of the ventral surface. Siphons are short, both on the upper surface, separated by about one-fourth the body circumference. The test is tough, translucent, and fairly flexible, with well spaced, short, irregular, and flattened or rounded hairs, or 'tag-like excrescences,' which are shorter but more dense on the siphons. The body wall with moderately developed longitudinal and circular bands, especially around the siphons. There are 8 or more many-branched larger tentacles alternating with smaller ones. The dorsal tubercle is large, with a wide U-shaped slit, open interval directed more or less posteriorly and to the left with both horns turned in to a greater or

less extent. The dorsal lamina is wide and short with a smooth margin, whereas, owing to the longer ventral curve of the body, the endostyle is very long. There are 9 well developed branchial folds on each side of the body with 6 to 13 internal longitudinal vessels on the folds and from 1 to 4, or more (sometimes 8), between the folds. Stigmata form large infundibula in the folds. There is only a single spiral in each mesh, so that the circumference of each spiral at the base of the fold is great and the stigmata here not very curved. Therefore between the folds the stigmata appear more or less straight and the spirals are apparent only from the back of the branchial sac. The gut loop is long and very narrow and deeply curved around the ventral border of the animal to form a deep secondary loop; the exact shape of the curve depends on the size of the individual. The left gonad in the second gut loop is directed toward the atrial siphon, and the extent to which it is embraced by the loop depends entirely on the depth and shape of this loop [see Millar, 1960, p. 129, text fig. 54]. There are dense liver lobes in the region of the stomach. The anus is bilabiate. The ovary is sausage-shaped, opening by a short oviduct, and the testis lobes form a coating on the free mesial surface of the ovary. In immature specimens the testis lobes are seen at the ends of branching seminal ducts, which join a more or less median duct along the surface of the ovary beneath the testis lobes. The oviduct is short and the vas deferens appears to open beside it. The opening of the vas deferens is inconspicuous, however, and the course of the duct is obscured by testis lobes. In one specimen only seminal ducts were observed joining the proximal and distal branches of the vas deferens on the mesial surface of the ovary. About two-thirds of the distance along the ovary these ducts join to form a short vas deferens, which opens on the surface of the gonad. The kidney, posterior to the right gonad, is long, curves around the end of the gonad, and is more or less dorso-ventrally oriented.

Remarks. The species is distinguished from the closely related *M. setigera* by the long and curved kidney, by the deeper curve of the gut loop, by the shape and orientation of the gonads and their ducts, and by the heavier encrustation of sand, which is present in *M. setigera.*

Molgula setigera Ärnbäck
Text fig. 202

? *Molgula kophameli* Michaelsen, 1900, p. 125; 1907, p. 80; 1915 [part], p. 367.—Van Name, 1945, p. 407.

Molgula setigera Ärnbäck, 1938, p. 7 [not Kott, 1954, p. 133 (< *M. pedunculata* Herdman, 1881, p. 234)].
? *Molgula platana* Van Name, 1945, p. 404.
? *Molgula falsensis* Millar, 1955, p. 217; 1960, p. 128; 1962, p. 203.
Molgula setigera f. *georgiana* Millar, 1960, p. 134.
Molgula setigera f. *marioni* Millar, 1960, p. 136.

New Records. Drake Passage: *Eltanin* Sta. 219 (115 meters), Sta. 369 (293 meters). Off Tierra del Fuego: *Eltanin* Sta. 981 (40–49 meters). Macquarie I.: *Eltanin* Sta. 1417 (79–93 meters), Sta. 1418 (86–101 meters).

Previous Records.

Antarctic: South Georgia [Millar, 1960].

Subantarctic: Falkland Is., Magellanic area [Michaelsen, 1900, 1960; Ärnbäck, 1938]; Marion I. [Millar, 1960].

Elsewhere: ? South Africa [Millar, 1955, 1962]; ? Río de la Plata [Van Name, 1945].

Distribution. Previously the species was thought to be confined to the shallower areas (up to 293 meters) off the Falkland Islands, the Magellanic area, and South Georgia; perhaps extending north on the Patagonian Shelf to Río de la Plata (21 meters). The recent record from Marion Island [Millar, 1960], the present records from Macquarie Island (*Eltanin* Sta. 1417, Sta. 1418), and the suspected synonym from South Africa (*M. falsensis*) may indicate a wider subantarctic distribution.

Description. Body globular to ovate, flattened basally, maximum dimension 2.8 cm, although the large number of specimens in the present collection are 0.4 to 1.5 cm. Both apertures on very short siphons at either end of the upper surface. Test is thin, soft, and semi-transparent and is usually produced into stiff or flexible bristles or hairs. The stiff bristles may cover the whole body surface but are most conspicuous in tufts around the siphons, whereas the rest of the body has more flexible hairs, which may protrude through the coating of sand usually adhering to the test. Occasionally the stiffer bristles are even absent from the siphonal region and only the softer hairs protrude through the sand coating. Body wall is thin, but strong muscle bands radiate from the siphons and circular bands are particularly strong in the siphonal region. Muscles are not present in the ventral part of the body wall. About 16 larger branchial tentacles alternate with smaller tentacles. The dorsal tubercle has a C-shaped, longitudinal, sinuous, or simple oval aperture. The dorsal lamina is fairly long, narrow,

and smooth. The branchial sac has 7 folds on each side of the body with up to 10 internal longitudinal vessels on the folds but none between them. Stigmata form about 6 irregular infundibula along each fold, each dividing into two in the summit. The base of each infundibulum extends into the interval between the folds and is there adjacent to the corresponding spiral from the next fold. The internal longitudinal vessels are mostly on the ventral side of the folds. The stomach is obscured by liver lobes, and the gut forms a long narrow loop curved along the ventral border of the body.

There is usually 1 gonad on each side of the body extending close along the dorsal side of the kidney and the descending limb of the gut, respectively. The oviduct is wide and fairly long and may be bent to open postero-ventrally or may be turned up toward the atrial siphon. In a single specimen from the present collection there are 2 gonads on the right: the most dorsal with the oviduct bent dorsally and the ventral gonad with its oviduct bent ventrally. In other specimens of the present collection the oviduct is bent ventrally, as in *M. setigera* f. *marioni* Millar, 1960. Gonads consist of sausage-shaped ovary fringed on both sides and around the ends by a border of pyriform testis follicles joined to a median vas deferens on the mesial surface of the ovary by a series of seminal ducts. There is sometimes a particular increase in the size of these lobes around the end of the ovary. The long vas deferens usually extends toward the atrial opening. The kidney is oval or long, more or less horizontal, and not very bent.

Remarks. The species is best characterized by the position of the gonads and length of their ducts rather than by the condition of the hairs or bristles on the surface, or by the form of the dorsal tubercle, which are both variable to some extent. In the present collection the oviduct is generally bent ventrally, as in Millar's [1960] form from Marion Island. It is unlikely that this character is significant taxonomically and may be associated with the maturity of the ovary, so that at the time eggs are liberated the oviduct turns ventrally to ensure viviparity. The length of the vas deferens is also apparently variable, and in specimens described by previous authors the vas deferens terminates near the base of the oviduct. The multiplicity of seminal openings in *M. setigera* f. *georgiana* is regarded as an individual variation. *Molgula falsensis* Millar is very closely related to the present species with the same gonads, gut loop, and regular infundibula in the branchial sac. It may be synonymous, and, if so, it indicates a much wider distribution for the species, especially in the Indian Ocean.

Van Name [1945] suggested the synonymy of *M. kophameli* Michaelsen with *M. setigera*. The gut and gonads of Michaelsen's single specimen and its location in the Strait of Magellan support this suggestion. *M. kophameli* probably represents a specimen of *M. setigera* in which the test bristles are not well developed or are obscured.

Molgula pyriformis Herdman

Text figs. 203, 204

Molgula pyriformis Herdman, 1881, p. 236; 1882, p. 79.—Hartmeyer, 1922, p. 316.—Van Name, 1945, p. 406.—Rodrigues, 1966, p. 105.
Caesira pyriformis Hartmeyer, 1912, pp. 373, 374, 378 [not *C. pyriformis* Michaelsen, 1900, 1907].

New Records. Drake Passage: *Eltanin* Sta. 219 (115 meters).

Previous Records.

Elsewhere: Buenos Aires, 1098 meters [Herdman, 1881].

Distribution. Probably confined to the Magellanic area and the Patagonian Shelf and slope areas, in 115–1098 meters.

Description. Almost spherical, 0.4 to 0.8 cm in diameter. Conspicuous siphons on opposite ends of upper surface directed horizontally away from each other. The test is thin, sand covered, with fine hairs on the surface extending between grains of sand. The body wall is thin with rather diffuse longitudinal and circular muscles absent from the ventral surface. Branchial tentacles are twice pinnate. The peritubercular area is long, almost to the esophageal opening, and the dorsal tubercle opening is simple and circular halfway down. The dorsal lamina is narrow, very short, and smooth margined. There are 7 flat folds on each side of the body with only 2 to 4 internal longitudinal vessels on the ventral side of each fold; none between. Herdman's specimen had up to 8 internal longitudinal vessels on the folds. Stigmata form 6 regular infundibula per fold, not extending very far into the fold. The gut loop is long and closed but fairly wide at the pole. It curves around the ventral border of the left side to form a secondary loop. The stomach is obscured by the usual arborescent liver lobes. In the present specimens the single gonad on each side of the body is flask-shaped, with pyriform testis follicles on the posterior border only, but Herdman's and Rodrigues' specimens had testis follicles all around the ovary and the gonads were more elongate. The vas deferens extends along the mesial surface of the ovary and is joined by seminal ducts from the testis follicles. Both oviduct and vas deferens are short and the oviduct may be turned posteriorly. Both gonads are almost vertical, forming an angle with the anterior end of the gut loop and kidney, respectively.

Remarks. Although Van Name suspects their identity, the present species is distinguished from *M. platana* Van Name, 1945, by the position of the gonads. The species is distinguished from closely related *M. malvinensis* by the conspicuous and horizontally directed siphons, the small number of internal longitudinal vessels, and the shorter and broader gonads and their orientation. It resembles *M. setigera* only in the absence of vessels between the folds and in the disposition of testis follicles around the ovary. The present specimens differ from Herdman's in the presence of testis lobes on one border and in the larger number of vessels on the folds. Herdman's specimen was, however, more than twice the size of these Magellanic specimens.

Molgula malvinensis Ärnbäck

Text fig. 205

Molgula malvinensis Ärnbäck, 1938, p. 5.—Van Name, 1945, p. 407.—Kott, 1954, p. 135.—Millar, 1960, p. 132.
Molgula spiralis Kott, 1954, p. 134.
Molgula herdmani Brewin, 1958, p. 451.

New Records. Drake Passage: *Eltanin* Sta. 219 (115 meters). Antarctic Peninsula: *Staten Island* Sta. 35/63 (46 meters). Weddell Sea: *Edisto* Sta. 21, TR 8 (413 meters). Commonwealth Bay: B.A.N.Z.A.R.E. Sta. 1820. Macquarie I.: *Eltanin* Sta. 1418 (86–101 meters).

Previous Records.
Antarctic: South Georgia [Millar, 1960]; Enderby Land [Kott, 1954].
Subantarctic: Falkland Is. [Ärnbäck, 1938; Van Name, 1945]; Kerguelen I. and Macquarie I. [Kott, 1954]; Stewart I., New Zealand [Brewin, 1958].

Distribution. Circum-subantarctic in shallow waters from a 'few' [Ärnbäck, 1938] to 100 meters; also circum-antarctic in waters up to 400 meters.

Description. Small, slightly dorso-ventrally flattened spheres up to 4.3 cm long but more often less. Test is very soft and transparent but brittle with sand particles, through which fine test hairs protrude. The atrial aperture is mid-dorsal and the branchial aperture on the upper surface anteriorly, both almost sessile and obscured by sand. The body wall has strong outer circular and inner longitudinal bands in the region of the siphons, but these bands do not extend beyond the upper half of the body. About 12 larger branchial tentacles with few and short primary branches and minute secondary branches alternate with smaller tentacles. Peritubercular area is a deep narrow V with a C-shaped tubercular slit turned to the left. The dorsal lamina is short with a smooth margin. Branchial folds number 6 to 8 on the left and 7 to 9 on the right, where the most ventral fold is rudimentary consisting of only one longitudinal vessel. There are 6 to 11 internal longitudinal vessels on both sides of each fold, although the vessels on the ventral sides of the fold are thicker. The stigmata form 8 infundibula in each fold, and these, in younger specimens, do not extend very far into the fold. There are no spirals or internal longitudinal vessels between the folds, but irregular short stigmata do occur there, or the base of the spiral extends out to the base of the corresponding spiral from the next fold. The gut forms quite a wide but closed horizontal loop, extending dorsally toward the atrial opening. The stomach is obscured by liver lobes. There is a single gonad on each side of the body, encircling the pole of the gut loop and the kidney, respectively. Both ducts may extend toward the atrial opening, but often the oviduct is shorter, opening just dorsal to the kidney or gut loop. A second shorter gonad on the right may occur posterior to the first [see Kott, 1954, fig. 13]. Gonads consist of central ovary fringed by testis follicles at the terminal branches of seminal ducts, which join the median vas deferens on the mesial surface of the ovary. The kidney is large and oval or slightly curved.

Remarks. The species resembles *M. setigera* and *M. pyriformis* in the test hairs, the absence of internal longitudinal vessels between folds, and the position of the testis follicles along the sides of the ovary. The gonads are longer than those of *M. setigera* and *M. pyriformis* and have a different relationship to the kidney and gut loop, and the gut loop is wider. *M. spiralis* Kott, 1954, differs only in the extreme regularity of the branchial sac and should not be separated from the present species. The longitudinal vessel in the interspace is only apparent and is actually associated with the transverse vessels in the fold.

Molgula pulchra Michaelsen
Text figs. 206, 207

Molgula pulchra Michaelsen, 1900, p. 128; 1907,

p. 81.—Sluiter, 1932, p. 1.—Van Name, 1945, p. 409.—Kott, 1954, p. 135.
Molgula pyriformis [part] Michaelsen, 1900, p. 131; 1907, p. 81.
Molgula georgiana Michaelsen, 1900, p. 132.—Sluiter, 1932, p. 2.
Caesira georgiana; Hartmeyer, 1909–1911, p. 1324.
Caesira pulchra; Hartmeyer, 1909–1911, p. 1324.
Caesira pyriformis var. *kerguelenensis*, Hartmeyer, 1911, p. 519.

New Records. Drake Passage: *Eltanin* Sta. 219 (115 meters), Sta. 369 (293 meters). Scotia Sea: *Eltanin* Sta. 370 (115 meters). Knox Coast: *Glacier* Sta. ?, Deep Freeze II (on ship's anchor, depth ?). Macquarie I.: *Eltanin* Sta. 1418 (86–101 meters).

Previous Records.

Antarctic: South Georgia [Michaelsen, 1900; Sluiter, 1932].

Subantarctic: Magellanic area [Michaelsen, 1900; 1907; Van Name, 1945]; Kerguelen Is. [Hartmeyer, 1911; Kott, 1954]; Macquarie I. [Kott, 1954].

Distribution. This species also appears to be circum-subantarctic and circum-antarctic, generally in shallow waters (13 to 130 meters) but has been taken off the Burdwood Bank in 293 meters, so that possibly the lack of records from deeper waters is due to the inconspicuous nature of the species.

Description. Spherical to oval, slightly dorso-ventrally flattened. Individuals in the present collection are from 0.2 to 2.0 cm. Mature individuals are from 1.0 cm. Maximum size recorded is 2.5 cm. The lower surface is usually fixed to the substrate and may be concave. Both apertures on short siphons, close together in the middle of the upper surface. Atrial and branchial siphons have 6 and 4 lobes, respectively, and the lobes correspond to furrows down the length of the siphons. The atrial siphon is directed upward and the branchial siphon directed laterally to the right; the siphons may be recessed into the body with a fold of test around them. The test is thin, heavily encrusted with sand particles between which fine hairs protrude. The body wall is not very adherent to the test and has inner longitudinal muscle bands radiating from the siphons and fine outer circular bands, but all musculature is limited to the region below the siphons. Branchial tentacles, of varying sizes, about 15 larger than others, with slender primary branches and only occasional secondary branches. The tubercular slit is a large C with inturned horns directed posteriorly and to the left. Dorsal lamina is short and plain. There are 6 or 7 branchial folds on each side of the body with 2 to 5 broad internal longitudinal vessels on the apex of the folds; none between the folds. The stigmata form infundibula in each fold. The gut forms a long, narrow, closed loop, bent to lie horizontally along the ventral surface. The left gonad is in the rather wide and open angle of the secondary gut loop and the right gonad lies vertically anterior and dorsal to the kidney. The gonads are very broad and characteristic: Distally pyriform testis follicles form a complete circle, their apex to the center and against the body wall, where short seminal ducts join to form the vas deferens which extends on to the mesial surface of the flask-shaped ovary and short broad oviduct, where it runs an extremely convoluted course. The oviduct terminates in a wide opening directed dorsally. However, the sperm duct extends for some distance, and, although sometimes is directed to the atrial opening, it is often turned in a complete semicircle anteriorly and ventrally on the left, or posteriorly and ventrally on the right. The kidney is curved and in the postero-ventral corner of the body.

The peribranchial cavity is often filled with embryos.

Larvae. Have anterolateral rows of large rounded ampullae but no suckers or papillae. They are tailed and have an otolith but no ocellus.

Remarks. The gonads and seminal ducts of this species are quite distinctive. *M. confluxa* has similarly shaped gonads, but the vas deferens is not convoluted and the right gonad is against the whole dorsal border of the kidney.

Molgula confluxa (Sluiter)

Text fig. 208

Caesira enodis Sluiter, 1912, p. 452; 1914, p. 4.
Microcosmus confluxa Sluiter, 1912, p. 454.
Caesira confluxa Sluiter, 1914, p. 6.
Molgula amokurae Bovien, 1922, p. 35.
? *Ctenicella mortenseni* Michaelsen, 1922, p. 366.—
    Brewin, 1958, p. 440.
Molgula confluxa; Van Name, 1945, p. 412.

New Records. Antarctic Peninsula: *Edisto* Sta. 189[23] (64 meters), Sta. 226[23] (74 meters), Sta. 234[23] (74 meters); *Staten Island* Sta. 67/63 (38 meters).

Previous Records.

Antarctic: South Shetland Is. [Sluiter, 1912]; Antarctic Peninsula [Sluiter, 1912].

Subantarctic: Auckland I., New Zealand [Bovien, 1922]; ? Stewart I., New Zealand [Michaelsen, 1922].

---

[23] U.S. Navy Antarctic Expedition, 1947–1948.

Distribution. Three specimens of *M. amokurae* were available, but it is not known how common the closely related *M. mortenseni* is. It is possible that the lack of records for this widespread species is due to its inconspicuous form and that its distribution is wider in the Antarctic, as well as the Subantarctic, as is true for so many species of this family. Depth range is from 18 to 75 meters.

Description. Spherical, oval; 0.6 and 1.7 cm, respectively. Both siphons short, wide, and one-third of the body circumference apart on the dorsal or upper surface. Apertures are rather indistinctly lobed. Test is thin but coriaceous and tough. Papillae and hairs with minute branches along their length closely placed on the outer surface. Body wall is thin with longitudinal muscles radiating from the siphons, but musculature is otherwise diffuse. About 30 branchial tentacles of two sizes, only slightly branched. Aperture of dorsal tubercle S-shaped or a simple crescent turned to the left. Dorsal lamina is wide, with irregular tongues or teeth posteriorly. There are 6 branchial folds on each side of the body with a maximum of 5 to 7 internal longitudinal vessels on the folds. The two most dorsal folds on the left terminate dorsally at the dorsal lamina. The internal longitudinal vessels of each fold tend to coalesce into a single vessel some distance before the posterior end of the branchial sac. The gut forms a long narrow and curved loop with the left gonad in the secondary loop. The right gonad is close to the kidney on its concave dorsal surface; the breadth of the gonad is parallel or at a slight angle to the long axis of the kidney. The broader-than-long gonads consist of a broad distal arc of pyriform testis follicles, around the end of the broad ovary. The vas deferens extends from a point on the body wall at the apices of the testis follicles on to the mesial surface of the ovary, where it may extend for a short distance to open on top of the oviduct; it may turn posteriorly and ventrally. The oviduct is especially broad and short with a wide opening directed anteriorly toward the branchial rather than the atrial opening. The kidney is along the ventral border against the endostyle.

Remarks. Although this species bears a superficial resemblance to *M. pulchra*, the specimen available in the present collection (although much smaller than the type) confirms the characters of the type species by which the species is clearly distinguished from *M. pulchra*: The siphons are farther apart and the apertures only indistinctly lobed; the dorsal lamina is longer; the testis follicles form an arc embracing the end of the ovary rather than a circle of lobes at the end; the end of the gonad on the right is embraced by the curve of the kidney, whereas in *M. pulchra* the whole gonad is anterior and dorsal to the anterior horn of the kidney; the vas deferens is short and not convoluted; the tendency of longitudinal vessels to coalesce at the posterior end of the fold occurs to a marked extent in the present species.

Van Name [1945, fig. 302] erroneously reproduced Sluiter's figure of *C. enodis* as representing Sluiter's type of *M. confluxa*. However, the figure does represent the same species, as *C. enodis* Sluiter is clearly a synonym of *M. confluxa*. *M. mortenseni* (Michaelsen) agrees with the type specimen in all characters and agrees with the present specimens except for the absence of test hairs. These hairs may have previously been obscured by sand, and *M. mortenseni* may also be a synonym of the present species.

The species is closely related to *M. sluiteri*; however, the oviduct in *M. sluiteri* is directed ventrally across the top of the gut loop on the left and is longer. It is possible that further collecting will demonstrate a variation in the length of the oviduct and perhaps with increasing maturity a longer oviduct of the *M. sluiteri* type may be inclined antero-ventrally. Both *M. confluxa* and *M. sluiteri* types of oviduct have been described from New Zealand [Michaelsen, 1922: *C. mortenseni* and *M. sluiteri*, respectively].

The position of the gonads resembles that of *M. cryptica* Millar, 1962, from South Africa; however, *M. cryptica* has distinctive branchial sac and body shape.

Molgula sluiteri (Michaelsen)

Text fig. 209

Molgula martensi; Sluiter, 1900, p. 32 [not *M. martensii* Traustedt, 1885].

Ctenicella sluiteri Michaelsen, 1922, p. 373.

Molgula sluiteri; Brewin 1950, p. 61.—Kott, 1954, p. 136.

New Records. Macquarie I.: *Eltanin* Sta. 1418 (86–101 meters).

Previous Records.

Subantarctic: Macquarie I. [Kott, 1954]; Chatham I. [Sluiter, 1900].

Elsewhere: New Zealand: Otago, Stewart Island [Brewin, 1950a]; Foveaux Strait [Michaelsen, 1922].

Distribution. Confined to the New Zealand-Macquarie Island area from the intertidal region to 69 meters. Unless the relationship to *M. confluxa* discussed above is found to be intraspecific, this distribution is one of the most limited known for a species of the Molgulidae in the subantarctic area. It is most likely a New Zealand species, Macquarie Island representing the limits of its range.

Description. Solitary or numerous individuals adherent together in clumps. Body more or less spherical and dorso-ventrally flattened or upright specimens, respectively. Maximum dimension 1 to 2.2 cm high. Both apertures on the upper surface on short siphons fairly close together. The dorsal surface is flattened or depressed into the body. The branchial aperture is mid-dorsal with 6 lobes; the atrial aperture toward the posterior border. The color of the test is yellow with purple lining the siphons [Brewin, 1950]. The test is thin but tough and leathery with a coating of sand over the whole external surface, excluding the siphons. The body wall has strong outer circular muscles and radiating longitudinal bands in the upper half of the body only. There are 10 to 18 larger branchial tentacles, branched twice, alternating with smaller ones with primary pinnate branches only. The dorsal tubercle opening is either a transverse slit or an upright or recumbent S. The dorsal lamina is a very broad membrane, continuous to the right of the esophageal opening. There are irregular tongues or teeth toward the posterior end of the dorsal lamina. There are 6 or 7 branchial folds on either side of the body with a maximum of 4 internal longitudinal vessels accumulated at the summit or on the ventral surface of the folds. No internal longitudinal branchial vessels have been recorded from between the folds. Regular spiral infundibula present in the folds, but the stigmata between the folds are shorter, curved or straight. In larger specimens spirals also occur between the folds [Brewin, 1950]. The gut forms a narrow closed loop, curved to form a secondary loop enclosing the gonad on the left side. On the right the gonad is against the anterior concave border of the gently curved kidney, which lies almost dorso-ventrally across the posterior end of the body. An arc of pyriform testis follicles embraces the end or dorsal side of the short, broad ovary, from which the oviduct is directed ventrally. The vas deferens, from the apices of the testis lobes in the center of their arc extends dorsally to open near the anus at the base of the atrial siphon.

Remarks. As discussed above, this species is distinguished from *M. confluxa* by the orientation of the longer oviduct and ovary toward the ventral border of the body and by the slightly fewer internal longitudinal vessels on the folds. The dorsal lamina, dorsal tubercle, and position of the gonads in relation to the kidney are all similar. Neither Michaelsen [1922] nor Brewin [1950] has described the course of the male duct. Both have described the ovaries as long, thin structures, but Brewin's fig. 4 [1950, p. 61], made from specimens with larvae in the peribranchial cavity, shows that the oviduct is filled with eggs, thus increasing the apparent length of the ovary. The partial evacuation of the ovary itself has reduced its diameter. The swollen oviduct thus gives the appearance of a long continuous ovary. A similar condition is probably represented by Michaelsen's fig. 3 [1922, p. 375].

Molgula euplicata Herdman

Text fig. 210

Molgula lutulenta Herdman, 1923, p. 14. [Not *Caesira lutulenta* Van Name, 1912, p. 468; or *Molgula lutulenta* Van Name, 1945, p. 397.]
Molgula euplicata Herdman, 1923, p. 15.—Kott, 1954, p. 132.

New Records. Antarctic Peninsula: *Staten Island* Sta. 32/63 (46 meters), Sta. 37/63 (49 meters).

Previous Records.
 Antarctic: Enderby Land, Mac. Robertson Land [Kott, 1954]; Adélie Coast, Wilkes Land [Herdman, 1923].

Distribution. Probably a circum-antarctic shelf species; maximum depth 200 meters.

Description. Oval to spherical and up to 5 cm in diameter. Both apertures are sessile, and about one-fourth the body circumference apart. The test is thin and tough, produced externally into a 'feltwork' of fine hairs with mud or sand and shell fragments adhering. The body wall is muscular, thick, and closely adherent to the test, with strong muscle bands radiating from the base of the siphons and a layer of outer circular muscle fibers. There are 12 short and thick branchial tentacles with primary branches but very few and short secondary branches. These alternate with rudimentary tentacles. The peritubercular area is large, with a comparatively small tubercle with a simple longitudinal slit; the anterior end or both ends sometimes turned over to the right, both ends forming a wide C-shape directed laterally, postero-laterally, or antero-laterally. The dorsal lamina is fairly short with a crenate or lobed margin. There are 7 to 9 branchial folds on each side of the body with 6 to 13 internal longitudinal vessels on the larger folds. Between the folds internal longitudinal vessels are often absent, but there are sometimes as many as 3. Stigmata form spiral infundibula in the folds but between the folds

they are very short and irregular. Primary transverse vessels are wide and parastigmatic vessels irregular. The gut loop is long, narrow, closed, and curved to form a deep but open secondary loop. The ovaries, one on each side of the body, are very wide and shallow. On the left they occupy the secondary gut loop curving ventrally over the pole of the first loop; on the right the end of the ovary extends along the length of the long narrow kidney, which lies ventrally along the antero-posterior axis of the body. A short broad oviduct extends from the mid-dorsal border of the ovary. Testis follicles are scattered over the surface of the ovaries in clumps, and each clump of testis lobes has its own short duct, sometimes turned ventrally.

Remarks. This species is distinguished by the closely placed test hairs, the highly muscular body wall, the large peritubercular area and small simple tubercular opening, the crenulated margin of the dorsal lamina, the irregularity of the stigmata, and the disposition and shape of the gonads and their ducts.

Molgula kerguelenensis Kott

Text fig. 211

Molgula kerguelenensis Kott, 1954, p. 137.

New Records. None.

Previous Records.
 Subantarctic: Kerguelen Is., 4 to 45 meters [Kott, 1954].

Distribution. This species is apparently endemic and isolated in fairly shallow waters around Kerguelen Islands, in 4 to 45 meters.

Description. More or less circular, laterally compressed and 1.5 cm in diameter. The test is smooth and gelatinous. The siphons are fairly short, the branchial longer than the atrial, separated by about one-fifth the body diameter. The body wall has radiating longitudinal bands and outer circular muscles, particularly around the base of the siphons. The branchial tentacles are twice pinnate of two sizes. Rudimentary tentacles alternate with these larger ones. Dorsal tubercle is large, completely filling the peritubercular area, and the opening is an E-shaped slit directed to the right and posteriorly. The dorsal lamina is a plain broad-edged membrane. There are 7 thick high folds on each side of the body with about 12 internal longitudinal vessels on the folds, but none between them. Stigmata form spiral infundibula in the folds. The gut loop is narrow and gently curved, forming only a shallow secondary loop. The gonads are long, curving around against the descending arm of

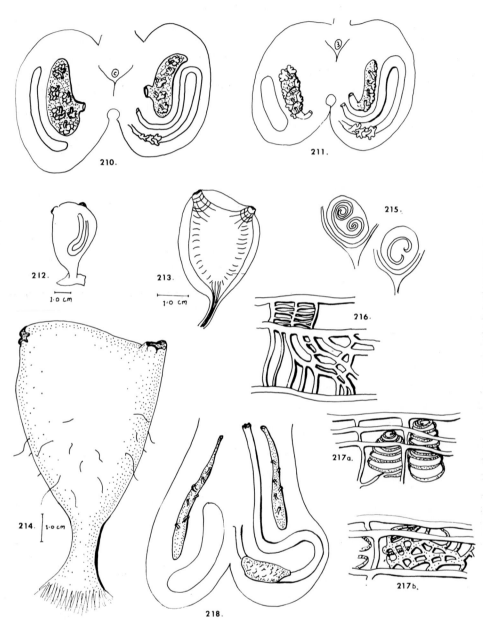

Molgula euplicata

210. Inner body wall showing gut, gonads, and kidney.

Molgula kerguelenensis

211. Inner body wall showing gut, gonads, and kidney.

Molgula gigantea

212. Young specimen showing gut loop.

213. Young specimen showing muscles.
214. External appearance of older specimen.
215. Dorsal tubercles.
216. Portion of branchial sac between folds.
217. Branchial sac in summit of folds: (a) Younger specimen; (b) older specimen.
218. Inner body wall.

the intestinal loop on the left and on the right lying parallel and adjacent to the dorsal border of the long, gently curved kidney in the postero-ventral corner of the body. Pyriform testis follicles fringe the ovary on one or both sides. Their ducts extend across the surface of the ovary, meet a corresponding duct from the other side, and open immediately by a series of independent openings along the surface of the ovary.

Remarks. This rare species resembles *M. euplicata* in the multiplicity of vas deferens openings. However, the shape of the gonads and the nature of the test differ. The gonads also resemble the Australian-Indonesian species *M. calvata* Sluiter [see Kott, 1964], but the branchial sac of *M. calvata* has far fewer internal longitudinal vessels.

Molgula gigantea Herdman

Text figs. 212–218

Ascopera gigantea Herdman, 1881, p. 238; 1882, p. 62.—Hartmeyer, 1909–1911, p. 1328; 1911, p. 421.—Ärnbäck, 1938, p. 19.—Van Name, 1945, p. 426.—Millar, 1960, p. 138.

Ascopera pedunculata Herdman, 1881, p. 239; 1882, p. 65.—Hartmeyer, 1909–1911, p. 1328.—Ärnbäck, 1938, p. 20.

Ascopera bouvetensis Michaelsen, 1904, p. 188.—Hartmeyer, 1911, p. 424.

Caesira bacca; Hartmeyer, 1909–1911, p. 1739; 1911, p. 414.

Molgula bacca Herdman, 1910, p. 13.—Ärnbäck, 1938, p. 12.—Van Name, 1945, p. 411.—Millar, 1960, p. 134.

Molgula longicaulis Herdman, 1910, p. 14; 1923, p. 11.

New Records. Knox Coast: *Glacier* Sta. 1 (120 meters). Antarctic Peninsula: *Edisto* Sta. 28, TR 14 (129 meters); *Staten Island* Sta. 5/63 (48 meters), Sta. 6/63 (7 meters), Sta. 32/63 (46 meters), Sta. 67/63 (38 meters). South Shetland Is.: *Eltanin* Sta. 410 (240 meters), Sta. 435 (73 meters), Sta. 436 (73 meters) Sta. 732 (265 meters). South Orkney Is. ?: *Eltanin* Sta. 1081 (631–641 meters).

Previous Records.

Antarctic: McMurdo Sound [Herdman, 1910, 1923]; Wilhelm II Coast [Hartmeyer, 1911]; Antarctic Peninsula, South Shetland Is. [Ärnbäck, 1938; Millar, 1960]; South Georgia [Ärnbäck, 1938; Millar, 1960]; South Sandwich Is. [Millar, 1960]; Bouvet I. [Michaelsen, 1904].

Subantarctic: South of Kerguelen Is. [Herdman, 1882].

Distribution. This species is recorded from all around the antarctic continental shelf, and its occurrence in the Kerguelen region may be explained by its extension along the Kerguelen Plateau. The species must, however, be considered as typically antarctic, and its extension to the Kerguelen Islands probably represents the most northern extent of its range. It is surprising that it does not also extend along the Scotia Ridge to the Falkland Islands area, particularly as it is plentiful around South Georgia and the South Sandwich Islands. It has been taken in from 25 meters to about 668 meters. As it is large and conspicuous and unlikely to be overlooked, it probably does not extend very much deeper.

Description. Sometimes oval to globular without a stalk, but usually more or less triangular and laterally flattened with a contractile stalk of variable length from the apex of the triangle. The length of the stalk rarely exceeds the length of the body. Basally the stalk is fringed by a feltwork of fine hairlike rootlets. Apertures anteriorly at each corner of the upper surface. The branchial aperture with 5 shallow lobes is sessile and directed laterally, whereas the 4-lobed atrial aperture is on a short, wide, anteriorly directed siphon, with 4 shallow longitudinal furrows corresponding to the lobes around the aperture. The test of older specimens is thin and flaccid but tough and semitransparent, or brown and almost opaque. In younger specimens the test is firmer, glassy, and completely transparent. The test is always firm in the region of the apertures. Evenly distributed papillae or tubercles or fine filamentous hairs present on the surface of the test. The hairs tend to be lost in older specimens. Some preserved specimens are faintly tinged with green. The smallest specimens (about 1.0 cm long) have previously been described as *M. bacca*, and there is a gradation of characters to the *M. gigantea* condition in individuals up to 20 cm in length. The body wall is thin and delicate with short transverse muscle bands around each side of the endostyle. These bands are interrupted by the kidney on the right and by the gut on the left. The muscles from the posterior part of the body continue along the portion of body wall that extends into the stalk.

There are about 12 very bushy tentacles of varying sizes. The dorsal tubercle is large with a U-shaped slit with the opening directed to the left, either anteriorly or posteriorly. The horns turn or spiral inward. The dorsal lamina is a short but wide membrane.

The branchial sac has 7 high folds on each side of the body, with from 7 to 18 internal longitudinal vessels on the folds and up to 11 between the folds. Stigmata increase in complexity with the age of the individual, and sometimes quite regular meshes with 5 to 8 stigmata and parastigmatic vessels may occur in parts of the branchial sac and some regular conical infundibula extend into or almost into the apex of the folds. With age, however, the transverse vessels subdivide and branch irregularly and the branchial sac is broken up into irregular meshes with short irregular stigmata. In larger specimens especially not all the branchial sac is perforated by stigmata and areas of plain membrane occur. On the left side of the body the gut forms a closed narrow loop, open at the pole, which is bent at right angles across the posterior end of the body. The stomach is obscured by compact liver lobes. The anus is fringed by small rounded lobes. On the left a very long kidney curves around the postero-dorsal border of the body. The kidney is 7 mm long in an individual 1.5 cm tall, and specimens of 6 cm in the present collection had kidneys up to 14 mm long. Single long thin gonads on each side of the body extend longitudinally from the concavity of the kidney and gut loop, respectively. A portion of the left gonad occasionally projects into the open part of the pole of the gut loop. Gonads consist of a long tubular ovary surrounded by testis follicles with numerous (6 to 15) male ducts opening over the entire surface of the ovary. In smaller specimens gonads may be completely absent and often the male glands are not developed.

Remarks. The synonymy indicated above was arrived at by a careful survey of species characteristics in relation to zooid size. The elaboration of the branchial sac and the number of longitudinal vessels particularly between the folds both steadily increase with the size of the individual. The stalk length is variable and does not constitute a specific character [Millar, 1960]. Larger specimens, together with the increasing flaccidity of the test, tend to be more triangular than globular or oval.

The long narrow kidney and long narrow gut loop, flexed at right angles only at the pole, and the arrangement of the muscles, together with the long narrow gonoducts with multiple vas deferens openings, constitute the characteristics of the species.

There seems no justification for the genus *Ascopera* as distinct from *Molgula*, since, although spiral infundibula are not present between the folds or even in the base of the folds, the younger specimens examined clearly have spiral infundibula in the folds. Similarly, Herdman (despite his definition of *Ascopera*

as lacking spirals) describes for *A. gigantea* infundibula in the folds. These are also described for *M. bacca* [Hartmeyer, 1911; Herdman, 1910]. Spiral infundibula are therefore generally present in younger specimens (previously described as *M. bacca*) and often also in larger specimens. The branchial sac, thought to characterize the genus *Ascopera*, merely represents elaborations of a typically molgulid branchial sac, which, in this species, occurs with age. Owing to their large size and complicated branchial development, there is every reason to believe that the individuals of this species live to a comparatively great age, as has been suggested for other species of this family. *Molgula longicaulis* Herdman, 1910, appears to be identical with the present species, and both Herdman [1923] and Hartmeyer [1911] have suggested the relationship.

Genus *Molguloides* Huntsman, 1922

Type species: *Caesira immunda* Hartmeyer, 1909–1911

Similar to *Molgula* with branchial folds and spiral stigmata; however, the left gonad is inside the primary gut loop.

The genus is rare. The two species recorded from Antarctica also occur in the tropical west Pacific. Only two other species have been recorded, from Japan [Huntsman, 1922].

KEY TO ANTARCTIC SPECIES OF *Molguloides*

Stigmata form flat spirals in the branchial sac. . . . .
. . . . **immunda,** p. 156
(South Shetland Is., Chile, New Guinea, Kermadec Trench)
Spirals form infundibula projecting into the folds. . . . .
. . . . **vitrea,** p. 159
(Enderby Land, Indonesia, Philippine Is.)

Molguloides immunda (Hartmeyer)

Text figs. 219–221

Caesira immunda Hartmeyer, 1909–1911, p. 1324, footnote; 1912, pp. 245, 374, 378.

Molgula sordida Sluiter, 1904, p. 118 [not *M. sordida* Stimpson (< *M. manhattensis*, vide Van Name, 1945, p. 425)]

Molgula (Molguloides) immunda; Van Name, 1945, p. 425.

Molgula immunda f. *monocarpa* Millar, 1959, p. 201.

New Records. Off Valparaiso, Chile: *Eltanin* Sta. 87 (5929 meters). South Shetland Is.: *Eltanin* Sta. 439 (165 meters), ? Sta. 991 (2672–3020 meters). Knox Coast: *Edisto* Sta. 44[24] (184 meters).

----
[24] U.S. Navy Antarctic Expedition, 1947–1948.

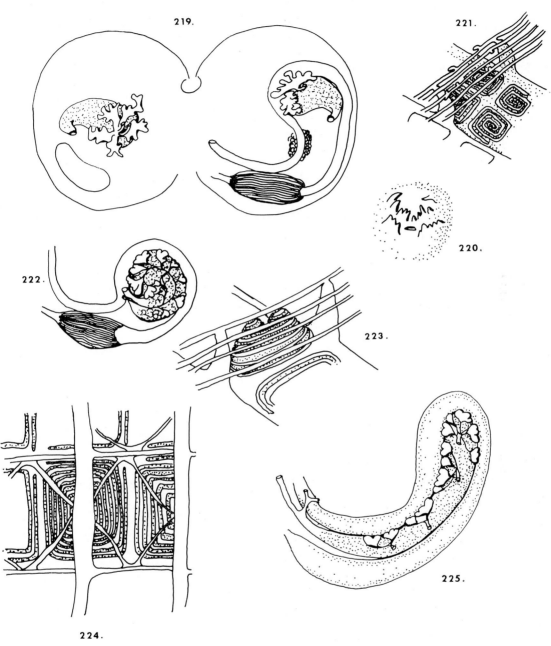

Molguloides immunda
219. Inner body wall.
220. Papillae around branchial opening.
221. Portion of branchial sac.

Molguloides vitrea
222. Inner body wall on left.
223. Portion of branchial sac.

Eugyra kerguelenensis
224. Portion of branchial sac.
225. Left gonad in gut loop.

Previous Records. Off Chile: 20°29′S, 103°26′W [Van Name, 1945]. South of New Guinea: 05°46′S, 134°00′E [Sluiter, 1904]. Kermadec Trench [Millar, 1959].

Distribution. This smooth and inconspicuous species may have a very wide distribution in the deeper temperature and tropical waters of the world, as specimens have been taken off Chile and in the South Shetland Islands since Sluiter originally described the species from Indonesia (south of New Guinea in the Arafura Sea). The specimen from the Knox Coast in 184 meters indicates that the species also occurs off the antarctic continent. The depth distribution suggests 'tropical submergence,': a species adapted to lower temperatures in southern seas surviving in lower latitudes but at greater depths [Sverdrup et al., 1942, p. 849]. Depth range is from 165 to 5929 meters.

Molguloides vitrea (Sluiter) has a similar distribution, but also occurs in shallower waters in the tropics. There may, therefore, be some other explanation for the distribution of both these species.

Description. Small spherical or oval species. Maximum size 1.7 cm. The test covered with hairlike filaments that may be longer posteriorly. Sometimes sand particles adhere to the hairs. The test is thin but tough and semitransparent. It is thickened posteriorly. Sessile apertures present at opposite ends of the dorsal aspect of the body. Stout pointed fingerlike hollow extensions of the test are sometimes developed around the dorsal aspect of the branchial aperture. These are arranged in two more or less concentric circles and may be simple, forked, or several may arise from an elongate common base. In the inner circle the number of projections varies from 4 or 5 up to about 15; and in the outer circle they are sometimes reduced to 2 rudimentary processes. In many specimens hollow extensions of the test around the apertures remain rudimentary. The body wall is thin with longitudinal muscle bands extending into the base of the tentacular ring. These bands are more sparse ventrally. Extensions of the body wall extend into the hollow tentacular projections of the test from the margin of the branchial siphon. About 15 branchial tentacles with only primary branches alternate with smaller sometimes unbranched tentacles. The dorsal tubercle is a small papilla with a simple longitudinal slit at the base of a deep V-shaped peritubercular area extending halfway down the dorsal surface of the body. The neural gland and ganglion are adjacent to the dorsal tubercle. The dorsal lamina is plain. The branchial sac has 6 to 8 branchial folds on each side of the body, each fold

formed by up to 10 internal longitudinal vessels, supported by extensions from the transverse vessel. Short transverse vessels confined to the folds help to hold the longitudinal vessels together. These usually consist of a median or parastigmatic vessel and two intermediate vessels between each pair of primary transverse vessels.

In the large specimens (1.5 cm) from *Eltanin* Sta. 87 (off Valparaiso) these connectives are not present although papillae are present along the internal longitudinal vessels. The stigmata are regularly arranged flat double spirals of 6 to 7 coils in a single row under the folds but not extending up into folds at all. Smaller specimens from *Eltanin* Sta. 439, and those mentioned by Van Name [1945] have single coils between successive transverse vessels. Both in Sluiter's [1904] account and in the present specimens from Valparaiso, however, the arrangement of coils is less regular: In the present specimens there are two and sometimes accessory spirals in each mesh; in Sluiter's description the number of spirals is not given but the arrangement of connectives along the folds indicate that there are at least two spirals between each mesh. The gut forms a fairly short open loop enclosing the gonad on the left, and the distal part of the intestine is especially long. The stomach is marked by longitudinal glandular plications. The kidney is fairly long, postero-ventral, and closely applied to the endostyle and stomach. The gonad on the right is dorsal to the kidney.

The form and orientation of the gonads show some variation. The testis follicles are clustered around the proximal end of the circular to claviform ovary. The male ducts join on the mesial surface of the ovary and immediately open by 1 or 2 openings. The terminal part of the ovary with oviducal opening is always directed toward the atrial aperture. Where the ovary is longer, however, the proximal end, surrounded by testis follicles, is directed dorsally and the whole gonad has a dorso-ventral orientation, whereas the oviduct and adjacent part of the ovary turns posteriorly and dorsally. In Millar's [1959] specimens the gonad on the left is absent.

Remarks. Variations in the small number of this species taken to date make the taxonomy very confusing. Although the gonad, gut, test, body form, and probably the branchial sac of the present specimens from the Chilean coast agree entirely with Sluiter's type from Indonesia (1.5 and 1.7 cm, respectively), the branchial sac differs from that of Van Name's specimens from the Chilean coast. As indicated above, this difference is probably due to growth, as the elaboration and loss of regularity of stigmata coils is generally associated with growth in other genera of this family. The small (0.6 cm) specimen from the South Shetland Islands in the present collection has a branchial sac identical with that described by Van Name from Chile, although the gonads are differently oriented and are a different shape, but this is due to different stages of maturity of the ovary. In *Molguloides vitrea*, a close relative from Enderby Land and Indonesia, the same variation in gonads has been observed.

Molguloides vitrea (Sluiter)

Text figs. 222, 223

Molgula vitrea Sluiter, 1904, p. 119.—Van Name, 1918, p. 68.
Caesira vitrea; Hartmeyer, 1909–1911, p. 1324.
Caesira bathybia Hartmeyer, 1912, p. 240.
Molguloides tenuis Kott, 1954, p. 138.
Molgula immunda; Millar, 1959, p. 200.

New Records. None.

Previous Records.

Enderby Land and Mac. Robertson Land [Hartmeyer, 1912; Kott, 1954]; Indonesia [Sluiter, 1904; Millar, 1959]; Philippines Is. [Van Name, 1918].

Distribution. This species, known from 3 specimens off Enderby Land, 4 specimens off Indonesia, and 5 specimens from the Philippine Islands, shares the first two localities with *M. immunda*. However, *M. vitrea* is taken from deeper waters in Antarctica than in the tropics, which is the reverse of the situation for *M. immunda*. Depth range is from 397 to 4636 meters.

Description. Rounded and laterally flattened or stalked. The stalk arising from one side of the body, not in the median line. Maximum size 3.5 cm. The test is whitish, almost gelatinous, semitransparent, but tough and is covered externally with hairs or taglike excrescences, especially on the stalk or posteriorly. The apertures are well separated anteriorly. The body wall has well developed longitudinal bands radiating from the siphons. Either 6 or 7 extensions from the branchial siphon and 4 extensions from the atrial siphon fit into pockets in the test. About 8 twice-pinnate branchial tentacles of varying sizes alternate with rudimentary ones. The dorsal tubercle has a conspicuous oblique slit, and the branchial sac has 7 or 8 folds on each side with 8 to 16 internal longitudinal vessels on each fold. Stigmata form funnel-shaped infundibula, which extend into the folds, sometimes breaking into two at the apex. The gut forms a long closed loop enclosing the gonad. The stomach is

spindle-shaped with longitudinal glandular plications (Hartmeyer's specimen had lost this part of the gut loop). The kidney is close to the endostyle and first limb of the gut loop. The gonads vary. In Hartmeyer's specimen they are rounded and, although it has not been described, the testis probably surrounds the proximal end of the ovary and opens on the mesial surface. In Kott's specimens the gonads spiral, clockwise on the left and anticlockwise on the right, so that ducts are directed toward the atrial opening. The testis lobes surround the ovary. These ducts join on the mesial surface to form many separate openings along the surface of the ovary.

Remarks. These specimens, of a similar range, resemble one another and differ from *M. immunda* primarily in the extension of stigmata coils into infundibula in the folds. They are also distinguished from *M. immuda* by the nature of the test with 'tag-like excrescences' and the depth of the peritubercular area. The variations in form of the gonads are interesting, and it appears that increasing growth of the ovary occurs from the distal end to form a spiral. This spiral has also been observed in *M. immunda* and in neither case is it thought to constitute a distinguishing character.

Genus *Eugyra* Alder and Hancock, 1870

Type species: *Cynthia glutinans* Moeller, 1842

Branchial sac without folds; 5 to 7 large widely spaced internal longitudinal vessels on each side crossed by 5 transverse vessels. Stigmata form regular double spirals forming conical infundibula under the longitudinal vessels. Single gonad on the left or one on each side; the gonad on left side entirely or partially in the primary gut loop.

Eugyra kerguelenensis Herdman

Text fig. 224, 225

Eugyra kerguelenensis Herdman, 1881, p. 237; 1882, p. 81.—Hartmeyer, 1922, p. 139.—Van Name, 1945, p. 435.—Kott, 1954, p. 319.—Millar, 1960, p. 142.
Paramolgula guttula Michaelsen, 1900, p. 135; 1907, p. 81.
Eugyrioides antarctica Hartmeyer, 1909–1911, p. 1321 [nomen nudum]; 1912, p. 231.
Eugyrioides guttula; Hartmeyer, 1909–1911, p. 1321; 1912, pp. 236, 239.
? *Eugyra guttula* Michaelsen, 1915, p. 350.

New Records. Antarctic Peninsula: *Staten Island* Sta. 67/63 (38 meters). South Shetland Islands: *Eltanin*

Sta. 997 (769 meters). Bellingshausen Sea: *Edisto* Sta. 146[25] (56 meters).

Previous Records.

  Antarctic: South Georgia [Millar, 1960].

  Subantarctic: Kerguelen Is. [Herdman, 1881, 1882; Hartmeyer, 1912, 1922; Kott, 1954]. Patagonian Shelf [Michaelsen, 1900; Van Name, 1945; Millar, 1960].

Distribution. Circum-subantarctic and extending into the antarctic area along the Scotia Ridge. As with other subantarctic species with a circumpolar distribution in comparatively shallow waters, the localities from which the present species has been recorded are widely isolated from one another. The depth range is from 10 to 769 meters.

Description. Rounded body, globular, ovate, or elliptical; maximum length 2 cm. Surface covered with moderately long unbranched hairs to which mud and sand adhere. The density of these hairs varies. Both apertures anteriorly, close together, are on low siphons in a flattened depressed area, surrounded by the raised rim of the test when siphons are retracted. Test is transparent, thin, but tough. The body wall is thin, with longitudinal muscle bands radiating from the siphons, circular bands around the siphons, and posterior to these narrow bands of transverse fibers across the ventral and dorsal borders of the body. There are 10 to 13 branchial tentacles of varying sizes with short primary and minute secondary branches. These alternate with smaller rudimentary tentacles. The dorsal tubercle slit on a small inconspicuous papilla on the left of the peritubercular area varies from crescentic, C-shaped, to almost circular. The dorsal lamina is short, wide, and smooth-edged. In the branchial sac the stigmata form open regular longitudinal rows of double spiral coils, 6 in the most dorsal row and 12 in the most ventral row. Each coil has 6 to 7 turns, and no intermediate coils have been observed. A single internal longitudinal vessel extends along the center of each row of coils except the most dorsal. There is a smooth area of unperforated membrane along each side of the endostyle. The gut forms a narrow gently curved open loop. The stomach is oval to elliptical with longitudinal glandular plications. The gonads are long, parallel, and adjacent to the dorsal border of the kidney on the right and contained in the primary gut loop on the left. The central tubular ovary with its duct directed toward the atrial aperture is surrounded around the proximal end and along one or both sides

by pyriform testis follicles, which open by many (5 or 6) separate short ducts along the mesial surface of the ovary. The oviduct may be considerably branched distally, forming several openings. The kidney is long and gently curved around the postero-ventral border of the right side.

Remarks. This is one of the most uniform species known from the area. The condition of the branchial sac is particularly stable, and the greatest variations observed occur in the distribution of testis lobes around the ovary. Despite records from the Patagonian Shelf and the isolated Kerguelen Islands area, the species has not been recorded from the subantarctic islands, as would be expected if the distribution is completely circumpolar. *Eugyra myodes* Millar, 1962, is a closely related but distinct species from South Africa.

Genus *Pareugyrioides* Hartmeyer, 1914

Type species: *Eugyrioides dalli* Ritter, 1913

Branchial sac without folds. Internal longitudinal vessels present. Radial vessels across spiral infundibula are numerous. The left gonad not enclosed in the primary gut loop.

Hartmeyer [1914] characterized the genus by the extent to which the stigmata, spiralling in the infundibula, were interrupted. Interruption of the stigmata also occurs, however, in *Eugyra* spp. and does not constitute a character sufficient to separate the genera. The stomach wall, thrown up into irregular convolutions, diverticula, and rounded pockets presents a condition often found in *Pareugyrioides*. However, *P. galatheae* has longitudinal glandular lamellae on the stomach wall and consequently this character cannot be considered typical. In all species known at present the position of the left gonad and the multiplicity of radial vessels across the infundibula, together with the absence of branchial folds, is constant and may be considered characteristic of this genus.

Apart from the type species from Alaska, the only known species are from Antarctica. (*P. japonica* Hartmeyer, 1914, is a species of the genus *Eugyra*.)

KEY TO ANTARCTIC SPECIES OF *Pareugyrioides*

1. Stomach with rounded pockets and diverticula......... 2
   Stomach with longitudinal glandular lamellae..........
   ....*galatheae*, p. 161
             (southeast Atlantic, South Pacific; abyssal)
2. Stalked ....*arnbackae*, p. 161
                                      (circum-antarctic)
   Not stalked.............................*filholi*, p. 163
                              (Macquarie I., Stewart I.)

---

[25] U.S. Navy Antarctic Expedition, 1947–1948.

Pareugyrioides galatheae (Millar)

Text figs. 226, 227

Molgula galatheae Millar, 1959, p. 202.

New Record. Southeast Pacific Basin: *Eltanin* Sta. 1140 (4731 meters).

Previous Records.

Elsewhere: Off West Africa (Guinea Basin), 2550–5160 meters [Millar, 1959].

Distribution. A cosmopolitan distribution in the deeper waters of the Atlantic and Pacific is suggested by these records.

Description. Ovoid body up to 2 cm in greatest diameter. The test is soft and semitransparent, with fine, hairlike processes, especially long posteriorly, forming a beard. Apertures are wide apart, almost at opposite ends of the upper surface, almost sessile, and set in an area of slightly thicker and firmer test. The borders of the apertures are raised into small papillae. The body wall is thin with slender inner longitudinal and outer circular muscle bands around the siphons and across the dorsal surface. Muscles are absent from the ventral part of the body. There are 6 to 8 large branchial tentacles with primary, secondary, and sometimes tertiary branches. These alternate with smaller tentacles. Tentacles on the dorsal side of the opening are joined basally by a thin fold or velum. The dorsal tubercle has a simple opening. The dorsal lamina is a plain-edged double membrane. In the branchial sac there are 5 wide internal longitudinal vessels on either side, and 5 wide transverse vessels separate single rows of spiral infundibula. Each infundibulum is a flat weblike spiral of about 15 turns beneath each longitudinal vessel and crossed by about 8 radial vessels in each quarter. There are usually extra infundibula between the endostyle and the next internal longitudinal vessel. There are small papillae on the radial vessels.

The gut forms a short simple loop, open at the pole, in the posterior part of the body. The rectum is wide and turns anteriorly toward the atrial opening. The anal border is plain. The stomach has longitudinal glandular plications that are especially deep and apparent externally at the wide cardiac end of the stomach. There is a single gonad on either side of the body consisting of wide flask-shaped ovary surrounded distally by an arc of testis follicles, which sometimes overgrow the whole mesial surface of the ovary. The ovary opens by a short oviduct directed dorsally, and testis ducts join on the mesial surface of the ovary to form a short vas deferens. The left gonad is anterior to the gut loop. The proximal end of the right gonad lies against and overlies, to varying extents, the curved dorsal border of the kidney.

Remarks. The longitudinal glandular plications separate this species from others in the genus, although they are present in other genera of the Molgulidae and especially among closely related *Eugyra* spp. The papillae present on the radial vessels and the number of internal longitudinal vessels are also distinguishing characters.

Pareugyrioides arnbackae (Millar)

Text figs. 228, 229

Eugyra ärnbäckae Millar, 1960, p. 144.

New Records. Robertson Bay: *Edisto* Sta. 5 (400 meters). Weddell Sea: *Edisto* Sta. 20, TR 6 (394 meters). Antarctic Peninsula: *Staten Island* Sta. 48/63 (70 meters). South Shetland Is.: *Eltanin* Sta. 410 (240 meters). Bellingshausen Sea: *Edisto* Sta. 146[26] (56 meters), Sta. 148[26] (55 meters), Sta. 161[26] (56 meters).

Previous Records.

Antarctic: South Sandwich Is. [Millar, 1960].

Distribution. Probably circum-antarctic on the continental shelf. Depth range is from 55 to 400 meters.

Description. Rounded head up to 2 cm in diameter on a long, wiry stalk 10 cm or longer. The length of the stalk is apparently independent of head size. The stalk is from the anterior end of the body, and both apertures, almost sessile, are situated at opposite ends of the dorsal surface, directed laterally if the head is held upright. Basally the stalk has a beard of fine rootlets. Living specimens have been described as 'white "jack-in-the-pulpit".' The test is thin and transparent and externally is covered with evenly spaced, minute papillae. The body wall is closely adherent to the test and has fine circular muscle strands, mainly around the siphons, and a few longitudinal bands radiating from the siphons down either side of the body. Sixteen branchial tentacles of two alternating sizes are stout with few primary and some short secondary branches. These alternate with rudimentary tentacles. The dorsal tubercle is small with a slightly curved slit, longitudinal or oblique. The dorsal lamina is a broad plain-edged membrane. The branchial sac has 7 tall internal longitudinal vessels, each corresponding to a row of flat double spirally coiled stigmata with 6 to 7 coils in each.

[26] U.S. Navy Antarctic Expedition, 1947–1948.

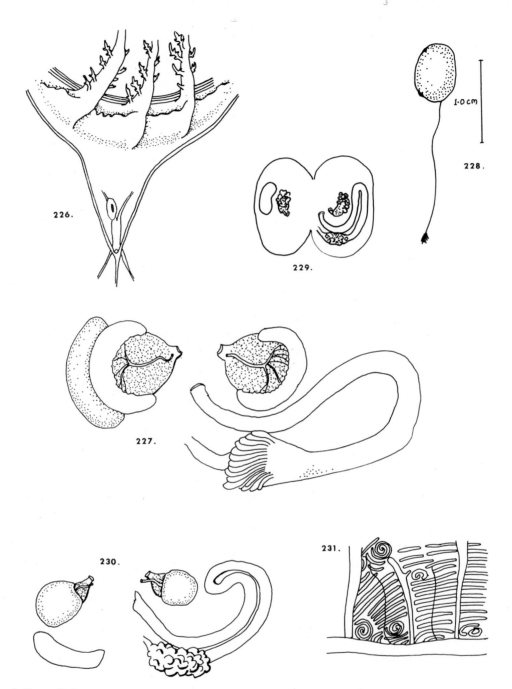

Pareugyrioides galatheae

226. Dorsal branchial tentacles and neural region showing
     tentacular velum.
227. Inner body wall showing gonads and gut loop on both
     sides of the body.

Pareugyrioides arnbackae

228. External appearance, small specimen.
229. Inner body wall, small specimen.

Pareugyrioides filholi

230. Inner body wall showing gut, gonads, and kidney [after
     Brewin, 1960].
231. Portion of infundibulum from branchial sac [after Bre-
     win, 1960].

These coils are occasionally broken. Up to 12 vessels radiate from the center of each coil and extend to the periphery, where they meet vessels from the adjacent coil.

The gut forms a closed, deeply curved, narrow loop that may or may not be open at the pole, where the dorsal or descending limb curves dorsally and posteriorly before turning ventrally to close the loop. The rectum extends for a short distance anteriorly to open in a two-lipped anus at the base of the atrial opening. The gut abruptly expands in diameter where the esophagus joins the stomach, but the stomach gradually tapers into the intestine. The stomach wall is marked by rounded glandular swellings and diverticula. The right gonad is dorsal and parallel to, but separated from, the kidney; the left gonad lies in the secondary gut loop. Each gonad consists of a large long central ovary with short terminal oviduct directed toward the atrial opening. Testis follicles surround the sides and end of the ovary or extend on to the mesial surface, where they obscure the several openings of the male ducts. Testis follicles from the distal end of the ovary near the oviduct open by a common duct on the mesial surface of the oviduct, 2 or 3 supplementing the short common male ducts opening along the surface of the ovary.

Remarks. Characterizing this species is its always present wiry stalk, which supports the animal above the substrate with its branchial aperture directed downward and its atrial aperture directed into the water above, as with other stalked species (p. 132). Internally it is very similar to *P. filholi* but is distinguished from it by the flask-shaped ovary and single vas deferens opening of *P. filholi*.

Pareugyrioides filholi (Pizon)

Text figs. 230, 231

Molgula filholi Pizon, 1898, p. 347; 1898b, p. 272.
Molgula inversa Sluiter, 1900, p. 32.—Hartmeyer, 1914, p. 11.
Caesira filholi + *C. inversa;* Hartmeyer, 1909–1911, p. 1323.
Paramolgula filholi; Michaelsen, 1922, p. 378.—Brewin, 1958, p. 450; 1960, p. 120.
Pareugyrioides macquariensis Kott, 1954, p. 169.

New Records. Drake Passage: *Eltanin* Sta. 219 (115 meters), juvenile (identification doubtful).

Previous Records.

Subantarctic: Stewart I., South Island, and Cook Strait, New Zealand [Pizon, 1898; Sluiter, 1900;

Michaelsen, 1922; Brewin, 1958, 1960]; Macquarie I. [Kott, 1954].

Distribution. Although at present records suggest a confined range from the South Island of New Zealand to Macquarie Island, it is possible that the species has a wider distribution in the subantarctic area. Depth range is from intertidal to 47 meters and possibly more.

Description. Rounded individuals up to 5 cm in longest diameter. Test is thin and flexible, smooth externally and usually with sand grains or shell fragments embedded. Apertures are close together and sessile. The body wall is thin with fine longitudinal bands radiating from the siphons on the anterior part of the body only. Fine circular bands are present superficially around the siphons and across the anterior part of the dorsal surface. There are 16 to 20 branchial tentacles with primary, secondary, and often tertiary branches. The dorsal tubercle has a simple U-shaped opening. There are 7 internal longitudinal vessels on each side of the branchial sac and sometimes an additional vessel on the left. On the right there is a row of infundibula adjacent to the endostyle without a corresponding internal longitudinal vessel. There are 4 to 6 transverse vessels, the number related to the size of the individual. Generally, single infundibula occur between the transverse vessels to form rows under the internal longitudinal vessels. In the seventh and eighth rows, however, there are 2 infundibula in each mesh. The stigmata are wide and interrupted along the course of the 4 to 5 spirals that form conical infundibula. The infundibula in the ventral rows are more flattened, and spiral from a wider base. Three primary radial vessels are present in each quarter of the infundibula, alternating with secondary radial vessels. In larger specimens the stigmata tend to form secondary and interstitial spirals only to a limited extent. The gut forms a curved narrow loop, sometimes open at the pole. The stomach wall is complicated and broken up into pockets and diverticula.

The gonads on each side of the body consist of a flask-shaped to elongate ovary and a circle of pyriform testis follicles around the proximal end of the ovary, sometimes extending over the ovary on its mesial surface. On the right the gonad is anterior and more or less parallel to the long axis of the curved kidney and on the left the gonad extends from the middle of the secondary gut loop. In the specimens from Macquarie Island [Kott, 1954] the oviduct, distended with eggs, is turned ventrally. Male ducts join on the mesial surface of the ovary and the vas deferens opens with the oviduct.

The juvenile taken in the Drake Passage is minute and sandy with the mantle strongly adherent to the test. The gut loop is small and simple in the posterior part of the body. The stomach is covered with rounded swellings. The branchial sac has 6 long vessels crossing short, randomly oriented stigmata, some curved. Thus the condition of the branchial sac indicates a species of *Eugyra*, or *Pareugyrioides*, and the rounded stomach swellings suggest that this is a juvenile of either *P. arnbackae* or the present species. Since *P. arnbackae* is not now known in the subantarctic area, this fact, together with the absence of stalk and the sandy coating around the test, indicates a possibility that the specimen represents a juvenile of *Pareugyrioides filholi*.

Remarks. The species is distinguished by the position of the apertures, close together on the dorsal surface, by the pockets and diverticula of the stomach wall, and by the single opening of the vas deferens with that of the oviduct at the distal end of the ovary.

Genus *Paramolgula* Traustedt

Type species: *Paramolgula schultzii* Traustedt 1885

Complete suppression of branchial folds, which are represented by single wide internal longitudinal vessels. Transverse branchial vessels irregular. Stigmata small and short, forming many small irregularly distributed infundibula. Left gonad outside primary gut loop.

The genus is monotypic, closely related to *Pareugyrioides*, and confined to the Magellanic area of the Subantarctic.

Paramolgula gregaria (Lesson)

Text figs. 232, 233

Cynthia gregaria Lesson, 1830, p. 435; 1830a, p. 157.
Cynthia gigantea Cunningham, 1871, pp. 125, 263; 1871a, p. 489.
Cynthia magellanica Cunningham, 1871, p. 488.
Molgula gigantea; Herdman, 1881, p. 234; 1882, p. 69.
Molgula gregaria; Herdman, 1881, p. 234; 1882, p. 73.
Molgula horrida Herdman, 1881, p. 235; 1882, p. 76. —Michaelsen, 1900, p. 142.
Paramolgula schulzii Traustedt, 1885, p. 20.—Michaelsen, 1900, p. 141.
Molgula glomerata Pizon, 1898, p. 354; 1898a, p. 1817; 1898b, p. 274.

Ctenicella lebruni Pizon, 1898, p. 364; 1898a, p. 1817; 1898b, p. 274.
Ctenicella rugosa Pizon, 1898, p. 372; 1898a, p. 1817; 1898b, p. 273.
Stomatropa villosa Pizon, 1898, p. 379; 1898a, p. 1817; 1898b, p. 273.
Paramolgula gigantea; Michalesen, 1900, p. 138; 1907, p. 81.—Hartmeyer, 1922, p. 321.—Ärnbäck, 1938, p. 15.
Paramolgula patagonica Michaelsen, 1900, p. 141; 1907, p. 81.
Paramolgula schultzei; Michaelsen, 1907, p. 81.
Paramolgula gregaria; Hartmeyer, 1909–1911, p. 1326.—Herdman, 1912, p. 306; 1915, p. 88.—Van Name, 1945, p. 428.—Millar, 1960, p. 140.
Paramolgula horrida Herdman, 1912, p. 307; 1915, p. 89.
Paramolgula villosa; Michaelsen, 1912, p. 176.
Paramolgula chilensis Hartmeyer, 1914, p. 18.
Paramolgula gigantea f. *capax* Ärnbäck, 1938, p. 16.

New Records. Scotia Sea: *Eltanin* Sta. 370 (115 meters). Off Tierra del Fuego: *Eltanin* Sta. 981 (40–49 meters).

Previous Records.

Antarctic: South Georgia [Millar, 1960].

Subantarctic: Magellanic area and Tierra del Fuego [Cunningham, 1871; Herdman, 1882; Traustedt, 1885; Pizon, 1898; Michaelsen, 1900; Ärnbäck, 1938]; Falkland Is. [Lesson, 1830; Michaelsen, 1900; Herdman, 1882, 1912; Ärnbäck, 1938; Millar, 1960]; Patagonian Shelf [Herdman, 1882; Millar, 1960]; Chilean coast [Hartmeyer, 1914; Van Name, 1945].

Distribution. Is very limited in waters from 1 to 130 meters, on the Patagonian Shelf as far north as Río de la Plata, from the Magellanic and Falkland Islands areas and extending only as far south as South Georgia. The species has also been taken from the Chilean coast. The three specimens from South Georgia [Millar, 1960] represent the southernmost record at present.

Description. One of the largest simple ascidians. The five specimens from the Burdwood Bank in the present collection are between 20 and 30 cm long and about 12 cm wide. Herdman records one that is 33 cm. Body is a rounded oval or oblong upright sac. The atrial aperture is almost sessile, directed upward on the antero-dorsal corner of the body. The branchial aperture adjacent on the antero-ventral corner is 4-lobed on a conspicuous siphon more or

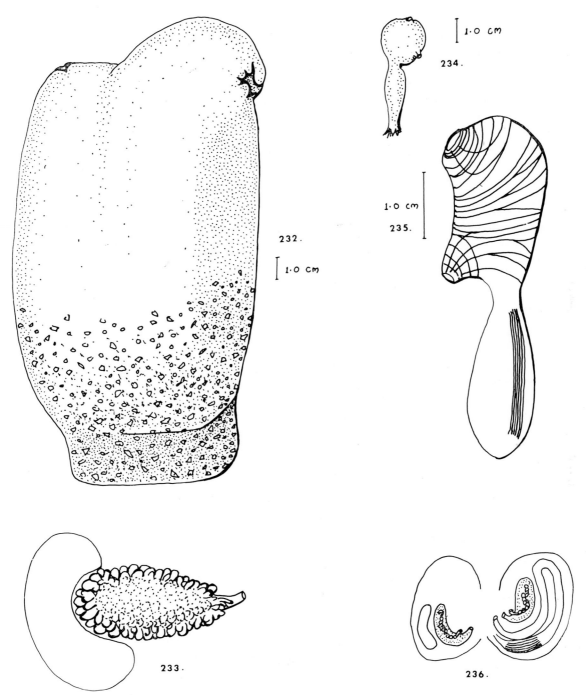

232.

1·0 CM

234.

1·0 CM

1·0 CM

235.

233.

236.

Paramolgula gregaria
232. External appearance.
233. Kidney and gonads from right side of body.

Fungulus cinereus
234. External appearance.
235. Body removed from test showing muscles.
236. Inner body wall.

less recurved toward the posterior end or base of the individual. As the individual grows, the body lengthens but does not increase greatly in diameter and the apertures remain close together. The test is thin but tough, and out of water the animal is collapsed and flaccid, especially in older individuals. Posteriorly there may be a tuft of rootlike hairs, or the test is thickened into a keel-like anchor, or sometimes a stalk, often encrusted with sand. Pebbles may be embedded in the basal test. The surface of the test is smooth or wrinkled or granular and is often covered with sand, shell, or debris. Younger preserved specimens may have gray, yellowish, or white test, but in larger specimens the test is usually discolored and appears brown.

The body wall has well developed, variously directed muscles forming a thick network, whereas around the base of the siphons the muscles are arranged in the usual outer circular and inner longitudinal layers. Basally there are extensions of the body wall into the keel or stalk, if either is developed. About 16 branchial tentacles vary in size and are much branched. The dorsal tubercle is usually C-shaped with inrolled horns to form a double spiral cone with the open interval to the left or right. The plain-edged dorsal lamina is very short, owing to the great curvature of the body in this species in which the siphons are almost adjacent. Consequently, the branchial sac is also very curved, with 7 wide internal longitudinal vessels crossed by 5 transverse vessels radiating from the dorsal lamina. The transverse vessels, as the animals grow, give off increasingly numerous branches that anastomose on the surface of the sac to form a complicated network, sometimes almost covering the short stigmata spiraling to form numerous low, irregularly arranged infundibula. In small young specimens (*Eltanin* Sta. 981) there are 2 rows of infundibula between the internal longitudinal vessels and 1 row beneath each vessel. All traces of these rows of infundibula have disappeared in the branchial sac of larger and older individuals. The gut loop on the left forms a compact double loop postero-dorsally. The tapering stomach is partly obscured by dense liver lobes. The anus is smooth and bilabiate. The kidney is fairly long and curved, embracing the end of the circular or elongate gonad. On the left a similar gonad is enclosed by the secondary gut loop. The ovaries are flask-shaped to long and are surrounded by, or sometimes covered by, conglomerations of testis follicles, which may open by a single vas deferens on the mesial side of the oviduct, both directed toward the atrial opening.

There may be numerous seminal openings (up to 12, Ärnbäck [1938]) at the base of the oviduct.

Biology. Millar [1960] found that individuals under 3 cm had not reached sexual maturity. In mature individuals gonads become active in November; the main spawning period is from February to May. He also observed the presence of crustacean particles in the gut together with unicellular algae. It is most likely that these algae form the principal food of the species and that the presence of crustacean particles is fortuitous. The ramifying network of secondary transverse vessels on the surface of the branchial sac may assist in trapping zooplankton. However, this would have to be considerably broken down before it could be passed along the endostyle. There is no suggestion that these are not filter feeders, and it is most likely that their enzyme systems are adjusted to a herbivorous rather than carnivorous diet.

Remarks. In younger specimens the stigmata are arranged in regular rows of spirals in meshes formed by the intersecting transverse and longitudinal vessels as in the genera *Eugyra* and *Pareugyrioides*. As the primary gut loop does not enclose the left gonad, it seems probable that *Paramolgula* may represent a species of *Pareugyrioides* in which increasing complexity of the branchial sac accompanies tremendous increase in size, perhaps due to longevity. Thus the situation parallels that of *Molgula gigantea* in which a similar phenomenon has been observed. Van Name [1945] also drew attention to taxonomic difficulties caused by the great variability. This variability appears, however, to be due mainly to size increase and the body curvature, which affects the shape of the branchial sac. The position of the gonads in relation to the kidney and gut determine the species even in the unlikely event of the complete absence of the secondary network resulting from ramification of transverse vessels in the branchial sac.

Genus *Fungulus* Herdman, 1882

Type species: *Fungulus cinereus* Herdman, 1882

A stalked abyssal genus with folds in the branchial sac; without stigmata. Typical molgulid kidney present on right side of the body. Stomach with longitudinal glandular plications.

Only two specimens were previously known: one each from Kerguelen Islands and the South Orkney Islands. The genus was thought to have strong affinities with the genus *Culeolus*. Examination of ten generally well preserved specimens in the present collection indicates that this genus properly belongs with the Molgulidae.

Fungulus cinereus Herdman

Text figs. 234–236

Fungulus cinereus Herdman, 1882, p. 127.
? *Fungulus antarcticus* Herdman, 1912, p. 308; 1915, p. 90.—Hartmeyer, 1912, pp. 374, 378.—Van Name, 1945, p. 367.

New Records. South Shetland Is. *Eltanin* Sta. 365 (4385 meters). Antarctic Peninsula: *Eltanin* Sta. 268 (2818 meters). Drake Passage: *Eltanin* Sta. 451 (4026 meters). Northeast of South Sandwich Is.: *Eltanin* Sta. 596 (5673–5918 meters).

Previous Records.

Antarctic: ? South of South Orkney Is. [Herdman, 1912].

Subantarctic: Between Cape of Good Hope and Kerguelen Is. [Herdman, 1882].

Distribution. Records at present indicate a distribution on either side of the Scotia Ridge in depths from about 2500 to 5918 meters. As the species tolerates great depths, there are no apparent barriers to a wider distribution, and Herdman's record from the southern Indian Ocean supports an hypothesis of a general distribution of the species at least in the southern Pacific and Atlantic basins. As is to be expected at these depths, there is no biological boundary at the antarctic convergence.

Description. Spherical to oval body on a short, wide, hollow stalk from the anterior end of the body. The unlobed apertures, when extended, are on very short siphons, but when closed they appear to be sessile. The branchial aperture is about two-thirds the distance down the dorsal side of the body, directed laterally or down toward the stalk; the atrial aperture is terminal on the upper or posterior end, or is posterodorsal, directed upward or slightly laterally. The stalk is 'bulging,' i.e. narrowest where it joins the head and constricted again toward the base where there is a fine felt of hairlike rootlets. The test is thin, papery, transparent, and covered with minute processes.

Specimens from 1.5 to 5 cm body diameter and 1.5 to 7 cm stalk length have been taken in which the maximum diameter of the stalk is from 0.4 to 2.0 cm. The body wall is not closely adherent to the test, but this may be the result of collection and preservation during which the body has contracted away from the test. A hollow mesenchymatous exten-

sion of the body wall richly supplied with blood vessels projects to the base of the stalk and is bulged in the same way as the stalk. The body musculature is confined to about 14 longitudinal bands, well spaced but branching into two across the dorsal and ventral surfaces. One branch each of the most anterior and posterior of these muscle bands extends along the siphons, and the other branch extends over the dorsal surface. Circular muscle bands are present around the siphons. Along the ventral aspect of the stalk from the base to the neck, where it joins the rest of the body, there is a ribbon of thick muscle bands. These muscle bands have no apparent connection with the longitudinal bands of the body, to which they run at right angles. The muscle bands of the larger specimens appear to branch more than those of the smaller specimens.

There are 9 stout branchial tentacles, the 4 largest radially arranged. These tentacles all carry lateral branches with minute branched filaments. The dorsal tubercle, just to the right of the ganglion, has a simple circular opening directed to the right. The dorsal lamina is a plain broad-edged membrane. The branchial sac is delicate. There are 5 'folds' on each side represented by approximations of 2 to 4 internal longitudinal vessels. The internal longitudinal vessels are tall and in preserved specimens flattened and sometimes folded along their length, so that one vessel may at first appear to be 2 or 3. There are no vessels between the folds. There are 5 transverse vessels radiating from the dorsal lamina, and they form, with the longitudinal vessels, the meshes of the branchial sac. There are very occasional connectives joining the transverse vessels, running parallel to the longitudinal vessels. In larger specimens an unperforated membranous extension of the branchial sac projects into the stalk with the body wall.

The gut loop is narrow and slightly curved around the ventral border of the left side, the pole of the loop extending almost to the tentacular ring. The stomach enlargement has yellow internal longitudinal glandular plications and gradually tapers to the intestine. The kidney is long and gently curved around the postero-ventral corner of the right side of the body.

A single elongate hermaphrodite gonad is present on each side of the body, consisting of a tubular ovary with compact white testis lobes along the mesial surface in an undulating line. In some specimens the testis lobes occupy only the proximal two-thirds of the ovary, although arranged in a similar undulating line.

On the right the gonad lies parallel and dorsal to the kidney with both ducts reflected up toward the atrial opening. On the left the gonad occupies a similar position in relation to the gut loop.

Biology. The specimens from the Falkland Islands area in the present collection were taken in association with *Culeolus murrayi:* the long thin stalk of the *Culeolus* specimen adherent to the stalk and part of the head of the largest *Fungulus* specimen. Long fine branching hairs from the *Culeolus* stalk spread over the surface of the *Fungulus,* anchoring it firmly.

Other specimens of the present species have cirripedes, hydroids, or both adhering to the test.

Remarks. Herdman [1912] states 'The looseness of the branchial sac and the minute undulations in practically all the muscle bundles of the mantle give the impression that when alive and filled with sea-water the animal had the power of expanding to a considerably larger size than it now shows.'

This may explain why the muscle bands of Herdman's specimens seemed closely placed; in other respects *F. antarcticus* is apparently similar to the present species.

Hartmeyer [1912] regarded *Fungulus* as a member of the family Pyuridae. However, only Herdman's two specimens were known at that time, and the molgulid kidney had not been observed. Moreover, in the present specimens the longitudinal glandular plications of the stomach are similar to those found in *Molguloides* spp. and in some species of *Eugyra.* The digestive gland of Pyuridae is invariably arborescent, concealing the stomach.

Van Name [1945] suggests that the elongate gonads open near the atrial opening, radiating therefrom, a character reminiscent of Styelidae. The gonoducts in the present specimens are, however, reflected toward the atrial openings, as is usual in Molgulidae.

Genus *Oligotrema* Bourne, 1903

Type species: *Oligotrema psammites* Bourne, 1903
Branchial sac greatly reduced. Branchial aperture extended into a high collar-like circular fold with 6 large branched lobes that curl inward over the aperture. Molgulid kidney on right side of body.

Synonyms of this monotypic genus include species assigned to the genus *Hexacrobylus* Sluiter, 1905, that were previously distinguished by characters resulting from different states of contraction. The genus is of particular interest because of considerable modifi-

cation of musculature and gut for a carnivorous way of life.

Oligotrema psammites Bourne

Text figs. 237–239

Oligotrema psammites Bourne, 1903, p. 233.—Oka, 1913a, p. 9.
Hexacrobylus psammatodes Sluiter, 1905, p. 135.
Hexacrobylus indicus Oka, 1913a, p. 6.—Millar, 1959, p. 203.
Hexacrobylus arcticus Hartmeyer, 1923, p. 133.— Ärnbäck, 1928, p. 76.—Van Name, 1945, p. 442.
Hexacrobylus sp. ? Kott, 1957b, p. 147.

New Records. North of South Shetland Is.: *Eltanin* Sta. 991 (2672–3030 meters).

Previous Records.

Elsewhere: New Britain, 92 meters [Bourne, 1903]. Indian Ocean, 4158–4350 meters [Oka, 1913a; Kott, 1957b; Millar, 1959]. Faroes and Iceland, 891–1264 meters [Hartmeyer, 1923].

Distribution. In deep waters of the Indian Ocean, the Norwegian Sea, and the southern Pacific Ocean. It therefore seems possible that the species has a cosmopolitan distribution in the deeper waters of the world. The species occurs in shallower water off New Britain, as do other deep-water species in the Indonesian area (p. 204).

Description. The body is upright, ovoid, generally about 1.5 cm long and 1 cm wide. The whole test is covered with short tentacular projections or papillae, which get longer posteriorly and develop into long hairs forming a fairly sparse beard from the posterior half of the body. Around the upper surface of the body the test is produced to form a crown of 6 large hollow tongue-like tentacular projections, their borders lobed and produced into fingerlike extensions. The 3 ventral projections are longer than the dorsal ones. The branchial aperture is a large slit in the center of the circular area enclosed by the crown of tentacular projections. The atrial opening is about one-fourth of the distance down the dorsal surface and is often inconspicuous externally. The test is moderately thick and soft and gelatinous internally. The body wall is very muscular in its anterior two-thirds. Strong superficial circular muscle bands surround both siphons. The bands on the atrial siphon extend well down the dorsal surface. On the branchial siphon the circular muscle bands are in two groups, one immediately around the aper-

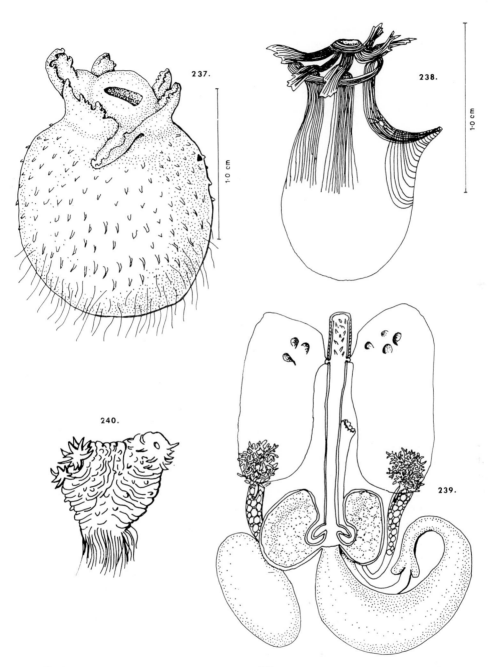

Oligotrema psammites
237. External appearance.
238. Body removed from test showing musculature.
239. Internal organs (esophagus and glandular prestomach sectioned horizontally).

Oligotrema sp.
240. External appearance.

ture and anteriorly invaginated into the siphon lining. Another band circles the body posterior to the tentacular projections. Longitudinal bands extend from the siphons and out along the upper surface of the tentacular projections. In the extremities of the fingerlike lobes they break up into fibers. Further longitudinal bands extend from the extremities of the lobes along the under surface of the tentacular projections, beneath the band of circular muscles circling the body. These longitudinal muscles from the two most ventral projections and from the one on the right extend down the body in a single wide band of muscles ventrally. Those from the projection on the left extend down the body in a single band down the left side. The longitudinal muscles from the two most dorsal projections extend along either side of the upper surface of the atrial siphon beneath the circular muscles and beneath the dorsal ganglion. There are no longitudinal muscles on the right side of the body.

The longitudinal muscles extend into the branchial siphon beneath the circular musculature, which forms a sphincter at the base of the siphon. Branchial tentacles are present at the base of the siphon [Bourne, 1903] but were not observed in the present specimens, which have randomly distributed small tentacular papillae lining the siphon. Just below the internal circular siphonal muscles small pharyngeal pores perforate the esophageal wall on either side. These pores open out into very delicate paired branchial sacs, together occupying the greater part of the body cavity and overlying, on the left, the anterior part of the gut loop and gonad, and on the right overlying the anterior part of the large kidney and the right gonad. The walls of these branchial sacs are perforated by only 3 or 4 openings in their antero-dorsal aspect. These openings are reminiscent of the reduced stigmata in the dorsal part of the branchial sac of *Pyura obesa* (p. 138).

The long fibrous esophagus with thick folded walls extends straight down the body and extends into a valve at its posterior end before opening out into a glandular prestomach with rounded internal swellings. The opening to the glandular prestomach may be opened by the withdrawal of the esophagus, possibly by muscular action. The stomach itself is large and crescent-shaped, with glandular ridges on the internal wall. From the distal horn of the stomach crescent the gut loops dorsally and posteriorly, and there is another valve before the distal extent of the gut loops dorsally and anteriorly to extend forward and terminate near the atrial opening in a lobed anus. On the right side of the body, posteriorly, is a very large kidney.

Single gonads are present on each side of the body. Each arborescent testis extends from the middle of the anterior half of the body to open in a very short vas deferens where the testis overlies a tubular ovary distally. The ovary on the left extends down into the second gut loop and the oviduct turns forward with the rectum and opens near the atrial opening. On the right side of the body the gonad is in a similar position, the oviduct turning forward anterior to the kidney.

Remarks. In this species the main organs affected in achieving the high degree of specialization associated with a carnivorous habit [Bourne, 1903] are the body wall musculature and the gut. The homologues and functions of the structures developed are, in some cases, confused and have led to difficulties in the taxonomy of the genus. The functions of the muscles associated with the tentacular projections are related to the capture of food and protection of the individual. Their arrangement suggests the adaptation of the circular and longitudinal musculature generally found in ascidians to operate the highly specialized tentacular projections. These projections and their musculature are not homologues of any part of the branchial siphon of other ascidians but are developed from the body wall as accessory organs to the branchial opening. They may be considered homologues of the ridge of test found in certain species of Phlebobranchia (Corellidae, Agnesiidae) which, by the action of the body muscles is closed across the apertures. When the longitudinal muscles on the anterior surface of the projections are contracted in association with the contraction of the internal and external circular siphonal musculature, the branchial aperture will be closed, the tentacular projections closed over the apertures, the branchial siphon and esophagus descreased in diameter and consequently lengthened, and the glandular prestomach will be separated off from the lumen of the gut. When the longitudinal muscles from the undersurface of the tentacular projections are contracted and those on their upper surface are relaxed, the tentacular projections will open and, in association with the relaxation of the outer and inner circular siphonal muscles, the branchial aperture will open, the diameter of the esophagus will increase, while its length decreases, and the glandular prestomach will become continuous with the lumen of the rest of the gut.

It is apparent that the variations in body shape and in the shape of the internal organs are due to the operation of the body muscles and are not true morphological differences. Especially in this regard *H. psammatodes* Sluiter, 1905, fig. 17, has a wide open branchial opening, and the distortion of the ovarian tubes could result from the contraction of the external longitudinal muscles affecting this opening. Similarly, the lumen of the glandular prestomach is continuous with the lumen of the rest of the gut. Bourne's [1903] account of this species is very detailed histologically, but only a single ventral branchial sac is demonstrated with but a single restricted opening from the esophagus. However, in view of the excellent agreement in all other respects with the present specimens, its seems most likely that the apparent absence of a second branchial sac is due to difficulty of interpreting the sections of this damaged specimen.

The similarity of testis structure and its position in relation to the ovary, together with the structure of the tentacular projections, the musculature, the gut, and the nature of the surface of the test suggest that this species includes all the synonyms listed above.

Oligotrema sp.
Text fig. 240

An empty ascidian test taken from 6006 meters in the Peru-Chile Trench (*Eltanin* Sta. 37). Although the test was not apparently damaged, the tissues inside it were completely disintegrated.

Description of Test. The animal is triangular, laterally flattened and fixed by one corner of the triangle, from which there is a feltlike beard of long fine hairlike roots. The apertures are sessile, close together at the antero-dorsal corner of the triangle. At the postero-dorsal corner of the body there are two hollow moundlike projections of the test, from each projection transversely wrinkled pointed fingerlike processes radiate. Anteriorly the test is leathery with thickened ridges and wartlike, elongate, or rounded extensions, especially around the apertures. However, the basal half of the test is thinner, smooth, almost transparent, with hairlike extensions.

Remarks. This distinctive test is not like that of any ascidian species so far described. External extensions of the test are developed in *Molguloides* spp., but here they are directly associated with the branchial aperture. In *Culeolus* spp. tufts of papillae are developed, and, as in the present specimen, they are not associated with the apertures. This character alone would, however, be insufficient to establish a relationship with *Culeolus*. It is possible that the test processes of this specimen and *Oligotrema* spp. are analogous.

7. BEHAVIOR

ADULT ASCIDIANS, INVARIABLY SESSILE and protected by an inert test, respond to chemical or tactile stimuli received through the branchial and atrial apertures. Pelagic larvae react more directly with the environment and are generally equipped with specific organs sensitive to light and gravity.

FEEDING

MacGinitie [1939] most recently has observed the method of feeding in *Ciona intestinalis*, *Ascidia californica*, and *Diplosoma pizoni*. The process has also been investigated by other authors in other species [see Berrill, 1950] and is similar. The following account can be regarded as representative of the feeding process generally within the class.

Solid material filtered from the water passing through stigmata of the branchial sac are enmeshed in a stream of mucous secreted by the endostyle. This mucous is moved dorsally by the action of cilia on the branchial bars, on ridges, and in grooves. In the region of the dorsal lamina sheets of mucous from either side of the body are organized into a food-laden thread that passes into the esophagus. Particles of undesirable food that are enmeshed in the cilia may be rejected, possibly by ciliary action; however, larger undesirable particles are generally prevented from entering the branchial sac by the tentacles at the base of the branchial siphon and are ejected by quick contraction of the body wall. Stronger disturbances of this nature cause the animal to stop feeding; i.e., mucous secretion stops although the cilia lining the stigmata will continue to beat, causing the current of water through the branchial sac to continue. Eventually, feeding will be resumed. If further disturbing stimuli are received, however, the animal will eject all water from the branchial sac and will remain contracted with the apertures closed for some time. The ejection of the water, which occurs with considerable force, gives the simple ascidians their common English name of 'sea squirts.' Van Weel [1940] has shown that at least part of the mucous stream is diverted to the mouth of the neural gland or the ciliated pit on the dorsal tubercle. Carlisle [1950] has postulated that the ciliated pit may therefore act as the sensory receptor involved with the nervous control

of feeding, although as yet this has not been demonstrated.

FERTILIZATION

As mentioned above, a portion of the mucous food thread formed in the dorsal lamina is diverted to the ciliated pit or opening of the neural gland on the dorsal tubercle [Van Weel, 1940]. Carlisle [1951] has demonstrated, in *Ciona intestinalis* and *Phallusia mammillata*, that gametes of the same species present in the food stream will, on reaching the ciliated pit, stimulate the neural gland to release the gonadotrophin, which, acting on the neural ganglion, initiates the nervous activity resulting in the release of gametes. Although the species with which Carlisle worked are both oviparous, the mechanism is probably similar in viviparous species in which the presence of male gametes in the incurrent stream of water would, in the same way, stimulate the release of mature ova into the peribranchial cavity or into the oviduct, where fertilization may take place. This mechanism provides efficiently for the cross fertilization of fixed organisms, particularly since the release of gametes is always accompanied by cessation of feeding for a sufficiently long time to ensure their dispersal, thus preventing self-fertilization [Carlisle, 1951]. It also ensures that gametes in the incurrent stream are available for fertilization and are not enmeshed in the mucous food stream, since secretion of mucous ceases when feeding stops.

The initiation of the process leading to fertilization is therefore dependent on the presence of gametes of the same species in the water drawn into the oral siphon. This will be affected by the population density, the viability, buoyancy, and density of the gametes, and the turbulence of water and velocity of current flow. With increasing viviparity the male gametes only are exposed to dispersal, and there is an increase in the number of male gametes produced and a relative decrease in the number of ova. This is reflected in the relative size of the respective organs concerned.

MIGRATION

The availability of a suitable physical environment, the duration of free-swimming larvae and fertile eggs, the turbulence of water, and the velocity of current flow all influence the dispersal of ascidians. The likelihood of a resulting spread of the existing populations and the establishment of viable new populations is, however, reduced in relation to the extent of this dispersal as it affects their ability to satisfy the minimum population density necessary to ensure fertilization. Mechanisms preventing wide dispersal of larvae assist in maintaining the minimum population density necessary for subsequent sexual reproduction. Consequently, a long external embryonic period and a long free-swimming larval life are not necessarily advantageous in ensuring the spread of populations. For these reasons reduction both in the buoyancy of eggs and in the duration of free-swimming larvae are especially advantageous for oviparous and viviparous species in turbulent or swiftly flowing currents. Berrill [1935] has suggested that the increase in egg density, which does in fact occur with the evolution of this class, results from long established viviparity (chapter 8, Phylogeny), which is, in itself, an especial advantage in preventing a wide dispersal of larvae by reducing their free-swimming life. The extent to which viviparity is developed is inversely related to the duration of the free-swimming phase and involves the suppression of larval organs in favor of adult ones.

In still waters, however, where the dispersal rate is not so great, species with more buoyant eggs and longer external embryonic and larval stages are at an advantage in seeking suitable places for settlement, thus ensuring the establishment of a sufficient population density imperative for fertilization where species are oviparous. This is well demonstrated by the distribution of Ciona intestinalis, which is present in high-density populations in harbors and estuaries throughout the northern and southern hemispheres, having probably been transported by ships. The species has not, however, spread outside these isolated and protected localities where, presumably, larvae become too widely dispersed to result in sufficiently dense populations to ensure external fertilization of ova.

SETTLEMENT

Berrill [1955], in a discussion of the adaptive value of the tadpole larvae of ascidians in site selection, suggests that they have developed in response to genetic selection pressures related to the type of habitat available to the species. When these pressures are removed (i.e. by access to unlimited areas of suitable substrate for settlement such as are presented by the open sea bed as opposed to special and protected sites in clefts and on vertical and under surfaces), the necessity for

a pelagic larval form to seek a site for settlement is removed and the larval form is, in fact, lost. It is here suggested that the loss of a free-living larval form is the terminal point in a selection process operating throughout the class, where reduction of the duration of free-swimming larvae has a survival value in limiting the dispersal of offspring. This becomes especially valuable where changes in the body shape and in the nature of the test enable species to exploit localities beyond those available to the more primitive forms, which, owing to their size, growth pattern, small area of fixation, and oviparous habit, favor calm waters or are drawn into specialized sites for settlement.

Oviparous enterogonid ascidians (mostly Phlebobranchia), which are fixed by a comparatively small area of their test and grow three dimensionally to a relatively large size, have small, long-lived larvae equipped with otolith and ocellus. The initial response of these free-swimming larvae is negatively geotactic and positively phototactic to ensure dispersal. This is followed by a movement downward and into shaded areas where clean under and vertical surfaces provide suitable sites for fixation and growth. These forms, which require a long larval life to find a suitable substrate for settlement, are therefore at an advantage in calmer waters where dispersal of larvae by currents does not occur.

Viviparous Aplousobranchia, fixed by a comparatively large surface area, are able to exploit more confined crevasses and to survive in areas where encrusting growth is necessary for permanent attachment [Berrill, 1955]. These species require some minimum of pelagic existence to find a suitable site for settlement, and their dispersal is inhibited by shorter-lived, strongly swimming larvae that are attracted into protected situations by well developed light-sensitive organs.

Pyuridae remain most closely related to Phlebobranchia in their habits of site selection and related larval form [Berrill, 1955], although, because of their leathery test and special provision for fixation, the adults are able to survive in more exposed conditions. The duration of free-swimming larvae is reduced, and thus dispersal is limited.

In the solitary Styelidae larvae are known in the following species:

Styela partita Stimpson occurs on wharves and under harbor installations [Van Name, 1945] but also occurs under rocks and other similar underwater objects. It may be confined in harbors because of its oviparous habit, which results in too wide a dispersal of gametes and larvae to allow its survival in more turbulent waters. The ocellus is degenerate [Berrill, 1929].

Styela clava Herdman (> *Styela mammillata* Carlisle) has a wide distribution around the coast of Japan and has been introduced into European waters [Millar, 1960a]. The larva [Wallace, 1961] contains a degenerate ocellus, and its situation is probably similar to that of *Styela partita*.

Styela yakutatensis Ritter has been taken from reef flats and under ledges in exposed conditions [Huntsman, 1912a; Van Name, 1945]. The ocellus is degenerate and the larva is viviparous [Berrill, 1948].

Styela coriacea (Alder and Hancock) is attached to stones and shells from a wide north boreal area down to a depth of 600 meters. It completely lacks an ocellus and is at least occasionally viviparous [Millar, 1963b].

Dendrodoa grossularia (Van Beneden) is attached to stones and shells on the sea bed and in sheltered localities on exposed shores [Millar, 1954], as well as being attached to sides of rocks in enormous aggregates [Berrill, 1955]. Larvae are viviparous and the ocellus is absent.

Pelonaia corrugata (Forbes and Goodsir), a circumarctic species, is partially embedded in sand and mud. It is oviparous and its development is direct and anural [Millar, 1954b]. The yolk accumulation and the density of the egg are similar to the conditions that usually occur in viviparous species where viviparity is long established and results in the accumulation of yolk material [Berrill, 1935]. The species is therefore probably only secondarily viviparous.

Polycarpa pomaria (Savigny) from the Mediterranean to the north coast of Scandinavia is sometimes free but is usually attached to stones or shells or in large clusters on rocky or shady bottoms [Berrill, 1929 and 1950]. It is sometimes viviparous, and the larval ocellus is absent.

Polycarpa rustica (Linnaeus), attached to slopes in limited areas in estuaries [Berrill, 1950], is viviparous and the ocellus is absent.

Polycarpa fibrosa (Stimpson), arctic boreal, on clay or muddy bottoms with sand and stones down to 1200 meters [Berrill, 1950], is oviparous and the larva lacks an ocellus.

Polycarpa tinctor (Quoy and Gaimard), a sand dwelling ascidian from the east and northwest coasts of Australia, Indonesia, and Japan [Kott, 1964], is viviparous and anural [Millar, 1962b].

Berrill [1955] considers that the solitary Styelidae occupy localities similar to those occupied by the larger Pyuridae and Phlebobranchia. From the data above, however, it appears that, owing to their small size and the plasticity of their tough test, species of this family are able to exploit a wider variety of substrates, and the selective pressures imposed by the survival value of larvae responding to light stimuli are not great, which eventually results in the loss of the light-sensitive organ. Where larvae are not drawn into protected sites for attachment, and especially where species inhabit the open sea bed, dispersal of eggs and larvae is avoided by the development of viviparity, often to the anural stage in which larval organs are completely suppressed. The species *Styela yakutatensis* and *Dendroa grossularia*, without light-sensitive larvae, are able to colonize not only on the sea bed but also on exposed shores because of the short duration of their free-swimming larvae, which settle near the parents in protected localities [Berrill, 1955].

In colonial Styelidae budding, developed independently of the process in Enterogona [Berrill, 1955], forms colonies that extend the surface area for attachment and by causing a reduction in size of zooids results in encrusting sheets. Both adults and larvae are related to *Polycarpa* spp. [Berrill, 1955]. However, the large viviparous, strongly swimming larvae develop secondarily a light-sensitive photolith, which prevents their dispersal by attracting them to settle in shaded environments which favor encrusting forms. They thus demonstrate convergence with Aplousobranchia in their adaptations for exploiting a similar environment.

Molgulidae are highly adapted for life on the open sea bed. Their test is generally thin, with outgrowths of hairs, which enable them to rest on or root themselves in a sandy or muddy substrate. They have generally lost the leathery test, which in the Styelidae provides a firm surface for attachment to rocks and vertical surfaces. As is true for free-living Styelidae, the open sea bed provides limitless areas for settlement, and site selection by light-sensitive larvae is no longer advantageous. Consequently, the ocellus is lost and dispersal is prevented by viviparity or by completely anural development. Some species of this family inhabit rocks and weeds of shallow areas along the shore. Here they do not reach a large size, and Berrill [1955] has suggested that this colonization has only a limited success because of the inability of light-insensitive larvae to seek out the protected locations necessary for survival in these areas. However, populations of the styelid species, *D. grossularia* and *S.*

yakutatensis (see above), which also have light-insensitive larvae, are successful in similar situations because of the marked reduction of the free-swimming duration. It is probable that the lack of success of molgulids in exposed conditions is due to the loss of the leathery test which inhibits the formation of a sufficiently firm attachment for the adult.

Successful colonization by any species of ascidian is therefore determined primarily by environmental pressures acting on the adult, and the nature of the larval form is most likely the result of the habitat adopted by the adult. The selective pressures operating on the larvae are to some extent involved with site selection but are primarily involved with the prevention of dispersal. Generally, with the evolution of the class, there is an increasing degree of viviparity developed to ensure sufficient density of populations. Species adapted for exposed conditions, where turbulence imposes a need for larvae that are not subject to dispersal but are capable of selecting protected sites for attachment, have strongly swimming, light-sensitive larvae of minimal duration. Further increase in viviparity and loss of light-sensitive organs are observed as adults adapt to a free existence in open waters, where site selection is unimportant but where open conditions and current flow require measures that prevent dispersal.

In Antarctica large numbers of species are adapted for life on the open sea bed, since the wide continental shelf provides the principal habitat available for colonization. Gravel, sand, mud, and shell constitute the substrates available. The fauna clearly demonstrates a morphological adaptation to this type of environment. Large numbers of sand- or mud-living molgulids are present, and species of Pyuridae, Styelidae, and Agnesiidae are adapted for this type of substrate. Other species of the Pyuridae and the Styelidae and species of Corellidae and Ascidiiae are modified for attachment to small stones or shells and shell fragments by the development of a stalk or by an adjustment of the size or shape of their attachment area. Unfortunately, the life histories of these phlebobranch and stolidobranch ascidians are not known.

Larvae are known for the majority of antarctic species. The larvae of *Sycozoa sigillinoides, S. georgiana, Hypsistozoa obscura, Protoholozoa pedunculata, Tylobranchion speciosum, Aplidium caeruleum, Synoicium adareanum, S. tentaculatum,* and *Aplidiopsis georgianum* have all lost their ocellus. The loss of the light-sensitive organ in the deep-sea species *H. obscura, P. pedunculata,* and *S. tentaculatum* is not surprising, since this loss is often a characteristic of abyssal species [Shipley, 1901]. Of the known aplousobranch

species of the antarctic continental shelf, however, only *Distaplia cylindrica, Aplidium circumvolutum, A. radiatum,* and *A. vastum* have retained their larval ocellus. In aplousobranch larvae from other parts of the world the ocellus is known to be absent only in the southern genus *Sycozoa* [Kott, 1954, 1957; Millar, 1963a] and in the arctic species *Polycitor vitreus* (Sars, 1851) (< *Atapozoa vitreus*; Kott, 1967) [Berrill, 1948c].

Therefore, the aplousobranch species that have been successful on the wide antarctic continental shelf are also adapted for life on the open sea bed.

ORIENTATION

Owing to their fixed habit, either stalked or not or rooted by outgrowths of the otherwise inert protective test on firm substrates or in sand or mud, the Ascidiacea react with their environment largely through the branchial and atrial apertures. The orientation of these apertures in relation to the environment is therefore significant.

Hecht [1916] showed, in *Phallusia nigra*, that the affluent current is drawn into the branchial siphon from a region within a few millimeters of the apertures, whereas water filtered from the branchial sac is shot out to about ten times this distance. The normal current through the branchial sac when feeding, or not feeding, is effected by the cilia lining the stigmata [MacGinitie, 1939], and muscular action is involved only when unfavorable stimuli are received. The disparity in the force of the incurrent and excurrent streams must therefore be achieved by the relatively smaller diameter of the atrial aperture.

The two streams are also separated by the orientation of the apertures, which are generally pointed in different directions. Often the branchial aperture is terminal and the atrial aperture antero-dorsal, or both apertures rise from the dorsal surface (especially in Stolidobranchia) and are directed away from one another. There are, however, in many species throughout the class morphological adaptations that ensure that the effluent current is directed upward and away from the animal although the branchial aperture is directed horizontally or downward toward the substrate.

This orientation of branchial and atrial siphons is achieved in the following ways:

1. By development of terminal common cloacal openings while branchial apertures open to the exterior around the surface of the colony as in *Sycozoa* spp., *Distaplia* spp., and many species of the Polyclininae and Didemnidae.

2. By orientation of thorax of zooids so that atrial

apertures open above branchial apertures on slight elevations of the test as in *Podoclavella kottae* Millar, 1960; *Podoclavella detorta* Sluiter, 1904; *Protoholozoa pedunculata* (p. 000); and *Atapozoa marshii* Brewin, 1956.

3. By a distortion of the branchial sac involving shortening of dorsal lamina and enlargement of atrial cavity as in *Podoclavella cylindrica* (Quoy and Gaimard, 1834–1835) [see Millar, 1960] and *Podoclavella mollucciensis* Sluiter, 1904 [see Kott, 1957].

4. By the orientation of the whole body on top of a stalk so that the animal virtually 'stands on its head' as in *Corynascidia suhmi* Herdman, 1882; *Polycarpa clavata* Millar, 1963; *Pyura pachydermatina* (Herdman, 1881) [see Kott, 1952]; *Pyura legumen* (Lesson, 1830); *Culeolus murrayi* Herdman, 1881; *Pareugyrioides arnbackae* (Millar, 1960); *Fungulus cinereus* Herdman, 1882.

5. By differential growth of the siphons causing them to be turned in the appropriate direction as in *Podoclavella dagysa* Kott, 1957; *Phallusia depressiuscula* Heller, 1878 [see Kott, 1966]; some specimens of *Pyura georgiana* (Michaelsen, 1898) (see above); *Molgula gigantea* (Herdman, 1881); *Paramolgula gregaria* (Lesson, 1830).

6. By differential growth affecting the shape of the colony as in *Ritterella asymmetrica* Millar, 1966b.

7. By special development of the test as in *Adagnesia opaca* Kott, 1963a.

8. By muscular action as in *Clavelina baudinensis* Kott, 1957.

The advantages to the animal resulting from this orientation of the apertures are especially apparent in still waters and in areas where the population density is high. In these circumstances the dispersal of the effluent water in the area considerably above the animal is more effective and interferes less with adjacent individuals than an effluent stream of water, projected partly or completely horizontally where it could dilute the water available to adjacent animals for the supply of oxygen and food material. Where the bottom is uneven, the upward projection of the effluent stream would also prevent disturbance of the substrate causing particles of sand, rock, etc., to interrupt the feeding of individuals in the population [MacGinitie, 1939]. The downward direction of the branchial apertures enables individuals to exploit, as food, particulate organic matter lying close to the bottom, and in environments where debris and sand are disturbed it protects the animal from constant interruptions in

feeding, interruptions that would be caused by these particles falling into rather than past the branchial aperture.

Other advantages derived by the downward direction of the branchial aperture and the upward direction of the atrial aperture are related to the release of gametes, fertilized eggs, and larvae and their dispersal and survival. The risk of reproductive products falling into the branchial opening of parents or adjacent individuals is obviated and their dispersal and settlement are better effected.

There are only a few stalked species in which the atrial aperture is not higher than the branchial aperture, and, with the exception of species that lie on their side (*Adagnesia opaca* and some specimens of *Phallusia depressiuscula*), the species cited above are stalked, or at least raised off the substrate by the height of the individual or colony. In calm waters a stalk augments the advantages to the animal of this special orientation of its apertures by carrying the effluent stream even higher above the substrate and by raising the branchial opening to ensure that more dense particles are separated from particles in suspension before the ingestion of the suspended particles. A long stalk is probably most advantageous in turbulent waters, where it provides a firm anchorage for individuals that are undoubtedly swept to some extent in the direction of the current with the result that the opening of the branchial aperture is presented against the direction of the current flow, whereas the atrial opening directs the effluent stream with the current. Thus particles that otherwise might be swept past the branchial opening are swept into it by the force of the current reinforcing the strength and direction of the ciliary stream into the branchial sac. The advantages of a stalk in providing a firm anchorage where turbulence exists are therefore augmented by this orientation of the apertures in utilizing the direction of current flow to the advantage of the animal.

Stalked species are found either upright or fixed to the undersides of rocky ledges, caves, overhangs, or harbor installations. There is no evidence to suggest that this influences the orientation of apertures, which maintain the same relationship to the substrate whether the animal is hanging from it or fixed upright on it. The habits of some larvae appear to favor fixation to the undersurface of objects, and *Ciona intestinalis* is again remarkable in that an air bubble is secreted in the larval test before fixation, which causes the organism to float and possibly accounts for its settlement on ships' bottoms or other undersurfaces.

8. PHYLOGENY

CIONIDAE IS CONSIDERED the ancestral ascidian family from which two main lines of evolution proceed, characterized mainly by the function of the epicardium. In the Aplousobranchia the epicardium is utilized in an increasingly efficient process of vegetative reproduction which interrupts the growth of the individual zooid. Relations within the group depend on the development of this budding process, consequent reduction in zooid size, and development of colonial systems. The epicardium in Phlebobranchia and Stolidobranchia is modified for an excretory function, vegetative reproduction generally does not occur, and relations within the group are dependent mainly on the branchial sac development.

In Aplousobranchia, as the body of the mature zooid decreases in size, various mechanisms are adopted to accommodate the eggs (e.g. brood pouches and reduction in numbers of eggs). These changes, which tend to keep the egg longer in the parent zooid or colony, contribute to the efficiency of viviparity and consequently facilitate its establishment. Berrill [1935] has examined the rate of development of the embryo in relation to its size and the yolk-to-cytoplasm ratio. He concluded that, where viviparity is long established, the egg increases in size by an accumulation of yolk material. Increase in egg size is only advantageous where viviparity is long established. The rate of development of the egg is inversely affected by the ratio of the volume to the surface area of the egg, as in larger eggs the volume is increased relative to the surface area over which gaseous exchange can take place. The rate of development is also inversely affected by the increasing density of yolk in the egg, tending to dilute the cytoplasm. Therefore, in species with increased yolk-to-cytoplasm ratio, resulting in either increased density of yolk material or increased size of egg, the metabolic rate is reduced. This decrease in metabolic rate enables the embryo to develop in isolation in the parent colony or zooid without any special mechanism for the nutrient and respiratory requirements of the developing embryo. Where embryos are thus retained for longer periods the free-swimming larval phase is delayed and reduced and the development of larval structures is suppressed by the earlier development of adult organs before metamorphosis.

There is an increase in the yolk-to-cytoplasm ratio in the Clavelininae, and this ratio becomes even greater in the Perophoridae, Polycitoridae, Polyclinidae, and Didemnidae. In Perophoridae, Clavelinidae, and Didemnidae the increase in egg size from the primitive diazonid and cionid egg is especially marked. In Polycitoridae and Polyclinidae, however, the eggs are not so large, and in these families and in the Didemnidae the increased amount of yolk in the egg is accommodated by its increased density [Berrill, 1935]. Therefore, in species of these families crowding inside the egg forces the adhesive papillae into a median vertical line, away from the primitive triradiate arrangement that persists in the Clavelinidae.

Generally in Phlebobranchia and Stolidobranchia individuals are large, eggs remain small, and the species are oviparous. Vegetative reproduction occurs only in the Perophoridae and Styelidae, where it is associated with reduction in zooid size, development of colonies, a development of viviparity, and increase in egg size, as in Aplousobranchia. Millar [1966], agreeing with Van Name [1945, p. 14] that budding (present otherwise only in the lower invertebrate phyla) must be a property of the ancestral ascidian rather than a process acquired within the class, considers that the process of pallial budding in Styelidae is homologous with the process in Aplousobranchia. Although the ectoderm initiates the process in all cases, the endoderm is also involved only in the Aplousobranchia. The proximity of the site of bud formation to gonadial and epicardial elements in both groups is probably merely fortuitous and cannot be considered as establishing an homology between aplousobranch and styelid forms of budding. It is most probable that vegetative reproduction is a process secondarily acquired in the Phlebobranchia and Stolidobranchia, causing trends within these groups that are parallel to, but independent of, the general evolutionary trend within the Aplousobranchia.

Viviparity also occurs in *Polycarpa* in the Styelidae and in the Molgulidae and Agnesiidae, but in neither of these groups is it associated with budding or re-

179

duced zooid size. The distance of the oviducal opening from the atrial opening appears to be the mechanism that ensures the retention of eggs within the peribranchial cavity. As with all viviparous species, the size of eggs increases owing to an accumulation of yolk.

With the development of viviparity there is also a change in the relative sizes of testis and ovary. In oviparous species both are large, producing large numbers of gametes to ensure sufficient density for fertilization. As viviparity develops, the size of the ovary relative to the size of the testis decreases, since the eggs are no longer subject to dispersal as are the male gametes. This change in relative size of gonads is observed from a comparison of these organs in genera of Euherdmaniinae (e.g. *Tylobranchion*) and Polyclininae.

The relationship within the class suggested by these functional and morphological characters is confirmed by the vanadium content. Records available at present suggest that all species of this class accumulate one or more elements of the group titanium, vanadium, chromium, manganese, iron, and niobium [Levine, 1961]. The most primitive forms accumulate principally vanadium to a marked degree. The extent to which the vanadium content is reduced and apparently replaced by a related metallic ion varies directly with the degree of phylogenetic development of the species concerned.

Primitive aplousobranch genera have a high vanadium content: *Ciona intestinalis, Diazona violacea* [Bertrand, 1950], *Eudistoma ritteri* [Levine, 1961], *Pycnoclavella stanleyi* [Trason, unpublished, see Levine, 1961], and *Euherdmania claviformis* [Goldberg et al., 1951]. More specialized aplousobranch genera have lower concentrations of vanadium: *Clavelina lepadiformis, Eudistoma vitreus, Didemnum* spp., *Aplidium* spp., *Morchellium* spp., and *Sidnyum* spp. [Bertrand, 1950].

A high vanadium content has also been recorded for phlebobranchiate genera: *Ascidia* spp., *Phallusia* spp. [Bertrand, 1950], *Perophora* sp. [Ciereszko et al., 1963], and *Chelyosoma* sp. [Kobayashi, 1949].

In stolidobranch genera vanadium is often present in small quantities, but it is more generally absent. It is known to be replaced in this group by iron in *Pyura stolonifera* [Endean, 1955], manganese in *Microcosmus glacialis* [Vinogradov, 1953], or niobium in *Molgula manhattensis* [Carlisle, 1958].

Only *Molgula manhattensis* [Carlisle, 1958] has been shown to retain the faculty to accumulate vanadium as an alternative to the related ion niobium. This fact was demonstrated by the presence of vana-

dium in a large proportion of the specimens of *M. manhattensis* examined.

Of particular note here is that *Pycnoclavella, Euherdmania*, and *Eudistoma* have a high vanadium content, whereas *Clavelina lepadiformis* and *Eudistoma vitreus* have only small quantities. This is in complete agreement with the relationships of *Polycitoridae, Pycnoclavella*, and *Euherdmania* hypothesized below and confirms the specialized nature of *Clavelinidae* and the inclusion of *Eudistoma vitreus* (Sars, 1851) (< *Atapozoa vitreus*; Kott, 1967, p. 187) in the Holozoinae.

CIONIDAE Lahille, 1890

Berrill [1936, 1950] considers *Ciona intestinalis* Linnaeus the most primitive known species of the class Ascidiacea. He bases his arguments on the morphological simplicity of the unfused epicardial sacs with a persistent opening into the branchial cavity and on the condition of the egg and larval and post-larval forms. Millar [1966], Van Name [1945], and Ärnbäck [1934] prefer to regard the species as secondarily specialized, on the basis of the increase in size of the individual, consequent loss of budding, elaboration of the branchial sac, and secondary retention of the epicardial openings. Further arguments are discussed below in favor of Berrill's hypothesis:

1.   The aplousobranch process of vegetative reproduction involving the epicardium requires a degree of specialization of that organ that is not present in *Ciona*, in which even regeneration does not involve the epicardium [Berrill, 1950], although it is involved in other Aplousobranchia [Nakauchi, 1966 and 1966a]. It is likely that the process of vegetative reproduction, once established, interrupts the growth of the individual zooid, thus causing a reduction in size. Therefore, it is unlikely that a larger solitary species would evolve from forms in which the pattern of vegetative reproduction was already established. Thus, the commitment of the epicardial sacs to specialized functions (vegetative reproduction, regeneration, or excretion) is considered a later development in the evolution of the class that is not yet achieved in *Ciona*, which is primitive both morphologically and functionally.

2.   Internal longitudinal vessels are continuous in this and smaller closely related species (e.g. *Diazona* spp.), and the branchial papillae fail to unite to form these vessels only in species that are considerably less primitive in other ways. Continuous internal longitudinal vessels may therefore be considered the terminal component in the normal sequence of develop-

ment of the branchial sac, which, under certain circumstances (e.g. size reduction), is interrupted.

3. The eggs are small and oviparous and the oviduct extends to the atrial aperture. The triradiate larval papillae are simple and are formed by enlarged ectodermal cells without accessory suckers or ampullae. Thus, the eggs, larvae, branchial sac, and epicardium of *Ciona intestinalis* probably represent a primitive rather than a secondarily acquired condition

from which ascidians, as they are known today, can be derived. *Ciona intestinalis* itself may have evolved from a slightly smaller stalked species [Ärnbäck, 1934], but in all probability that species was solitary and closely related to the present species.

DIAZONIDAE Garstang, 1891a

The family can be derived from *Ciona* by a reduction in the size of the zooids and the gradual development

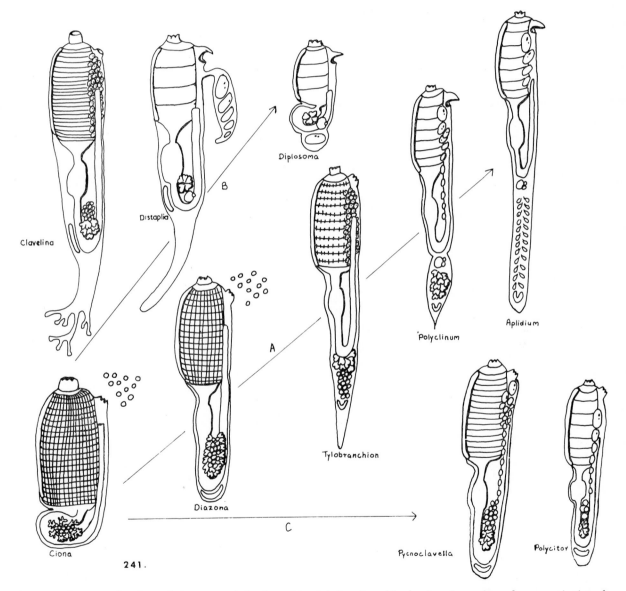

Fig. 241. Diagram of major evolutionary trends in the zooids of Aplousobranchia showing: increasing colony organization, decreasing size, branchial sac reduction, loss of longitudinal vessels; increasing viviparity, decrease in size of ovary, increase in size of egg, fertilization increasingly in oviduct.

A. Cionidae, Diazonidae, Euherdmaniinae, Polyclinidae.
B. Cionidae, Clavelininae, Holozoinae, Didemnidae.
C. Cionidae, Diazonidae, Polycitoridae.

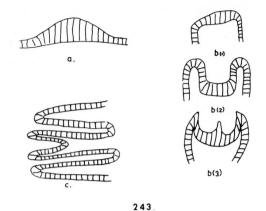

243.

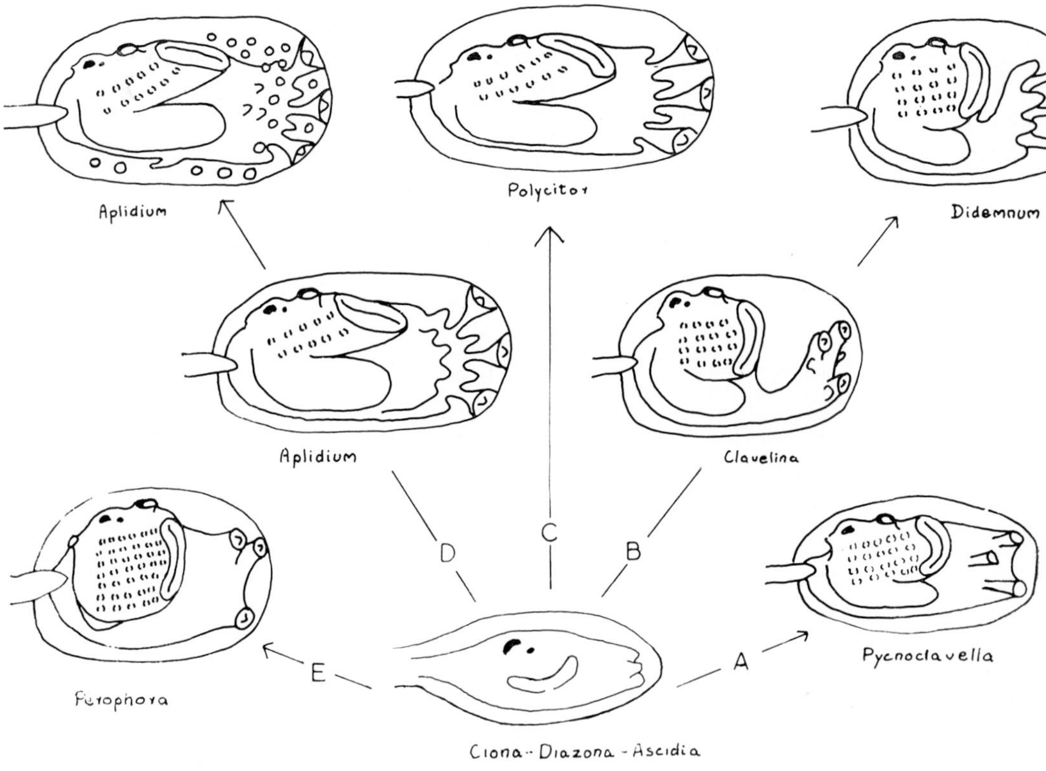

Aplidium

Polycitor

Didemnum

Aplidium

Clavelina

D   C   B

E   A

Pterophora

Pycnoclavella

Ciona - Diazona - Ascidia

242.

Fig. 242.   Diagram showing major trends in the evolution of larvae of Aplousobranchia.

A.   Papillary tubes.

B.   Larvae with frontal stalk.

C.   Absence of frontal stalk.

D.   Development of ampullary vesicles.

Fig. 243.

a.   Simple papilla of *Ciona.*

b.   Development of ectodermal papilliary cup (from *Clavelina baudinensis,* Kott 1957).

c.   Papilliary tube of *Pycnoclavella* [after Trason, 1963].

of vegetative reproduction. By a simple abdominal strobilation, a zooid may produce from 2 or 3 buds in *Rhopalea* [Ärnbäck, 1927] to 6 or 7 buds in *Diazona*. The solitary condition of the zooids is gradually lost with the development of budding, and, although some species of *Rhopalea* remain solitary, other species are joined by stolons and other genera are completely colonial (e.g. *Diazona*). The epicardium is present as a perivisceral sac, but in all species the cavities have become fused and have lost their connection with the branchial cavity. The internal longitudinal vessels of the branchial sac are uninterrupted.

The oviduct accompanies the rectum to the atrial opening; the eggs are small and oviparous. The larval papillae are arranged in a triangle [Berrill, 1950, p. 139, fig. 43E] and are developed by a local elongation of epidermal cells to form adhesive cells, as in *Ciona*.

The gut loop of the developing zooid is horizontal and posterior to the branchial sac, as in *Ciona*, but later it extends into the stalk as a characteristic vertical loop with the V-shaped heart at the base of the loop (e.g. *Diazona violacea*; Berrill, 1950, p. 139).

CLAVELINIDAE Forbes and Hanley, 1848

The family is here considered to comprise the subfamilies Clavelininae Seeliger, 1907, p. 1203, and Holozoinae Berrill, 1950.

The more primitive genera of the Clavelininae are in many ways closer to the genera of Cionidae than are the extant genera of the Polycitoridae. However, the clavelinid genera exhibit a wide range of characters that demonstrate increasing specialization of colony and zooid, culminating in the highly specialized Holozoinae.

As in other families of Aplousobranchia, the primary cause of differentiation appears to be asexual reproduction interrupting the growth of individual zooids and leading to size reduction and consequent loss of internal longitudinal vessels in the branchial sac. Vegetative reproduction in this group is highly specialized from the hypertrophied cionid vascular stolon, involving the epicardium in Holozoinae, although in Clavelininae the epicardium remains as an unspecialized perivisceral sac that does not extend into the vascular stolon. In view of the similarity of larval forms, it is proposed that the mechanism of budding in the Holozoinae developed from that in the Clavelininae by an involvement of the epicardium independent of the diazonid type of budding, which involves not only the epicardium but also the gut.

Thus, the family Clavelinidae may have evolved from the Cionidae before the development of the process of vegetative reproduction by abdominal strobilation, which characterizes the Diazonidae and Polycitoridae.

The specialized methods of budding in the Clavelinidae, involving the posterior abdominal vascular stolon only, interferes less with the functioning of parent zooids, and highly organized colonies develop, especially in the Holozoinae. These highly organized colonies provide ideal situations for the development of a high degree of viviparity.

Larval papillae usually have an ectodermal cuplike sucker, as in Polycitoridae. These papillae are arranged in a primitive triangle and are supported by short thick stalks from a stalked frontal plate, which is carried forward from the body of the larva, possibly a precursor of the vascular stolon. The oviduct terminates at the base of the peribranchial cavity and does not continue to the base of the atrial siphon as it does in oviparous families.

The heart is straight and situated vertically against the gut loop. In all other families of the Aplousobranchia the heart is V-shaped and more or less horizontal. It is possible that the enlargement of the blood vessel from one end of the heart into the hypertrophied vascular stolon has pulled the heart around into a vertical position and caused its straightening [Berrill, 1936].

(a) CLAVELININAE

Here the zooids are still fairly large and the branchial sac has a varying number of rows of stigmata, up to about 25 (*Clavelina enormis*; Kott, 1957), although there are only 2 in *Archiascidia neapolitana* Julin, 1904. The gut forms a long vertical loop with gonads enclosed in the loop. The zooids may be completely enclosed in the test or may still be more or less free, connected by stolons or partly embedded in common test. They open separately to the exterior by smooth-rimmed siphons, having lost the lobed apertures that are otherwise retained throughout the Ascidiacea.

Vegetative reproduction is achieved by budding from the isolated terminal ampullae of the stolonic vessel without involving the epicardium [Berrill, 1936 and 1950], a process exclusive to the Clavelininae.

Although genera are viviparous, remnants of primitive conditions persist and eggs are still numerous and fairly small and are fertilized in the peribranchial cavity or the anterior end of the oviduct [Berrill, 1936 and 1950], where they develop in great numbers. The larvae are not retained for very long and have a long free-swimming period [Berrill, 1935]. Eggs are not found developing from the base of the oviduct.

In *Clavelina lepadiformis* (Mueller) the close relationship of the Clavelininae with the primitive stock is further demonstrated. The frontal plate characteristic of clavelinid larvae supports the three triradiate stalked papillae, but these papillae do not have epidermal cups, and the adhesive cells are merely differentiated from the epidermal cells of the end of the papilla, as in Cionidae and Diazonidae. Gastrulation in *C. lepadiformis* is halfway between embolic (as in *Ciona* and *Diazona*) and epibolic (all other aplousobranchs) [Berrill, 1950].

Unless *C. lepadiformis* is exceptional, vegetative reproduction from a hypertrophied vascular stolon occurred in Clavelinidae before the development of epidermal papillary cups in the larvae. It is unlikely that, once this hypertrophy and mechanism of vegetative reproduction had been established, there would be a reversion to simple abdominal strobilation, which would be necessary if a direct relationship were to exist between Polycitoridae and Clavelinidae. Epidermal papillary cups therefore probably developed independently in both Polycitoridae and Clavelininae.

(b) HOLOZOINAE

The zooids are considerably reduced in size and the number of rows of stigmata is reduced to 3 or 4. The abdomen is reduced and the gut forms a more or less horizontal loop still enclosing the gonads. Although the gonads may extend from the gut loop in a stalked sac (e.g. *Distaplia* spp.) [Brewin, 1953], this extension does not represent a true continuation of the abdomen. Extension of the gonads into the proximal part of the stolonial stalk does occur, however, in *Hypsistozoa fasmeriana*, resembling the condition in Polyclinidae [Brewin, 1956b], although the heart remains alongside the gut loop, as is typical of Holozoinae.

Zooids are always enclosed in a common test, and, with the exception of a number of species in the genus *Atapoza* Brewin [Kott, 1967], they have lost their independent openings to the exterior, and the atrial siphon has been replaced by a sessile aperture with an anterior lip. Thus, highly efficient colonies are developed in which the zooids function as part of the colony and not as individuals. Often the sexual maturity of the individual is sacrificed for the sake of the colony, and sufficient gonad tissue for sexual reproduction is accumulated only after a number of asexual generations [Berrill, 1948a; Brewin, 1959],

which, nevertheless, produce zooids that contribute to the efficiency of the colony.

Although there is not complete agreement on the mechanism, budding occurs from the enlarged vascular stolon, into which the epicardium extends at the time of vegetative reproduction to become involved in the process [Berrill, 1948c and 1950; Brewin, 1959; Van Beneden and Selys Longchamps, 1913; Salfi, 1925]. This process sometimes commences in the larva [Brewin, 1959].

These highly organized colonies of Holozoinae provide ideal conditions for the developing embryo, and viviparity is enhanced by the formation of a brood pouch from a diverticulum of the oviduct, which projects into a sac from the postero-dorsal corner of the thorax and is consequently isolated from the zooid. The functioning of the zooid and of the colony is thus not prejudiced by developing embryos in the peribranchial cavity. The eggs are few and large. Berrill [1948a] states that fertilization occurs in the brood pouch; however, a developing embryo has been found in a pouch from the abdomen of *Atapozoa vitreus* (Sars, 1851) (> *Polycitor vitreus*; Berrill, 1948c). Eggs are therefore fertilized in the oviduct, although not always at the base of it.

The Holozoinae therefore have a more efficient mechanism of vegetative reproduction in which the epicardium has become involved, are considerably more advanced than the Clavelininae in colonial organization, and are more specialized for viviparity. They have achieved a great stability of the zooids, for all species greatly resemble one another in branchial sac, gut, and apertures. The main distinguishing characters between genera and species are found in the organization of the colonies.

POLYCITORIDAE Michaelsen, 1904a

(> DISTOMIDAE Giard, 1872)

Polycitoridae are conveniently described as 'dwarfed diazonids' [Berill, 1936 and 1950]. They probably developed from the Diazonidae by an increase in vegetative reproduction, which may be the cause of their considerable reduction in size and consequent modifications of the branchial sac, which result in the reduction of the number of stigmata in each row, the reduction in the number of rows of stigmata, and the loss of internal longitudinal vessels.

Zooids still bud by simple abdominal strobilation [Berrill, 1947; Nakauchi, 1966b]. Other differences indicate that considerable development has occurred and the family is further separated from the Diazonidae than is indicated by the form of the zooids. The family differs from the Diazonidae in characters associated with viviparity: The oviduct stops at the base of the peribranchial cavity; the eggs are few and large, are fertilized at the base of the oviduct, and commence their development as they pass up the duct into the peribranchial cavity, where they reach maturity. A limited number of embryos at different stages may be present in the atrial cavity at the same time. Larvae are generally smaller than the larvae of the Clavelinidae. The three anterior papillae have lost their triangular arrangement and have been forced into the mid-line, where they are arranged in a vertical row. The papillae have become stalked and an epidermal cup or sucker develops around the adhesive cells. Accessory adhesive ampullae develop from the larval epidermis between the bases of the suckers. Occasionally, lateral ampullae also develop from a lateral ridge on either side of the suckers [Kott, 1952a].

The increased rate of vegetative reproduction results in a large number of small zooids that remain completely embedded in the common test. The zooids in the colony do not, however, form systems, and both the atrial and the branchial apertures of each zooid remain unmodified and open independently to the exterior.

Polycitor circes Michaelsen [see Millar, 1963a] has an unusually large number of eggs developing in the oviduct and atrial cavity and may represent a more primitive condition similar to the situation in *Pycnoclavella* and in Euherdmaniinae, where the reduction in the number of embryos in relation to the development of viviparity has not been great.

Polycitor proliferus (Oka), the only described species of the family with ampullary vesicles in the larva, does not conform with the characteristics of this family and, on closer investigation, is found to belong to the genus *Ritterella* [see below; also Tokioka, 1953, pl. 25, fig. 8, and 1962, pl. 1 fig. 1] in the family Polyclinidae.

Pycnoclavella Garstang, 1891a has usually been considered a genus of the family Clavelinidae, closely related to *Clavelina* spp., which it resembles in the form of the zooid and the colony. However, many characters of the genus suggest closer affinities with Polycitoridae.

As with primitive oviparous ancestors, *Pycnoclavella* spp. produce a large number of eggs. In Clavelininae the eggs, fertilized in the atrial chamber, are soon released. In *Pycnoclavella*, however, viviparity has developed further and the eggs, fertilized at the

base of the oviduct, undergo considerable development before liberation, as in more primitive species of the Polycitoridae and certain genera of the Euherdmaniinae [Trason 1957 and 1963]. Budding in *Pycnoclavella* is by abdominal strobilation, as in Polycitoridae [Trason, 1963]. The heart in *Pycnoclavella* also indicates an affinity with Polycitoridae in that the orientation of the heart is to some extent variable and may be horizontal and barely curved (*Pycnoclavella aurilucens;* Berrill, 1947a, *Archidistoma aggregata;* Berrill, 1947 and 1948, and *Eudistoma olivacea;* Berrill, 1947 and 1948) or oblique and more or less V-shaped (*P. aurilucens, A. aggregatum,* and *E. olivacea;* Berrill, 1936). In Clavelinidae the heart is decidedly vertical and ventral to the gut loop rather than V-shaped or curved, horizontal or oblique, and associated with the posterior end of the body as in Polycitoridae and *Pycnoclavella.*

The larvae of species of this genus are unique. In *Pycnoclavella stanleyi* [Trason, 1963; Berrill and Abbott, 1949] the larva has unusual deeply invaginated papillae that completely evert on fixation. *Pycnoclavella aurilucens* Garstang is also described as having adhesive organs with 'stalk deeply invaginated' [Berrill, 1947a, p. 245]. *Pycnoclavella minuta* Millar, 1953, has similar larvae, although here the number of papillae are reduced to 2. Larvae of *P. stanleyi, P. aurilucens,* and *P. minuta* are also unique in that an otolith is absent, although an ocellus is present. Berrill [1935] suggests that the larval form indicates a close relationship of the group with Synoicidae. However, the 'ectodermal ampullae,' which suggest homology with those of the Synoicidae, are, in fact, longitudinal foldings of the larval epidermis that extend forward around the base of the suckers and are not discrete anteriorly directed fingerlike processes [Trason, 1963, figs. 11, 14; Berrill and Abbott, 1949, fig. 2d]. The form of the larval papillae does, however, suggest a relationship with Euherdmaniinae, which is the only other group in which this unique type of papilla has been described [Trason, 1957, and *Placentela translucida,* p. 42].

The partial embedding of zooids, the branchial sac, the course of the gut, the triradiate arrangement of papillae, and the large number of eggs indicate an affinity with *Clavelina* spp., but they share only the characters that are relatively primitive. In maintenance of the unmodified form of vegetative reproduction, together with the more specialized process of fertilization at the base of the oviduct and the position of the heart, this genus resembles most nearly the Polycitoridae. The most likely explanation of its origin is that it is an early derivation from the diazonid stock by increased budding and increasing viviparity. The genus diverges from Polycitoridae by special development of the larval adhesive papillae, differing from the cuplike ectodermal suckers of other enterogonid ascidians.

POLYCLINIDAE Verrill, 1871

(> SYNOICIDAE Hartmeyer, 1908)

This family is characterized by the dwarfing and the withdrawal of the gut [Berrill, 1936 and 1950], which leave the gonads, epicardium, and V-shaped heart in the posterior abdomen. Reduction in the size of the branchial sac has led to a loss of internal longitudinal vessels, but in some species traces of these longitudinal vessels remain as papillae on the transverse vessels. There is always a primitive V-shaped heart. Vegetative reproduction is by primitive strobilation of the posterior abdomen and occasionally of the abdomen as well [Millar, 1962a; Nakauchi, 1966 and 1966a].

Carlisle [1953] has hypothesized an origin of the Polyclinidae from Polycitoridae based on the tendency of the gonads to 'spill over' into a posterior abdomen and a similarity of larval form in *Polycitor crystallinus* Renier. In *P. crystallinus*, however, the gonads, heart, and gut loop bear the same relationships as they have in the diazonids, from which both families are probably derived. The gut is not withdrawn from the heart, and it is unlikely that the gut is withdrawn from the gonads. The 'spilling over' of testis follicles, so that they extend posterior to the gut loop, occurs in many species of Polycitoridae with mature gonads, but it does not necessarily indicate a withdrawal of the gut. The condition may be contributed to by the general decrease in body size that is so marked in Polycitoridae. Further, the larval ampullae in Polycitoridae derived primarily from the mid-line between the suckers are not homologous with those of Polyclininae developed from the lateral ridges [Kott, 1957]. In *P. crystallinus* the long oviduct extends halfway up the branchial sac; there are a large number of rows of stigmata and a long gut loop, all primitive characters indicating that the species is closer to its diazonid ancestors than many other species of the genus, and, as indicated above, probably does not represent an immediate ancestor of the Polyclinidae.

A similar argument is given (*Hypsistozoa fasmeriana*; Brewin, 1956b) for the origin of Polyclinidae from Clavelinidae. However, here also the extension of gonads into the posterior abdomen is due to a general reduction in the size of the abdomen rather than a withdrawal of the gut from other structures, and the heart remains straight and alongside the gut.

Together with the position of gonads and heart in relation to the gut loop, the persistence of the longitudinal muscles on the posterior abdomen in Polyclinidae adds further to the evidence that the position of the gonads in this family is a result of gut withdrawal and shortening of the loop rather than the 'spilling over' of gonads indicated in Polycitoridae and in Holozoinae, in which the gut loop is already considerably shortened so that further withdrawal is unlikely. It will be seen in the discussion of polyclinid genera below that the family is probably polyphyletic, and, although some genera may share a common ancestor with Polycitoridae, the whole family cannot be regarded as being derived therefrom.

(a) EUHERDMANIINAE

This subfamily is distinguished by separate siphonal openings to the exterior. Common cloacal systems are not developed. The subfamily is, however, extremely variable and problematical affinities exist [Kott, 1957 and 1963, and below]. Generally, a relatively primitive condition is indicated by the large numbers of embryos developing in the oviduct, which represents a relic of oviparity. Genera comprising the subfamily are discussed below.

Tylobranchion Herdman, 1886 (monotypic)

This genus is represented only by the antarctic species *Tylobranchion speciosum* Herdman. The zooids are only partly embedded in the common test and exhibit many primitive characters. The gut is partly withdrawn from the gonads and V-shaped heart (posterior to the gonads) in a posterior abdomen. Biramous papillae representing internal longitudinal branchial vessels are present. The oviduct extends halfway up the peribranchial cavity, where the eggs are fertilized and many embryos develop. The ovary, posterior to the testis, is very large. Embryos are probably retained in the peribranchial cavity for a very short period, as only two colonies have been taken with embryos [Berrill, 1935; Millar, 1960] and, although many specimens exist in the present collection, no embryos are present. The larvae have triradiate stalked papillae with ectodermal cups but no ampullae [Millar, 1960].

The genus is therefore separated from the Diazonidae by an increased rate of budding, reduction of longitudinal vessels, partial withdrawal of the gut, and the development of viviparity. Viviparity has developed only to the stage (found also in the Clavelininae) at which eggs liberated from the oviduct are fertilized in the peribranchial cavity and produce numerous embryos all at the same stage of development. In more highly evolved forms, in which viviparity is further established, eggs, fertilized at the base of the oviduct, produce embryos at different stages of development.

Protopolyclinum Millar, 1960
(incl. *Pseudodiazona* Millar, 1963a)

This genus also retains traces of longitudinal vessels in the branchial sac, but zooids are completely embedded, the gut loop is completely withdrawn from the posterior abdomen, and numerous developing eggs are present in the oviduct. This genus has therefore achieved a greater degree of viviparity than *Tylobranchion* by the fertilization of eggs at the base of the oviduct. In both *Protopolyclinum pedunculatum* Millar, 1960, and *P. claviforme* Kott, 1963, the esophagus crosses the rectum and the gonads are in a cluster in the posterior abdomen. In these species the testis is particularly well developed and extends back into the posterior abdomen leaving the small ovary anterior, in contrast to *Tylobranchion*, in which the ovary is large and the testis is comparatively small. This special development of testis lobes and the reduction of the ovary reflect the condition of a species in which increased viviparity results in a reduction of the number of eggs and a relative increase in the concentrations of sperm in the surrounding medium. Gonads of *Pseudodiazona sabulosa* Millar, 1963a, were not present, but the shape of the abdomen suggests that they would be in a cluster similar to the cluster of *Protopolyclinum pedunculatum* and *P. claviforme*.

The three species mentioned above show a gradation from complete internal longitudinal vessels (*Pseudodiazona sabulosa*) to occasional complete vessels (*Protopolyclinum claviforme*) to all internal longitudinal vessels reduced to papillae (*Protopolyclinum pedunculatum*). *Pseudodiazona sabulosa* should therefore be known as *Protopolyclinum sabulosa* (Millar).

Larvae are known for *P. pedunculatum* Millar, 1960, and they were probably immature. However, they have stalked papillae with ectodermal cups and ampullae from the lateral ridge, as in Polyclininae, although vesicles are not present.

The genus is closely related to *Tylobranchion*.

Euherdmania Ritter, 1904

Zooids of this genus are not generally embedded in the common test. They have numerous rows of stigmata and usually 4 stomach folds. Larvae are identical with the larvae of *Pycnoclavella* spp., in which the papillae are deeply invaginated and often reduced to 2. The colonies also resemble the colonies of *Pycnoclavella* in that the zooids are not completely embedded in the common test; the zooids are similar in the great number of embryos developing in the oviduct. Larvae of *Euherdmania claviformis*; Trason, 1957, *E. vitrea* Millar, 1961, and *E. digitata* Millar, 1963a, are known. Larvae are not known, however, for *E. solida* Millar, 1953, and *E. australis* Kott, 1957. The latter species is unusual because it has parastigmatic vessels and 18 stomach folds. It probably does not belong in this genus. *Euherdmania claviformis* has an unfused epicardium reminiscent of *Ciona*. This may indicate an origin from a primitive *Pycnoclavella* spp. before the fusion of the epicardium.

Placentela Redikorzev, 1913 (> *Sigillinaria* Oka, 1933; *Homoeodistoma* Redikorzev, 1927)

Placentela is distinguished from *Euherdmania* [Kott, 1963] by the absence of folds in the stomach and by the presence of zooids embedded in the common test. The two genera are, however, closely related, and, in view of variations in the condition of the stomach [*P. areolata* Kott, 1963], generic separation may not be justified. Although seven species of *Placentela*, including *P. michaelseni* (Redikorzev) and *P. longigona* (Tokioka) [Kott, 1963, p. 72], have been described, larvae are known only from *P. translucida* new species in the present collection, in which, as in *Euherdmania* spp., there are 2 deeply invaginated adhesive papillae. However, the larva more closely resembles the larva of most *Pycnoclavella* spp., in which, in addition to the form of the adhesive papillae, the otolith is absent. The zooids of most species have large numbers of embryos developing in the oviduct, as in *Euherdmania* and in the genera *Pycnoclavella*, *Protopolyclinum*, and *Pseudodistoma*.

It is possible that *Placentela arenosa* (Brewin, 1950b), with parastigmatic vessels and a smooth stomach, like *Euherdmania australis* Kott, 1957, with parastigmatic vessels and numerous stomach folds, has been assigned to the wrong genus (see *Ritterella* below).

Pseudodistoma Michaelsen, 1924

Millar [1954c] states, '*Pseudodistoma* may be regarded as a genus of the family Synoicidae; but one which retains much of the organization that we may ascribe to the common ancestors of the families Polycitoridae and Synoicidae.' This pronouncement is mainly based on the 3 rows of stigmata in the branchial sac and on the distribution of branchial tentacles in more than one circle at the base of the siphon. The gonads in this genus are far back in the posterior abdomen, as if a withdrawal of the gut occurred without simultaneous development of the testis. However, eggs are fertilized at the base of the long oviduct and reach maturity in the peribranchial chamber. It is possible that a large number of developing embryos present in the oviduct force the gonads back into the posterior end of the abdomen. Serial arrangement of testis follicles occurs in all species except *P. fragilis* Tokioka (see below).

Larvae of *P. australis* Kott, 1957, *P. cereum* Michaelsen [Brewin, 1958], and *P. africanum* Millar, 1954a and 1962, are known and resemble the larvae of *Eudistoma renieri* (Hartmeyer), *E. pyriforme* (Herdman), and *E. arenosum* Kott, 1957, respectively. Therefore, although the number of embryos produced suggests a more primitive condition than generally found in the extant Polycitoridae, there are indications of an origin from an *Eudistoma*-like ancestor, in which the branchial sac is similarly reduced to 3 rows of stigmata. The serial arrangement of testis follicles is probably a subsequent development, resulting from their increase and a simultaneous increase in the length of the posterior abdomen. The increase in length of the posterior abdomen would make possible an increase in the rate of asexual reproduction by primitive strobilation in which a specialized mechanism of budding had not developed, as in Holozoinae.

Pseudodistoma fragilis Tokioka, 1958, is exceptional. The larvae are similar to the larvae of Holozoinae, with 3 triradiate papillae on broad short stalks from an expanded frontal plate. This arrangement of papillae, together with a holozoinid-type brood pouch from the postero-dorsal corner of the thorax and the 3 rows of stigmata, suggests the genus *Atapozoa*. The sac-like posterior abdomen is connected to the abdomen by a long stalk reminiscent of the condition in *Distaplia* spp. [Brewin, 1953]. The origin of this species is therefore probably from the Holozoinae.

Ritterella Harant, 1931

Here, as in *Pseudodistoma*, the testis follicles are often serially arranged, but *Ritterella* spp. are distinguished by a reduction in the number of ova and developing embryos and by the persistence of a larger number of rows of stigmata. Thus, viviparity is better developed here than in most genera of this subfamily, although the branchial sac is not so reduced as in *Pseudodistoma*. Where larvae are known, they have 3 stalked papillae with ectodermal cups in a median vertical line and generally ampullae from paired lateral lines, as in *Protopolyclinum* and in the Polyclininae. The ampullae often proliferate into vesicles, as in Polyclininae. The genus appears to stand somewhere between *Protopolyclinum* and *Aplidium* and may represent the immediate ancestor of the latter genus.

Polycitor proliferus (Oka) [Tokioka, 1953, pl. 25, fig. 8 and 1962, pl. 1, fig. 1] is identical with *Ritterella dispar* Kott, 1957 and 1963. Both species have, in the field, the same bluish-white tinge in the test. The arrangement of zooids in the test is similar, there are 5 rows of stigmata and about 20 stomach folds in each. The larvae of both are also similar and have the ampullary vesicles characteristic of Polyclininae. In the Australian specimens the posterior abdomen is larger than that described for specimens from Japan. However, the testis follicles in both forms are bunched and posterior to the ovary. The species should be known as *Ritterella proliferus* (Oka). *Ritterella yamazii* Tokioka, 1949a, is a similar species, with ampullary vesicles in the larvae, 5 rows of stigmata, a short posterior abdomen, and a similar colony. There are fewer stomach folds, however.

Ritterella sigillinoides (Brewin, 1958) also has 5 rows of stigmata and stomach folds, but the colony is stalked, and the posterior abdomen is correspondingly long. The larvae have median ampullae of polycitorid type, apparently not paired or broken into vesicles. This species may therefore be developed from a polycitorid ancestor and have affinities with *Pseudodistoma*, from which it differs mainly in the number of rows of stigmata in the branchial sac.

Ritterella pedunculata Tokioka, 1953, *R. australis* (Kott, 1957) (> *Euherdmania australis*), and *R. arenosa* (Brewin, 1950b) (> *Placentela arenosa*) all have 9 to 12 rows of stigmata, a long posterior abdomen, and parastigmatic vessels. The first two species mentioned have numerous stomach folds; however, the stomach of the third species is not described. They are all undoubtedly closely related and adequately accommodated in this genus, but unfortunately, no larvae are known and neither their affinities nor the significance of the parastigmatic vessels can be determined. Their presence in this genus is probably independent of analogous vessels in Holozoinae. Some species of *Aplidium* and

Synoicium also have parastigmatic vessels and may be related to these *Ritterella* spp.

Dumus areniferus Brewin, 1952, monotypic, with 4 rows of stigmata but with a smooth stomach, may have affinities with the genus *Ritterella*. Although the zooids are separate, this condition may not be as significant as previously thought, because *Euherdmania australis*, clearly a species of *Ritterella*, also has separate zooids.

(b) POLYCLININAE

Zooids are organized into systems and are, like the Euherdmaniinae, derived from several sources. However, most larvae of the Polyclininae have lateral paired lobes and often have median ampullary lobes as well, and both of these types of lobe may be broken into vesicles. This uniformity of larvae suggests a fairly recent common ancestor. *Polyclinum* Savigny, 1816, with twisted gut, sac-like posterior abdomen, and relics of internal longitudinal vessels as papillae in the branchial sac, is clearly related to *Protopolyclinum* in the Euherdmaniinae and possibly developed from it by proliferation of lateral ampullae in the larvae, by organization of cloacal systems, and by loss of longitudinal muscles from the posterior abdomen. *Aplidium* Savigny, 1816, *Synoicium* Phipps, 1774, and related genera with a straight gut loop and often serially arranged testis follicles are most closely related to *Ritterella* spp., from which they are distinguished only by the cloacal systems. The similarity of larval structure indicates an hypothesis involving *Protopolyclinum* as an ancestor for both *Ritterella* and *Polyclinum*, unless ampullae proliferated independently, which is not as likely in this case. Ectodermal cups, already present in *Tylobranchion* and in Polycitoridae, may indicate their early origin before Polycitoridae branched off the ancestral stock, but after differentiation of *Clavelina*. The presence of ectodermal suckers on the papillae in *Polycitor*, *Tylobranchion*, and *Protopolyclinum* may indicate an early common ancestry. *Synoicium tentaculatum*, new species in the present collection, has a larva with deeply invaginated triradiate papillae resembling the larvae of *Euherdmania* spp. and indicating a relationship with *Euherdmania* and *Pycnoclavella*.

DIDEMNIDAE Giard, 1872

As in all highly evolved forms (e.g. Holozoinae), this family is very uniform. Zooids of all species are small, with 3 or 4 rows of stigmata and a highly developed common cloacal system. Longitudinal muscles from the thorax extend away from the abdo-men of the zooid into the surrounding test as a retractor muscle. Paired epicardial chambers are present in the esophageal region and are thought to represent persisting anterior horns of the primitive paired outgrowths in *Ciona*. It is possible, however, that they are reduced paired chambers that have not fused. Stolonic vessels are present, originating from the esophageal region rather than from the end of the zooid. Viviparity is well advanced and developing ova are retained in the test of the colony; each zooid produces only very few ova. There is no oviduct. As in species of Holozoinae, for which there is specialized colonial organization, generations of sexually immature zooids occur before sexual reproduction can occur. Budding is a very specialized process from the esophageal region, involving the epicardium [see Berrill, 1950]. Precocious budding may also occur in the larvae, especially in *Lissoclinum* spp. Larvae have epidermal ampullae developed from the lateral line on either side of the papillae, which are stalked with epidermal cups.

The origin of the family is obscure because of its extreme specialization. The adult process of budding in Didemnidae is specialized but resembles the primitive strobilation of *Eudistoma* 'where the zooid tends to constrict into two parts at the level of the anterior horns of the epicardia, the anterior part regenerating a new posterior, and the posterior regenerating a new anterior part. The mysterious aspect of budding in *Diplosoma* thus becomes merely the factor that induces the regenerative processes of the anterior and posterior parts, while there is yet apparently a normal morphological continuity between them' [Berrill, 1935, p. 349]. The mechanism in *Distaplia* spp. is also a modification of simple strobilation involving a posterior abdominal stolonic extension [Berrill, 1948a]. Here, as in Didemnidae, the gut is not primarily involved. Therefore, no evidence is available from the budding process that suggests the phylogeny of Didemnidae. Larval budding occurs in both Holozoinae and Didemnidae, but this fact does not indicate a phylogenetic relationship. In larvae of Holozoinae buds develop from a stolonic extension of the epicardium [Berrill, 1948a], and in the larvae of Didemnidae they develop directly from the epicardium. Thus, the respective processes are merely extensions into the larvae of the adult processes.

In the present collection *Diplosoma antarcticum* new species has larval papillae with extended adhesive areas, as in *Atapozoa* spp. (Holozoinae as amended by Kott, 1967). Further, the testis lobes of *D. antarcticum* new species are numerous and are arranged in a rosette reminiscent of Holozoinae. Just these characters suggest the phylogenetic affinities of the Didemnidae and favor their evolution from the Holozoinae.

PEROPHORIDAE Giard, 1872

The branchial sac has internal longitudinal vessels or, in smaller species, traces of them as papillae. The gut loop curves up on the left of the branchial sac, as in Ascidiidae, and the heart lies across the right side of the branchial sac, as in all phlebobranch and stolidobranch ascidians. These characters support a relationship with Ascidiidae, possibly representing a stage in the 'trend from *Ciona* to the Ascidiidae' [Berrill, 1936, p. 61]. Unlike species of Ascidiidae, however, individual zooids are connected by stolons with mesenchymatous septa from which buds develop. This stolon (homologous with ventral test vessel of *Ciona*), having developed the power to bud, which is usually associated with dwarfed zooids, indicates a specialization characteristic of the family. In both Clavelininae and Perophoridae buds develop from the stolon and its mesenchymatous septum. The process is, however, different; organic continuity, lost in Clavelininae, is maintained in the Perophoridae and both processes may develop independently.

There is 'some abbreviation and much acceleration' in the development of the perophorid embryo [Berrill, 1935]. The eggs of Perophoridae are viviparous [Kott, 1952; Berrill, 1950] and gastrulation is embolic, as in Cionidae and Ascidiidae [Berrill, 1935], but the eggs are more yolky than the eggs of *Ciona, Diazona,* and *Ascidia.* Larvae have 3 papillae with ectodermal cups on short broad stalks and no ampullae, most nearly resembling larvae of *Clavelininae;* however, because of the abbreviation and acceleration, the perophorid larva is distinguished by many rows of definitive stigmata.

Berrill [1936, p. 61] remarks, 'There are two valves between the posterior end of the stomach and the hind part of the intestine that suggest forcibly that the gut-loop once occupied the stalk. . . .' In *Distaplia, Diplosoma,* and *Ecteinascidia,* however, the valves are at the base of the ascending part of the intestine and are probably evolved independently in association with the ascending intestine and are not necessarily indicative of an origin from the vertical abdominal gut loop of Aplousobranchia.

Despite the similarities of stolon and larval form with Clavelininae, the branchial sac, the position of heart, the gut loop, and the nature of eggs indicate an affinity with the Ascidiidae. These characters are here considered more important, and derivation from an early ancestor of the Ascidiidae before the loss of cionid stolon and before the epicardium became involved in excretion or budding is considered most likely, followed by great specialization involving budding from the stolon, consequent reduction in size, loss of the epicardium, development of viviparity, increase in yolk, and development of papillary suckers in the larvae.

CORELLIDAE Lahille, 1887; ASCIDIIDAE Herdman,
1880; AGNESIIDAE Huntsman, 1912

These three families are probably derived from *Ciona* by the shifting of the gut, gonads, and heart to a position alongside the branchial sac. Short transverse muscles are developed around the dorsal and ventral borders of the body; internal longitudinal vessels are retained; the epicardium is developed into renal vesicles. Species are usually oviparous with small eggs. Larvae are similar to the larvae of *Ciona* [see Berrill, 1950]. Coiled stigmata occur in the Agnesiidae and Corellidae.

In Agnesiidae the gut remains on the left, as in Ascidiidae, and the intestine, after leaving the stomach, loops anteriorly and dorsally. In Corellidae, however, the gut loop is on the right, the distal limb of the loop is posterior to the stomach, and the rectum crosses the esophagus. The gut loop does not actually turn in opposite directions in these families, but, from its primitive horizontal course in *Ciona*, where the intestine bends to the left and then dorsally to form the loop, it is forced up on the left or right in Ascidiidae and Corellidae, respectively, while maintaining the initial relationships of its various parts. Alternatively, Herdman's [1888] suggestion of the backward extension of the branchial sac to overlap the gut is a likely explanation of the situation and would also account for the position of the heart across the right side of the branchial sac, and in Corellidae above the stomach. Thus, Agnesiinae and Ascidiidae could be derived from Cionidae via Ciallusiinae by modifications of the branchial sac. Corellinae are probably also developed from Cionidae via Rhodosomatinae by a similar process.

In *Ciallusia longa* Van Name the epicardium has not been detected, and this fact, together with the presence of a stalk, has suggested a relationship with the Perophoridae [Millar, 1963]. The stalk is a primitive character, however, probably persisting from the ancestral cionid. The genus also resembles Perophoridae in the position of the heart and condition of the branchial sac, but these characters are shared by most phlebobranch ascidians. The musculature, as in Agnesiidae, consists of short independent transverse bands around the right and left borders of the body. The species is regarded here as a member of the family Agnesiidae, separating from the Agnesiinae before the coiling of stigmata, loss of stalk, or reduction of internal longitudinal vessels.

Pterygascidia mirabilis Sluiter, 1904, has body musculature and branchial sac similar to those of *Ciallusia longa*; Tokioka, 1967. The course of the gut is also similar: '. . . gerade nach vorn ohne eine Biegung oder Schlinge zu bilden' [Sluiter, 1904, p. 23]. In younger specimens the gut is on the left, as in *C. longa*, and in both the dorsal lamina has pointed languets. The two species, separated by the development of large atrial lips in *Pterygascidia*, comprise the Ciallusiinae.

The dorsal lamina has often been regarded as indicating affinities, and both *Caenagnesia* and Ascidiidae have a ribbed dorsal lamina, whereas in Corellidae the dorsal languets of *Ciona* persist. In *Agnesia* the dorsal lamina is reduced to a flat membrane and the transverse vessels continue as ribs across it, confirming the position of *Caenagesia*, as indicated by the branchial sac, as less specialized than *Agnesia*.

The short transverse muscles around the borders of the body are mainly responsible for any specialization in species of this group. These muscles by contraction effect the characteristic lateral flattening. There is a tendency for these muscles to divide across the mid-line. This is especially true for Agnesiidae, in which special lateral folds of test for the protection of the apertures are often associated with the shorter, independent, and more versatile transverse muscles on the right and left (e.g. *Caenagnesia bocki* and *Agnesia glaciata*). Generally, species are not very diverse and these families probably represent a very ancient group.

Chelyosoma Broderip and Sowerby, 1830, with test modified into horny plates, is probably the only genus of Ascidiacea for which a fossil record exists: a chelyosome-like organism from the Permian [Jaekel, 1951; *cf.* Colonization, p. 205].

Hypobythiidae Sluiter, 1895

This family has previously accommodated only *Hypobythius* Moseley, 1876, a genus closely related to the Corellinae. The gut forms an elongate loop on the dorsal edge of the branchial sac, as in *Corynascidia* Herdman, 1882, and the very irregular

arrangement of stigmata suggests a relationship with forms having spiral stigmata.

Benthascidia Ritter, 1907, is also considered to be related to *Corynascidia* and has been placed in the Corellidae (> Rhodosomatidae) [Ritter, 1907; Hartmeyer, 1912; Van Name, 1945; and Millar, 1955a]. Although its morphology is known only from two very damaged specimens, it also has a branchial sac similar to that of *Hypobythius* and is consequently considered here as a genus of the family Hypobythiidae.

Dicopia Sluiter, 1905, and *Megalodicopia* Oka, 1918, have similar irregular stigmata and the gut loop is posterior to the branchial sac with the opening slightly to the right. It therefore appears to be a more accurate representation of their phylogeny to group these two aberrant genera with *Hypobythius* in the family Hypobythiidae rather than with *Pterygascidia* Sluiter (a genus of the Ciallusiinae; see above) in the family Pterygascidiidae, as Hartmeyer [1912] had done.

The family therefore comprises four highly specialized genera related to the Corellidae, and in particular to the Corellinae. It is characterized by complete loss of internal longitudinal branchial vessels and by very irregular stigmata. It is especially closely related to *Xenobranchion* in the Corellinae, from which it is distinguished by the retention of vestiges of internal longitudinal vessels in the form of branchial papillae in *Xenobranchion*.

Styelidae Sluiter, 1895; Pyuridae Hartmeyer, 1908; Molgulidae Lacaze-Duthiers, 1877

These three families, comprising the Stolidobranchia, are distinguished by elaboration and folding of the branchial sac and duplication of the gonads so that they occur on both sides of the body. Vegetative reproduction occurs only in Polyzoinae and Botryllinae, subfamilies of the Styelidae, by a process of simple evagination of the body wall involving the ectoderm only [Berrill, 1950]. It is significant that here, as in Aplousobranchia, vegetative reproduction is associated with reduction in size, reduction in the branchial sac, and formation of colonies. Ectodermal ampullae develop in the larvae, but no ectodermal suckers are present around the papillae. Papillae themselves are often lost in the Molgulidae. Each family exhibits great stability in the structure of the branchial sac except in the dwarfed branchial sac, where folds are often completely lost and there is a considerable reduction in the number of internal longitudinal vessels. As with Phlebobranchia, the epi-

PHYLOGENY OF ASCIDIACEA

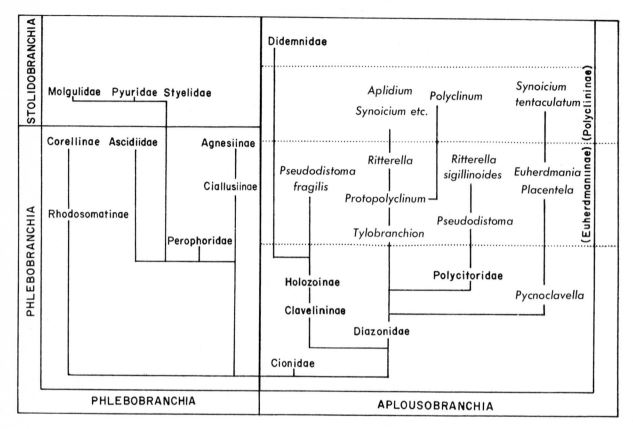

cardium is used in the process of excretion. Generally it breaks up into vesicles; however, the Molgulidae are distinguished by the persistence of a discrete renal organ on the right body wall, which thus maintains a more or less primitive position in relation to the heart.

The genus *Styela* has been distinguished from *Cnemidocarpa* because of the association of testis follicles with the ovarian tube in the *Cnemidocarpa*. This dichotomy is not always clearly expressed. Although in some species the mature testis follicles remain compactly beneath or around the ovary, this is not always the case (see *S. nordenskjoldi* above) and maturation of testis follicles involves an increase

in size that can result in the spread of these lobes to a position on the body wall, removed from the ovary. In the present work *Cnemidocarpa* is retained to accommodate the few species in which the testis follicles actually extend into and mingle with the ovary (*Cnemidocarpa verrucosa*). The testis follicles in *Polycarpa* spp. are mixed with ovarian tissue in the polycarps. A reduction in the number of the gonads and an increase in their length lead to the condition in *Cnemidocarpa* spp. in which the ovarian and testicular components remain mingled. In *Styela* the testis follicles are alongside the ovarian tissue on the body wall and may extend outward from the sides of the ovary, sometimes completely removed from it.

9. ZOOGEOGRAPHIC DISCUSSION

ANY DISCUSSION of the more obvious physical factors influencing the distribution of these benthic organisms, which generally occur below the intertidal zone in Antarctica, involves some consideration of the nature and topography of the ocean floor in the area concerned, as well as other aspects of oceanography and environment. The geological history of the area and the evolution of species and their phylogenetic relationships to species in adjacent geographical areas are also relevant to a consideration of the pattern of distribution of these benthic organisms.

ENVIRONMENT

Topography

The antarctic continent is surrounded by the waters of the Indian, Atlantic, and Pacific oceans, here collectively regarded as the Southern Ocean, which, in the Atlantic-Indian, South Indian, and Southeast Pacific basins, surround the continent with waters 4000 to 5000 meters deep. The only contemporary connection with subantarctic oceanic islands and land masses to the north is by a series of submarine ridges, which still have, to varying extents gaps in them up to 4000 meters deep. Thus, the topography of the ocean bottom surrounding the antarctic continent presents no barriers to the circumpolar distribution of species of the sublittoral continental shelf or of the deeper parts of the continental slope. The northward spread of the contemporary antarctic species, on the other hand, is limited by the oceanic basins and by the deeper gaps that interrupt the continuity of shallower water on the submarine ridges. Only abyssal species confined to depths greater than 4000 meters are limited by the topography of the ocean floor in their circumpolar range.

Oceanography

The antarctic convergence occurs at about 50°S, although it is forced farther to the south by warm east-Australian, Pacific, and Brazilian currents. North of the Weddell Sea, which is important oceanographically as the origin of all antarctic bottom waters affecting oceanographic and consequently biological conditions [Ostapoff, 1965], the convergence reaches its farthest point north. Thus the Falkland Islands are to the

north of the antarctic convergence, whereas South Georgia, although geographically not much farther south, lies to the east and is well south of the convergence. Also, affected by conditions in the Weddell Sea, the surface temperature at Marion Island is lower than that at Campbell Island, although Marion Island lies considerably to the north of Campbell.

Seasonal fluctuations are reflected by the extent of the pack ice around the antarctic continent. The pack ice reaches its northernmost limit (about 60°S) in September, and, with the onset of melting in December, reaches its most southern latitude (65° to 70°S) in March. February to March is the period of rising temperature and lowering salinity off South Georgia, where the temperature at 75 meters reaches a maximum of 1.5°C in March. The salinity is then at its lowest (33‰) [Discovery Reports 4, 1932; Mackintosh, 1946]. Pack ice continually surrounds the western side of Antarctica, except for the tip of the Antarctic Peninsula, whereas on the eastern side it recedes almost to the coast in the summer.

Owing to the circumpolar winds and the circulatory characteristics, little seasonal variation in temperature and salinity occurs in the waters around the antarctic continent below 200 meters. At the 75-meter level, however, seasonal trends prevail but diurnal variations are not apparent. The annual temperature variation at the surface is only 2°C; the variation in salinity in the immediate vicinity of melting ice [Sverdrup et al., 1942; Deacon, 1937] ranges from 32.0 to 34.5‰. These conditions extend to the north as far as the antarctic convergence. North of the convergence the surface waters are characterized by steadily rising temperatures, which subject the sublittoral and shelf fauna of the subantarctic islands to great seasonal variations in both temperature and salinity as terrestrial runoff and melting ice dilute the water. At greater depths, however, the antarctic water sinking beneath the warmer subantarctic surface water extends the antarctic conditions farther to the north, although the antarctic water becomes increasingly diluted with the warmer surface water. Thus, in the geographical regions that are characterized as subantarctic because of the physical conditions of their surface waters the temperature and salinity at depths greater than 4000 meters are the same as those of the shallower waters around the antarctic continent. Between 4000 and 1000 meters there is an increase of only 3°C, although at the surface the temperature may increase to 20°C.

Therefore, although climatic conditions, temperature, and salinity of the water may constitute limitations to the latitudinal range of species from antarctic to subantarctic regions at depths down to 1000 meters, they are unlikely to influence benthic fauna below this depth. Thus, the antarctic convergence, which marks the transition from antarctic to subantarctic fauna in the surface layers, is not so clear-cut a boundary for the benthic fauna [Broch, 1961].

Substrate

The antarctic continent for the greater part of the year is surrounded by ice. From the shore line to a depth of about 4 meters the area tends to be swept clean of macrofauna by moving ice [Powell, 1965, p. 333]. From about 4 meters down to about 50 meters, algae provide food and shelter for a great variety of animal life. In water deeper than 50 meters terrigenous and pelagic deposits increase over the continental shelf, which extends to a depth of 400 to 500 meters. The antarctic continental shelf is also unusual in that there are narrow 'inner shelf trenches,' especially around eastern Antarctica, where the depth may extend to 1000 meters [Andriashev, 1965].

Around the shore line of the oceanic islands ice is not present throughout the entire year, and the nature of the bottom varies in relation to the geological origin and nature of the island and according to the prevalent climatic conditions. Thus, around the Falkland Islands the bottom is sandy; around South Georgia the bottom is muddy; South Sandwich Islands to South Shetland Islands, on the Scotia Ridge, the bottom is composed of coarse volcanic sands. Kerguelen Island with its sheltered waters is particularly favorable to marine fauna, whereas Macquarie Island has an exposed coast line. These environmental differences will affect the distribution of the fauna and the species occurrences can probably be more often explained by the environment than by the zoogeographic conditions.

History

Paleontological evidence [Harrington, 1965] indicates that, following a glacial period in the late Paleozoic until the beginning of the present glacial period in the late Cenozoic, the antarctic continent was warm enough to support seed-bearing plants. In the interval between these two glacial periods the Antarctic appears to have had a normal fauna of cold and cold-temperate types

of life. There is good geological evidence to support the existence of a land bridge or an island chain, which facilitated the distribution of animals and plants from South America via the Scotia Ridge to the Antarctic during the Mesozoic and the Cenozoic. There is, however, no obvious evidence to support the existence of other land bridges.

Antarctic Biogeographical Regions or Areas

There has been considerable confusion about alignment and terminology of antarctic biogeographical areas (see Table 3). Generally, the provinces of Powell [1965], Knox [1960], and Andriashev [1965] together with the subregions of Andriashev [1965], the districts of Waite [1916], and the zones of Skottsberg [1960] are comparable, although their boundaries vary. The circumpolar area enclosed by the subtropical convergence has been divided for reference purposes into the 'antarctic' and the 'subantarctic' regions. From long usage 'antarctic' has come to mean the area south of the antarctic convergence and 'subantarctic' to mean the area between the antarctic and subtropical convergences. The use of 'antarctic' and 'subantarctic' to define more precise biological boundaries within the general area is confusing, and both Andriashev [1965] and Waite [1916] have dispensed with these terms in their nomenclature of the biogeographical areas, although they have retained the general term 'antarctic region' to define the area south of the subtropical convergence. Andriashev's use of 'antarctic region' as a general term is maintained here, and 'antarctic subregion' and 'subantarctic subregion' are used to subdivide that area into its major components. The following classification, which combines the nomenclature of Powell and Andriashev, is proposed for the biogeographical areas of Antarctica:

ANTARCTICA

Antarctic Subregion
  Continental Province (Antarctic Peninsula to Weddell Sea)
  South Georgian Province (Bellingshausen Sea, Antarctic Peninsula to South Georgia)
Subantarctic Subregion
  Magellanic Province (South Georgia to Patagonian Shelf)
  Kerguelen Province (Kerguelen, Heard, and Macquarie islands)
  Antipodean Province (New Zealand and Chatham, Auckland, and Campbell islands)

The distribution of the Ascidiacea within these areas is discussed in a separate section below.

ASCIDIAN FAUNA

Nature of the Fauna

The ascidian fauna of the Antarctic is highly specialized and characterized by the following features.

TABLE 3. Comparison of the Terminology for the Biogeographical Regions or Areas

Area Included	Andriashev (1965)	Knox (1960)	Powell (1965)	Wace (1965)	Waite (1916)	Scottsberg (1960)
	ANTARCTIC REGION					
Ross, Victoria	Eastern District	Rossian Subprovince		High Antarctic		
Enderby, Weddell	Continental Province — Western District — GLACIAL SUBREGION	Antarctic Subprovince	Continental Province — ANTARCTIC		GLACIAL DISTRICT	ANTARCTIC ZONE
Antarctic Peninsula		ANTARCTIC PROVINCE		ANTARCTIC		
South Shetland Is.		Scotian Subprovince				
South Orkney Is.						
South Sandwich Is.				Low Antarctic		
Bouvet I. *						
South Georgia	S. Georgian Province	S. Georgian Subprovince	S. Georgian Province			
Falkland Is.		MAGELLANIC PROVINCE	Magellanic Province	TEMPERATE	MAGELLANIC DISTRICT	MAGELLANIC ZONE
Magellanic						
Patagonia			SUB-ANTARCTIC			
Marion I.	KERGUELEN SUBREGION	KERGUELEN PROVINCE	Kerguelen Province	SUB-ANTARCTIC	KERGUELEN DISTRICT	KERGUELEN ZONE
Prince Edward I.						
Crozet Is.						
Kerguelen I.						
Heard I. *						
Macquarie I.						
	ANTIPODEAN REGION					
Auckland Is.		ANTIPODEAN PROVINCE (Part)	Antipodean Province	TEMPERATE	ANTIPODES DISTRICT	SUB-ANTARCTIC IS. OF N. Z.
Campbell I.						
Stewart I.						

* Bouvet Island and Heard Island are included in the Antarctic Subprovince of Knox.

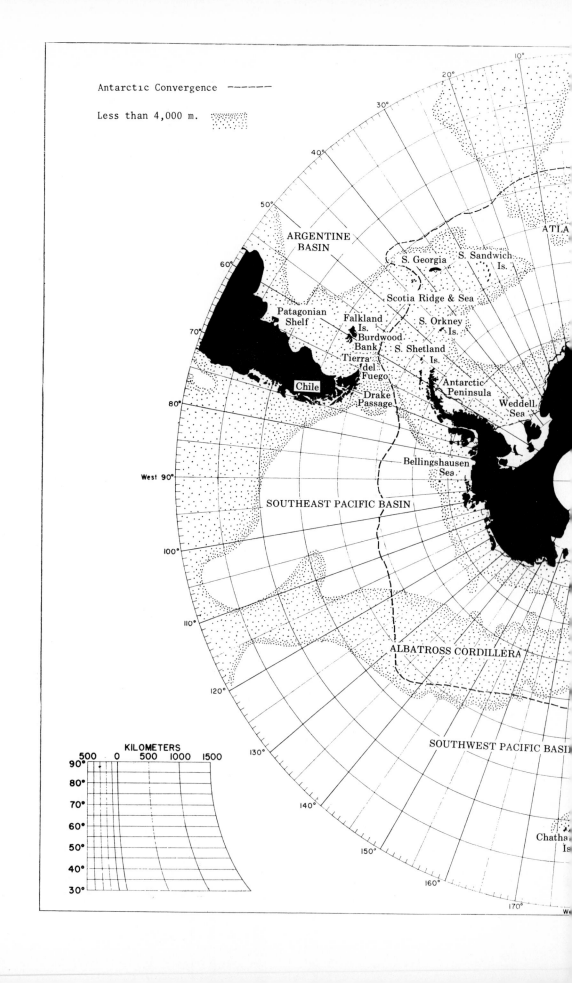

Antarctic Convergence - - - - - -

Less than 4,000 m. ⣿⣿⣿

ARGENTINE
BASIN

ATLA

S. Georgia

S. Sandwich
Is.

Scotia Ridge & Sea

Patagonian
Shelf

Falkland
Is.

S. Orkney
Is.

Burdwood
Bank

S. Shetland
Is.

Tierra
del
Fuego

Chile

Antarctic
Peninsula

Weddell
Sea

Drake
Passage

West 90°

Bellingshausen
Sea

SOUTHEAST PACIFIC BASIN

ALBATROSS CORDILLERA

SOUTHWEST PACIFIC BASI

Chatha
Is

KILOMETERS
500   0   500   1000   1500

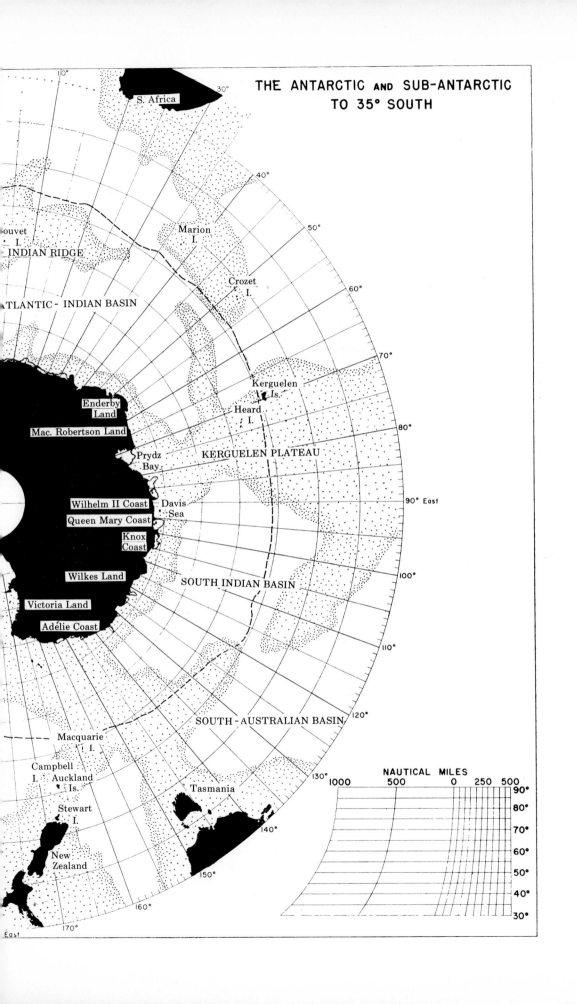

THE ANTARCTIC AND SUB-ANTARCTIC
TO 35° SOUTH

S. Africa

Marion
I.

Crozet
I.

ouvet
I.

INDIAN RIDGE

ATLANTIC - INDIAN BASIN

Kerguelen
Is.

Heard
I.

Enderby
Land

Mac. Robertson Land

KERGUELEN PLATEAU

Prydz
Bay

Wilhelm II Coast   Davis
                    Sea
Queen Mary Coast

Knox
Coast

Wilkes Land   SOUTH INDIAN BASIN

Victoria Land

Adélie Coast

SOUTH-AUSTRALIAN BASIN

Macquarie
I.

Campbell
I.   Auckland
     Is.   Tasmania

Stewart
I.

New
Zealand

NAUTICAL MILES
1000   500   0   250 500

30° 40° 50° 60° 70° 80° 90° 100° 110° 120° 130° 140° 150° 160° 170°

East

90° East

90° 80° 70° 60° 50° 40° 30°

Viviparity. Molgulidae, Agnesiidae, and Polyzoinae, in which there are many viviparous species, are especially well represented in the antarctic fauna. There are often special arrangements of gonoducts to ensure viviparity. In the generally viviparous Alpousobranchia, some species (i.e. *Synoicium adareanum, S. georgianum*) delay the liberation of the larvae to the extent that they metamorphose within the test of the adult colony. In other parts of the world species of the families Styelidae and Molgulidae demonstrate the high degree of viviparity and loss of the larval ocellus that are associated with a life on the open sea bed. It is not surprising, therefore, that these species have flourished on the wide antarctic continental shelf. It is of especial interest, however, that species of Phlebobranchia and Stolidobranchia have, in Antarctica, also adapted to this habitat by a similar increase in viviparity and loss of larval ocellus (see Settlement in chapter 7, Behavior).

Longevity. Longevity appears to lead to the development of large-sized zooids or colonies. Large colonial species invariably have highly developed cloacal systems, resulting from prolific vegetative reproduction (i.e. *Sycozoa sigillinoides, Distaplia cylindrica, Polysyncraton chondrilla, Aplidium* spp.). Species with large-sized solitary zooids (i.e. *Cnemidocarpa zenkevitchi, C. verrucosa, Pyura obesa, Molgula gigantea,* and *Paramolgula gregaria*) are distributed around the antarctic continent in notably shallow waters. The large size and the well developed parenchymatous tissue found in some of these species no doubt assist them in surviving in their rigorous, often frozen, environment.

In these large stolidobranch species considerable diversification of the branchial sac occurs with increasing age and size. In molgulid species the primary spiral arrangement of stigmata, present in the younger and smaller individuals, is lost; in styelid species there is a considerable increase in the dimensions of transverse vessels behind the branchial sac and in the number of stigmata in each mesh.

Plasticity. The majority of species are adapted for existence on the open sea bed and demonstrate considerable plasticity in shape and in the condition of developments from the test, according to the nature of the substrate on which they have settled. Species of Molgulidae, Pyuridae, Styelidae, and Agnesiidae are adapted for an existence on sand by the development of hairs from the test; other species of Pyuridae, Styelidae, Ascidiidae, and Corellidae have, by an adjustment of the body shape and the area available for fixation, become firmly attached to the surface of rocks and shell. In Molgulidae, Pyuridae, as well as the Clavelinidae and other Aplousobranchia, many species develop a stalk and strong basal roots for attachment to pebbles; these species are able to root themselves firmly in muddy substrates.

Most species of Aplousobranchia are stalked and only few of them form the characteristic encrusting colony generally typical of this order. The typically large phlebobranch forms that fix by a small surface area to clean surfaces are not represented in the fauna.

Protective closing mechanisms. In the family Agnesiidae the apertures are protected by thickened lips of test that close as they are withdrawn into the body. This mechanism is also found in a species of this family from Australia. In Antarctica the family has been especially successful; it is represented by three distinct species (*Caenagnesia schmitti, C. bocki,* and *Agnesia glaciata*). In some other species (family Pyuridae) the apertures are guarded by especially long, leathery, muscular siphons (*Pyura discoveryi*); in still others they are protected by thick coatings of long test hairs (*Pyura setosa, Molgula setigera,* etc.)

Primitiveness. Despite the generally highly specialized nature of the antarctic ascidian fauna, many of its species are representative of primitive families, such as Agnesiidae and Corellidae, which are represented in Antarctica, although rare in other parts of the world. Also, more primitive species of highly evolved families, such as *Tylobranchion speciosum, Placentela translucida,* and *Synoicium tentaculatum* in the Polyclinidae, and *Diplosoma antarcticum* in the Didemnidae, are common components of a fauna that may be considered, to some extent, a relict fauna.

Distribution of Ascidians

For discussion the antarctic ascidian fauna have been grouped according to the biogeographic subdivisions outlined above. In the antarctic region there is a large group of species with a general circumpolar distribution south of the subtropical convergence (Table 4).

Antarctic subregion. This region circles the antarctic continent and extends north along the Scotia Ridge to South Georgia. The majority of the species in the area have a circumpolar range. Only three species (*Ascidia meridionalis, Pyura setosa* and *Distaplia cylindrica*) extend beyond the northern boundary of the region (at South Georgia) and occur also on the Patagonian Shelf (Table 5).

Three species (*Molgula gigantea, Pyura georgiana,* and *Cnemidocarpa verrucosa*) have been taken from

TABLE 4. Distribution of Species of the Antarctic Region

Depth, m	Species	Ross Quadrant	Victoria Quadrant	Enderby Quadrant	Weddell Quadrant	Antarctic Peninsula	S. Shetland Is.	S. Orkney Is.	S. Sandwich Is.	S. Georgia	Falkland Is.	Magellanic Province	Chile	Patagonian Shelf	Atlantic and Indian Is.*	Kerguelen Is.	Heard I.	Macquarie I.	Chatham I.	Subantarctic N.Z. Is.	North Island, N.Z.	Elsewhere
36–637	Ascidia challengeri	X	X	X		X	X	X		X	X					X	X					Tasmania
40–600	Aplidium circumvolutum		X	X		X	X	X		X	X	X				X		X	X		X	
0–400	Molgula malvinensis		X	X	X	X				X	X					X		X		X		
55–1000	Polysyncraton chondrilla	X	X	X	X	X				X	X					?				X	X	
0–400	Styela pfefferi		X			X	X			X						X						
50–800	Synoicium adareanum	X	X	X	X	X	X			X						?						
25–668	Molgula gigantea	X		X		X	X	X	X	X					B	X						
100–500	Molgula pedunculata	X	X	X	X	X	X	X		X						X						
100–800	Pyura georgiana	X	X	X	X	X	X	X		X					B							Australia
18–548	Sycozoa sigillinoides		X	X		X	X			X	X	X		X		X	X	X	X		X	Atlantic Pacific
50–842	Corella eumyota	X	X	X		X	X				X	X	X	X	P			X	X	X	X	Auckland Is. Africa Australia
35–184	Agnesia glaciata		X			X						X	X								X	East Africa Japan California
100–5000	Styela nordenskjoldi	X	X	X		X	X	X		X	X	X	X	X	P	X						Australia California
25–437	Tylobranchion speciosum	X	X	X	X	X	X	X		X	X			X		X						
0–400	Cnemidocarpa verrucosa	X	X	X	X	X	X	X	X	X	X	X		X	BC	X						
50–1000	Aplidium caeruleum	X		X	X	X	X								M?							

*B, Bouvet Island; M, Marion Island; C, Crozet Islands; P, St. Paul Island.

Bouvet Island. *Pyura georgiana* is otherwise confined to the antarctic subregion, and therefore, although no evidence is available to confirm that Bouvet Island is part of the Continental or the South Georgian province, it may be considered within the limits of the subantarctic region.

1. *Continental province:* This province consists of the circum-continental area from the Antarctic Peninsula to the Weddell Sea more or less corresponding to the High Antarctic [Wace, 1965]. Five species of this province are completely circumpolar extending to the Antarctic Peninsula (*Molgula euplicata* and *Aplidium vastum*), or to the South Shetland Islands (*Didemnum biglans, Caenagnesia schmitti,* and *Styela serpentina*) (Table 5).

Within this province a few endemic species are recorded from the Victoria and the Enderby quadrants, but generally they are from specialized environments (*Pyura tunica, Synoicium ramulosum,* and *Cnemidocarpa zenkevitchi*).

2. *South Georgian province:* This province comprises an area extending from the Bellingshausen Sea along the Antarctic Peninsula to the South Shetland Islands, the South Orkney Islands, and the South Sandwich Islands to South Georgia. For the ascidian fauna the area is to some extent an 'overlap' area where six species from the subantarctic subregion (*Eugyra kerguelenensis, Aplidium fuegiense, Molgula confluxa, Aplidium irregulare, Aplidiopsis georgianum,* and *Styela schmitti*), extending as far south as the South Shetland Islands or the Antarctic Peninsula (Tables 6 and 7), overlap with nine species from the antarctic subregion with their northern limits mainly at South Georgia, but sometimes at the South Sandwich Islands (*Pareugyrioides arnbackae*) or the South Orkney Islands (*Pyura obesa* and *Bathypera splendens*) (Table 5).

Within this area there is some indication of a Scotian subprovince that is distinct from the rest of the South Georgian province, as four confirmed spe-

TABLE 5. Distribution of Species of the Antarctic Subregion

Depth, m	Species	Ross Quadrant	Victoria Quadrant	Enderby Quadrant	Weddell Quadrant	Antarctic Peninsula	S. Shetland Is.	S. Orkney Is.	S. Sandwich Is.	S. Georgia	Falkland Is.	Magellanic Province	Patagonian Shelf
74–780	Synoicium pererratum					X	X						
75	Pyura obesa						X	X					
0–75	Styela wandeli					X	X						
0–110	Styela grahami					X	X						
0–70	Cystodytes antarcticus					X	X						
375	Placentela translucida					X							
200	Diplosoma longinquum					X							
30	Polycitor glareosus					X							
?	Synoicium triplex					X							
25–439	Distaplia cylindrica (Planktonic?)	X	X	X	X	X	X	X	X	X		X	X
18–400	Pyura setosa	X	X	X		X	X	X				X	X
100–600	Ascidia meridionalis	X	X								X	X	X
75–680	Pyura discoveryi	X	X	X	X	X	X	X		X			
55–400	Sycozoa georgiana		X				X	X		X	X		
50–400	Aplidium radiatum					X	X	X	X	X	X		X
22–275	Distaplia colligans	X	X				X	X		X			
75–400	Styela insinuosa	X		X	X	X				X			
60–800	Caenagnesia bocki	X	X	X	X	X				X			
70–400	Pareugyrioides arnbackae	X		X	X	X					X		
75–1226	Bathypera splendens	X	X	X	X	X	X						
75–645	Styela serpentina	X				X							
50–1000	Caenagnesia schmitti	X				X	X						
30–600	Didemnum biglans	X		X		X	X						
100–300	Aplidium vastum	X		X		X							
50–100	Molgula euplicata	X	X			X							
2–3	Cnemidocarpa zenkevitchi	X											
134	Diplosoma antarcticum	X											
644	Aplidium loricatum	X											
380	Aplidium vanhoeffeni		X										
184	Synoicium ramulosum	X											
184	Pyura tunica	X											

cies (*Synoicium pererratum, Styela wandeli, Styela grahami,* and *Cystodytes antarcticus*) and four other species known only from single records, which were taken from the Antarctic Peninsula and the South Shetland Islands (Table 5), may all be endemic to the area. However, a further species, *Pyura obesa*, has been taken from the South Shetland Islands and from the South Orkney Islands, and further collecting may extend the range of these endemic species to the whole of the South Georgian province.

In the Bellingshausen Sea representatives of the subantarctic (*Eugyra kerguelenensis*), the antarctic (*Caenagnesia bocki, Sycozoa georgiana,* and *Pareugyrioides arnbackae*), and the endemic (*Styela wandeli*) components of the fauna of the South Georgian province occur.

At South Georgia only one species (*Styelopsis tricostata*) appears to be endemic, despite the high degree of endemism reported for other faunal groups in this area [Knox, 1960]. However, there is a diverse ascidian fauna in addition to the species of the antarctic subregion that occur here at their northern limit, since South Georgia also represents the southern extent of many species of the subantarctic subregion.

Subantarctic subregion. Many species have a general distribution between the subtropical and antarctic convergences, and most of them have their southern limits at South Georgia (Table 6).

1. *Magellanic province:* This province is considered to extend from the Patagonian Shelf to the Falkland Islands or South Georgia; only one species reaches Marion Island (Table 7).

2. *Kerguelen province* (Table 7): This province probably extends from Heard and Macquarie islands to the Kerguelen Islands. Many endemic species are confined to Kerguelen Island itself. Species may also extend into the Antipodean province.

TABLE 6. Distribution of Species of the Subantarctic Subregion

Depth, m	Species	Antarctic Peninsula	S. Shetland Is.	S. Orkney Is.	S. Sandwich Is.	S. Georgia	Falkland Is.	Magellanic Province	Chile	Patagonian Shelf	Marion I.	Kerguelen Is.	Heard I.	Macquarie I.	Chatham I.	Subantarctic N.Z. Is.	North Island, N.Z.	Elsewhere
0–500	Aplidium irregulare	X		X		X	X	X		X		X	X	X	X			
18–75	Molgula confluxa	X	X													X		
40–586	Aplidium fuegiense	X		X		X	X	X		X		X				X		
240	Sigillina moebiusi		X															E. & S. Africa
10–769	Eugyra kerguelenensis	X	X			X				X		X						
4–200	Polyzoa opuntia					X	X	X		X		X	X			X		
0–300	Aplidium variabile					X		X		X		X			X			
10–1693	Didemnum studeri					X	X	X				X	X	X		X		Gough Tasmania
0–300	Molgula setigera					X	X	X	X	X		X						S. Africa
0–842	Polyzoa reticulata					X	X	X		X		X		X		X		
100–300	Molgula pulchra					X				X		X		X				Victoria Quadrant Antarctica
0–100	Synoicium giardi					X						X						
20–250	Ascidia translucida					X						X						
0–148	Trididemnum auriculatum							X	X	X						?		
0–47	Paraeugyroides filholi								?					X		X	X	Africa
18–37	Polyandrocarpa placenta							X										
40–128	Aplidiopsis discoveryi									X							X	
0–80	Synoicium kuranui									X							X	
0–100	Aplidium stewartense									X				X		X		
0–485	Aplidium recumbens	X								X		X	X	X		X	X	

3. *Antipodean province:* This province comprises the fauna of the North and South Islands of New Zealand and extends to Chatham Island, connected by the Chatham Rise, and to the Auckland Islands and the Campbell Islands on the New Zealand island shelf. Some species from other provinces of the Subantarctic (from Kerguelen Island) spread to these islands and to New Zealand. One species only (*Molgula sluiteri*) extends from the South Island of New Zealand and Chatham Island to Macquarie Island. It appears that, although Chatham Island, in the region of the subtropical convergence, and the Auckland Islands and the Campbell Islands are faunistically related to New Zealand, Macquarie Island, which is also on the New Zealand island shelf, is faunistically part of the Kerguelen province, with a smaller New Zealand component. This conclusion is surprising, in view of the geographical proximity of other New Zealand islands. This relationship is probably determined by the environment of Macquarie Island, which is unprotected and bleak and favors the establishment of species inured to more rigorous conditions rather than the more temperate fauna of New Zealand.

The fauna of the Islas Guaitecas (44°S), like that of New Zealand, has some subantarctic components, representing the northern extent of their range. It shares with New Zealand a number of subantarctic species (*Corella eumyota*; *Didemnum chilense* > *D. tenue* ?; *Sycozoa sigillinoides*; and possibly *Trididemnum auriculatum*).

Very few species with a wide distribution in the Subantarctic reach as far as South Africa or southern Australia. More species range up the east coast of South America as far as the mouth of the Río de la Plata; the Patagonian Shelf provides continuity of this distribution.

On the west coast of the Americas, because of the upwelling from the Pacific Ocean depths, which keeps temperatures low, some species go northward: *Styela nordenskjoldi* extends as far as Panama and California; *Molguloides immunda* occurs off Chile at 20°S in 408 meters; *Didemnum tenue* persists in shelf waters at 50°S [Herdman, 1886] and possibly at 44°S. *Bathypera ovoida* (closely related to *B. splendens*) occurs off California and represents a similar northward extension of an Antarctic genus. Sverdrup et al.

TABLE 7. Distribution of Species of the Magellanic and Kerguelen Provinces

Depth, m	Species	Antarctic Peninsula	S. Shetland Is.	S. Orkney Is.	S. Sandwich Is.	S. Georgia	Falkland Is.	Magellanic Province	Chile	Patagonian Shelf	Marion I.	Kerguelen Is.	Heard I.	Macquarie I.	Chatham I.	North Island, N.Z.	Elsewhere
4–45	*Molgula kerguelenensis*											X					
275	*Polycarpa minuta*											X					
50	*Leptoclinides kerguelenensis*											X					
0–100	*Aplidium globosum*											X		X			
20–100	*Aplidium fuscum*											X					
100	*Aplidiopsis pyriformis*											X					
0–101	*Oligocarpa megalorchis*											X		X			
0?	*Synoicium kerguelenense*											X	X				
100–676	*Pyura vittata*										X	X		X			Cosmopolitan
0–84	*Hypsistozoa fasmeriana*											X	X			X	
0–101	*Molgula sluiteri*													X	X	X	
20–500	*Aplidiopsis georgianum*	X	X			X		X									
20–200	*Styela schmitti*		X						X								
1–130	*Paramolgula gregaria*					X	X	X	X	X							
0–150	*Alloeocarpa incrustans*					X	X	X		X							
23–1100	*Didemnum tenue*					X		X	X	X						X	
100	*Styelopsis tricostata*					X											
0–100	*Pyura legumen*						X	X		X							
2–100	*Styela paessleri*						X	X		X							
100–250	*Didemnum trivolutum*							X		X							
100–1000	*Molgula pyriformis*							X		X							
	Sycozoa gaimardi							X	X								
10	*Xenobranchion insigne*							X									
2–280	*Pyura paessleri*							X	X								
200–300	*Aplidium stanleyi*							X									
450	*Trididemnum propinquum*								X								
0–100	*Alloeopcarpa bridgesi*								X								
?	*Sigillina magalhaensis*								X								
27	*Styela ohlini*								X								
23	*Alloeocarpa bacca*									X							

[1942, p. 845] observed the same phenomenon in the northern hemisphere, where a northern temperate fauna spread from the Bering Sea as far south as Lower California. On the east coast *S. nordenskjoldi* and *D. tenue*, though present off the mouth of the Río de la Plata, are found only at depths of 1097 and 1100 meters, respectively (see next section).

Tropical Submergence

The phenomenon of tropical submergence may be used to explain the distribution of the following species, which occur on the continental slope at the northern limits of their range but at the southern limits are present on the shelf: *Didemnum tenue, D. studeri, Ascidia meridionalis, Styela nordenskjoldi, Pyura squamata, Bathypera splendens* (? > *B. ovoida*), *Molgula pyriformis,* and *Molguloides immunda.*

Pyura squamata occurs on the antarctic continental shelf and the adjacent slope. It is of particular in-

terest because of its similarity to *Pyura lepidoderma* [? > *P. squamata;* Pérès, 1949], which is found intertidally off Queensland and Japan [Kott, 1966] and off tropical West Africa [Pérès, 1949]. These littoral occurrences in the tropics are probably relics of an early cosmopolitan littoral species which originally populated Antarctica. In Antarctica the species, having survived a glacial period and having adjusted to only the most rigorous climatic conditions, appears to be independent of the tropical population, which now may represent a distinct species. The known depth distribution of this species in the Antarctic indicates a tropical submergence at its northern limit off the South Orkney Islands.

Styela nordenskjoldi in the Antarctic tolerates less rigorous conditions than *Pyura squamata.* It survives in the shelf waters of the Magellanic area but probably persisted in the Antarctic only by a retreat into deeper waters. Its occurrence with *Pyura squamata* on the antarctic continental shelf may be due to recolonization. Tropical submergence occurs to the north of the subtropical convergence in the South Australian Basin (as *Styela squamosa*) and in the Peru-Chile Trench. The occurrence of *Styela nordenskjoldi* on the slope of western America is probably associated with upwelling. On the continental slope off New Guinea *Styela orbicularis* may be synonymous with *S. nordenskjoldi*, and its occurrence here is also probably due to upwelling (see Abyssal Fauna and Colonization, below).

Molguloides immunda behaves exactly as does *Styela nordenskjoldi*; it occurs in deeper water north of the subtropical convergence and on the continental slope off New Guinea and the west coast of South America. Records for *Molgula pyriformis*, *Didemnum tenue*, and *Ascidia meridionalis* off Patagonia and *Didemnum studeri* off Tasmania suggest their retreat into deeper waters in the northern limits of their range.

Bipolarity

Bipolarity is demonstrated to some extent by a number of the more ancient components of the fauna, e.g., *Corynascidia suhmi*; *Culeolus murrayi*; *Pyura squamata* and closely related *P. lepidoderma* and *P. tessellata* Forbes; *Agnesia glaciata* and closely related *Agnesia septentrionalis* Huntsman. *Pyura haustor* from the northern hemisphere, which is closely related to *P. discoveryi*, may also represent bipolarity. This phenomenon is most likely explained for ascidian fauna by the assertion that the species are relicts of an ancient cosmopolitan fauna. There is no indication of bipolarity as a result of the spread of species by tropical submergence (see above), although many of these species also exist in deeper waters.

Endemism

There is a high degree of specific and generic endemism. Abyssal genera *Protoholozoa*, *Pharyngodictyon*, *Abyssascidia*, and *Fungulus*, eurybathic *Bathypera* and *Pareugyrioides*, and sublittoral *Caenagnesia*, *Alloeocarpa*, and *Oligocarpa* are known only from antarctic waters. Species of the genus *Sycozoa*, represented in the Antarctic by the prolific *S. sigillinoides*, are also present off Australia, South America, and South Africa. It is likely that the genus developed in the Antarctic and spread into adjacent waters in the southern hemisphere.

The generic endemism of Antarctica is due partly to the highly specialized deep-water fauna, of which *Protoholozoa*, *Pharyngodictyon*, and *Abyssascidia* represent primitive families, and may have derived from early littoral or sublittoral genera that have since disappeared because of glaciation. Primitive genera *Tylobranchion*, *Caenagnesia*, and *Xenobranchion* persist in the sublittoral and represent a relict fauna.

A small number of antarctic species extend north of the subtropical convergence. With the exception of abyssal and relict populations of cosmopolitan species (e.g. *Agnesia glaciata*), however, no representatives of littoral or sublittoral fauna from the adjacent southern cool temperate regions penetrate into the rigorous environment of the southern Atlantic, Pacific, and Indian oceans south of the subtropical convergence. The shelf and slope ascidian fauna of Antarctica is therefore almost exclusively endemic to the area.

Abyssal Fauna

It appears, from the frequency of their occurrence in relation to the number of hauls made, that specimens of Ascidiacea are common components of the abyssal benthic fauna. Certainly the nature of ascidians, with the tendency of their protective test to form stalks or roots, conforms with the ecological requirement for abyssal benthic fauna [Bruun, 1956] as a 'soft bottom community with dominance of burrowing or stalked species.'

Most abyssal ascidian species show the same modifications: The branchial sac is wide and open, with the meshes formed by longitudinal and transverse vesels; stigmata are considerably enlarged or completely lost; the test is delicate, usually transparent; body musculature is highly specialized, often into short bands and often associated with closing mechanisms for the siphons; species are often stalked, sometimes with long stalks, presumably an adaptation to raise them out of bottom ooze. The delicacy of the test, the reduction of general body musculature, and the reduction of the branchial sac all contribute to the extreme delicacy of the whole body of abyssal ascidians. The function of the considerable reduction in the surface area of the branchial sac is not known, although Berrill [1950] has suggested that this reduction, together with hypertrophy of the branchial siphon, enables the individual to exploit the slow, but steady, unidirectional currents that prevail on the slope and in the depths. Larvae of abyssal forms are known only for *Protoholozoa pedunculata*, *Hypsistozoa obscura*, and *Synoicium tentaculatum*, and in these larvae the ocellus is absent. Shipley [1901] has noted a tendency toward loss of light-sensitive organs and the reduction of respiratory apparatus in other groups of the abyssal fauna.

In the following species the branchial sac is not modified and regular stigmata are retained: *Podo-*

clavella sp., *Hypsistozoa obscura*, *Aplidium abyssum*, *Styela sericata*, *Styela nordenskjoldi*, *Minostyela clavata*, *Pyura squamata*, *Bathypera* spp., *Molguloides* spp., and *Pareugyrioides galatheae*. Of these species, however, *Styela nordenskjoldi*, *Pyura squamata*, *Molguloides immunda*, and *Bathypera hastaefera* have a wide range of distribution from the shelf region to greater depths, and they may be more recent additions to the abyssal fauna. Their presence in the abysses may be due to a spread from the continental shelf. The aplousobranch genera *Hypsistozoa* and *Aplidium* also may be more recent additions to abyssal fauna from the shelf region.

Other abyssal species shown in Table 8 may be considered truly abyssal, and generally show the morphological modifications described above and thus comprise an abyssal fauna that has long been established. Five of these species are from the phylogenetically primitive Clavelininae, Euherdmaniinae, Corellidae, and Hypobythiidae. *Synoicium tentaculatum* has a larval form that indicates its early phylogenetic relations. Other species belong to the highly specialized, exclusively abyssal stolidobranch genera *Culeolus*, *Bathyoncus*, and *Fungulus*. Only *Megalodicopia* and *Oligotrema* have retained stigmata, which are very irregular, and the branchial sacs of these two genera are,

TABLE 8. Distribution of Abyssal Fauna

Depth, m	Species	Ross Quadrant	Victoria Quadrant	Enderby Quadrant	Weddell Quadrant	Antarctic Peninsula	S. Shetland Is.	S. Orkney Is.	S. Sandwich Is.	S. Georgia	Falkland Is.	Magellanic Province	Chile	Patagonian Shelf	Kerguelen Is.	South Australian Basin	Elsewhere
3587–3817	*Minostyela clavata*	X															Atlantic Ocean Indian Ocean Tasman Sea
4636	*Bathyoncus enderbyanus*			X													
4636	*Bathyoncus herdmani*			X													
379–5000	*Molguloides vitrea*			X													
100–5000	*Styela nordenskjoldi*	X	X	X		X	X	X		X	X	X	X	X	X	X	St. Paul I. Australia California
320–2000	*Bathypera hastaefera*		X	X													California
518–5000	*Culeolus murrayi*	X		X		X	X			X	X						Japan California Indonesia
259–1226	*Pyura squamata*			X		X		X									
2000–5000	*Corynascidia suhmi*			X					X				X			X	Northern Hemisphere
300–1555	*Megalodicopia hians*				X								X				Japan
2500–4500	*Fungulus cinereus*						X	X	X	X	X			X			
3000–4709	*Protoholozoa pedunculata*					X				X	X						
165–6000	*Molguloides immunda*	X				X							X				Indonesia Kermadec Trench
?	*Pharyngodictyon reductum*					X											
891–4350	*Oligotrema psammites*					X											Indian Ocean Norwegian Sea
2800	*Synoicium tentaculatum*						X										
2800	*Podoclavella* ?						X										
1000–3000	*Pharyngodictyon mirabile*						X								X		
6500	*Aplidium abyssum*												X				
6000	*Hypsistozoa obscura*												X				
3000	*Bathyoncus mirabils*													X			
5000	*Abyssascidia wyvillii*															X	Kermadec Trench
2250–5160	*Pareugyrioides galtheae*			X												X	W. Africa
398–4820	*Styela sericata*			X												X	N. Atlantic Indian Ocean Tasman Sea

moreover, reduced in area. Only *Oligotrema* has modifications of gut and musculature demonstrating a carnivorous habit that Shipley [1901] suggested is common to all abyssal forms. *Megalodicopia* has large muscular hoods around the branchial aperture, which may assist in the capture of food. It is also possible that in *Megalodicopia* and other abyssal species nutriment is obtained from organic detritus.

The proportion of archaic forms of ascidians, as in other groups, is higher in the ocean's abysses, where, with a stable environment and sparse populations, these forms tend to be preserved. Evolution seems to proceed at a slower pace in the abysses than on the shelf. Thus, it is very probable that abyssal species were derived from the dominants of an ancient littoral fauna. Because of the general absence of fossil remains at great depths and the absence of littoral ascidian fossils, the age of the abyssal fauna can be assessed only on the basis of their phylogenetic relationships [see Zenkevitch and Birnstein, 1960; Ekman, 1953; Broch, 1961].

Broch [1961] states that the antarctic neritic community is interwoven to a high degree with deep-sea species. This relationship has not been confirmed by the Ascidiacea. Only *Bathypera* spp., *Styela nordenskjoldi*, and *Pyura squamata* are taken both on the antarctic continental shelf and in the abyssal basins around Antarctica. These species are not truly abyssal, however, and their distribution in those basins is probably due to a reinvasion or their contemporary spread into deeper water (cf. sections on Colonization, Tropical Submergence, and Bipolarity). Other truly abyssal ascidian genera occur in shallower waters off Japan and Indonesia [cf. the *Siboga* collections, Sluiter, 1904 and 1905a]. Ritter [1912] suggested that these collections indicate that no genus is truly abyssal. As suggested in the discussion of colonization (immediately following), however, there is probably some other explanation of the phenomenon. It may very likely be associated with upwelling in the Java Sea and the west Pacific Ocean [Wyrtki, 1962].

Colonization

The only known record of a fossil ascidian is of a *Chelyosoma*-like species in the Permian [Jaekel, 1915], which would seem to indicate that ascidians were then already well evolved. It is probable that some colonization of the Antarctic took place during the postulated 'warm period' in the Mesozoic and early Cenozoic.

Powell [1965], discussing the antarctic Mollusca, suggests that the fauna is a relict of a time when climatic conditions were more genial.

Despite the lack of fossil records, however, ascidians are a comparatively stable group, as evidenced by the large number of primitive types existing in the extant fauna. Thus, although colonization and subsequent isolation explain the general specialization of the antarctic fauna, a number of forms, particularly the ones that have adjusted to greater depths, have maintained their relationships with faunas of other geographic and climatic areas, suggesting the origin of the antarctic fauna. In particular, the species from northeast Australia, Indonesia, and the northwest Pacific, which are closely related to or identical with species in Antarctica, are indicated in Table 9.

Pyura vittata in the Antarctic may be distinct from the morphologically related species in the tropics, as is probably also true of *P. squamata* (see Tropical Submergence above).

As has been discussed (Abyssal Fauna), *Abyssascidia*, *Corynascidia*, *Megalodicopia*, and *Culeolus* are primarily abyssal genera and their presence in more shallow waters in the tropics may be due to upwelling from the Java Sea [Wyrtki, 1962]. However, *Agnesia glaciata*, *Styela nordenskjoldi*, *Molguloides* spp., *Pyura vittata*, and *Pyura squamata* are not modified for abyssal conditions and have a distribution from Japan, through Indonesia, or the Philippines, northeast Australia, and Antarctica to Chile and sometimes to California and the Atlantic Ocean. The persistence of these species in Antarctica and in the tropics suggests that at least some species of the antarctic ascidian fauna were derived from tropical regions. As conditions changed in the Antarctic, some of these species were driven into deeper waters. *Agnesia glaciata* and *Styela nordenskjoldi* persisted in shallower waters in the Antarctic. *Caenagnesia bocki*, *Caenagnesia schmitti*, *Protoholozoa pedunculata*, *Tylobranchion speciosum*, *Synoicium tentaculatum*, *Bathypera* spp., and *Diplosoma antarcticum* are primitive forms, apparently now confined to the Antarctic, and are probably related to early components of the fauna that developed in this way.

As discussed above (section on Endemism), there is a spread of contemporary species from south of the subtropical convergence northward into the more temperate waters of South America, South Africa, Australia, and New Zealand (*Sycozoa sigillinoides*, *Ascidia challengeri*, *Corella eumyota*). However, there is no extension of the contemporary cool temperate fauna from adjacent areas into the Antarctic: The physical barriers are most effective in restricting movement of organisms from more temperate areas.

TABLE 9. Distribution of Cosmopolitan and Closely Related Species Occurring in Antarctica*

Species	Antarctica	Elsewhere
Abyssascidia *A. wyvillii* Herdman *A. pediculata* Sluiter	(4758)	Kermadec Trench (5850–5900) [Millar, 1959] Indonesia (304) [Sluiter, 1904]
Corynascidia *C. suhmi* Herdman *C. sedens* Sluiter	(1574–5188)	Chile, North Atlantic (greater than 2000) [Van Name, 1945] Indonesia (694) [Sluiter, 1904]
Agnesia *A. glaciata* Michaelsen *A. septentrionalis* Huntsman	(13–184)	S. Africa (35); New Zealand (87) [Millar, 1960]. Moreton Bay Queensland (25) [Unpublished]. Japan (?–20) [Oka, 1915a, 1929a] British Columbia, Alaska, Bering Sea (27–78) [Van Name, 1945]
Megalodicopia *M. hians* Oka *Dicopia* *D. japonica* Oka *D. fimbriata* Sluiter	(810–1555)	Japan (300–368) [Oka, 1918] N.W. Pacific (?) [Oka, 1913a] Indonesia (1788) [Sluiter, 1905]
Styela *S. nordenskjoldi* Michaelsen *S. orbicularis* Sluiter	(0–1226)	South Indian Ocean, Chile, Panama, California (825–5314) N.W. Australia (littoral); Indonesia (1200) [Kott, 1964]
Pyura *P. squamata* *P. lepidoderma* Tokioka *P. mariscata* Rodrigues *P. vittata* (Stimpson) *P. jacatrensis* Sluiter	(259–1226) (0–676)	 N.E. Australia, Japan (littoral) [Kott, 1966]. Senegal, E. Africa (littoral) [Pérès, 1949] Brazil (140) [Rodrigues, 1966] Atlantic Ocean, West Indies (0–24) [Van Name, 1945]; Japan (littoral) [Tokioka, 1955] N.E. Australia, Indonesia (0–22) [Kott, 1952, 1966]
Culeolus *C. murrayi* Herdman *Culeolus* spp.	(2516–4804)	Wide distribution in Pacific and Atlantic (216–4820) Indonesia (450–2000) [Sluiter, 1904]
Molguloides *M. immunda* (Hartmeyer) *M. vitrea* Sluiter	(165–5929) (1226–4656)	Chile (4048); Indonesia (1788) [Van Name, 1945]. Kermadec Trench (4410) [Millar, 1959] Indonesia (397); Philippines (500–2000) [Van Name, 1918]
Oligotrema *O. psammites*	(2672–3030)	Indian Ocean (4158–4350); Norwegian Sea (891–1264); New Britain (92)

* Value in parentheses is depth in meters.

The degree of specific and generic endemism, the large number of primitive endemic genera, the specialized nature of the fauna, and the wide circumpolar distribution of so many species suggest that the area has been isolated for a very long time and that the ascidian fauna of Antarctica is a relict of a very ancient fauna.

Spread of Antarctic Fauna

The extent to which species centered in the Subant-arctic extend south across the antarctic convergence is limited; yet, many antarctic species have a wide distribution in the Subantarctic. Radiation of species in Antarctica therefore appears to occur from south to north. This is in agreement with the trend already observed for species distribution across the subtropical convergence, where the spread is from the south into more clement regions to the north, rather than the reverse.

Unless further reports indicate a greater depth tolerance to explain their distribution, many species of ascidians confined to littoral and shelf regions in the Subantarctic present the same problems that result from an attempt to explain the distribution of terrestrial forms in the same area.

Colonization of subantarctic islands is most popularly thought to have been facilitated by the West Wind Drift. Crisp and Southward [1953] point out, however, that a critical distance must exist, in relation to the current system and the duration of free-swimming stages, beyond which the rate of larval settlement is normally insufficient to reach the minimal population density (for colonization) within the lifetime of an individual. The duration of free-swimming larvae in antarctic ascidians is minimal, and, although benthic adults may be transported by debris, it seems unlikely that the requirements for circum-subantarctic colonization with respect to ascidians could be entirely satisfied by the theory of West Wind Drift (see chapter 7). The spread of the ascidian populations over shorter distances (e.g. from Kerguelen Island to Heard Island and even to Macquarie Island) might be accomplished in this way, as has been indicated for other groups [Knox, 1960].

From a study of the horizontal and vertical distribution of species in the Antarctic the following groups are identified:

1. Species distributed in the antarctic subregion, generally extending north into the subantarctic subregion or at least to the South Shetland Islands (30 species, Tables 4 and 5). These species, with few exceptions (*Agnesia glaciata, Distaplia colligans*), have a minimum depth range of 400 meters and extend over the continental shelf and on to the slope. Their minimum depth in the Antarctic is generally not less than 50 meters, although certain species have been recorded from shallower water in the Subantarctic.

2. Species with a limited distribution in the antarctic subregion, Continental province (8 species, Table 5). These few species are known from comparatively few records and only the specialized *Cnemidocarpa zenkevitchi* is known from less than 50 meters. *Aplidium vastum* has the greatest depth range of 200 meters. Only *A. loricatum* has been taken off the continental shelf.

3. Species with a limited distribution in the antarctic subregion, Georgian province (9 species, Table 4) are, with one exception (*Synoicium pererratum*), taken from a range of depths of less than 200 meters,

the minimum depth being 0 to 20 meters, and are confined to the continental shelf.

4. Species from the subantarctic subregion, circumpolar, or with a limited distribution in the Magellanic province (50 species, Tables 6 and 7). They generally have a depth range of 100 to 300 meters or less and are confined to the continental shelf. The majority are recorded from a minimum depth of from 0 to 20 meters. *Didemnum studeri, D. tenue,* and *Molgula pyriformis* are recorded from greater depths only at the northern limits of their geographic range. Otherwise, only *Aplidium irregulare, A. fuegiense, Aplidiopsis georgianum, Eugyra kerguelenensis, Polyzoa reticulata,* and *Pyura vittata* are exceptional and have been recorded from the continental slope.

The majority of species on the antarctic continental shelf are circumpolar and also extend northward into the subantarctic region, where many are also circumpolar. They are present over the whole extent of the shelf and into the deeper waters of the slope. It is probable that they radiated over the whole area by migration northward along submarine ridges, which have since submerged. Their persistence in the antarctic subregion is possibly due to a wide depth tolerance and a consequent ability to escape the effects of glaciation on the continental shelf by retreat into deeper waters. The few species with a limited vertical range in the antarctic subregion also have a limited horizontal range and may be the result of more recent speciation.

Circumpolar subantarctic shelf fauna, generally tolerating only a restricted depth, may be derived in a similar way by radiation from the antarctic continental shelf. Populations of these species are now isolated from one another in the Subantarctic. They have probably disappeared in the antarctic subregion because of their restricted depth tolerance and their inability to escape the effects of glaciation by retreat into the greater depths of the shelf and slope.

It is significant that the majority of species with a distribution apparently centered in the subantarctic subregion and overlapping into the antarctic subregion (to South Georgia or the Antarctic Peninsula) has a depth range restricted to about 200 meters and are generally confined to shallower parts of the continental shelf. Species from the antarctic subregion spreading into the subantarctic subregion have a greater depth range, which extends their distribution over most of the continental shelf and on to the slope. Thus, the hypothesis suggested above is again supported: Species that tolerate only shallow shelf waters become progressively isolated in the northern part of their range and survive there as subantarctic species, whereas species that tolerate greater depths survive also in the antarctic subregion.

Local endemic species in the Antarctic are few. This suggests a long established and continuous colonization, before isolation, from adjacent well established, large populations. One would otherwise expect a higher proportion of endemism in isolated communities resulting from speciation. This also supports the hypothesis suggested above that the antarctic ascidian fauna was derived during the early Tertiary and subsequently was isolated from the north by increasing glaciation. The species that persisted in the antarctic subregion survived the effects of the ice age by their ability to migrate into deeper waters. Others survived as relict populations isolated in the more clement islands of the subantarctic subregion.

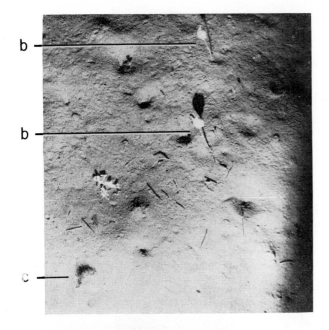

Fig. 1. Cruise 32, Sta. 33, Frame 15/0½–18. Taken in the Ross Sea, at 78°04′S, 162°23′W; depth, 607 meters (see footnote, page 132).

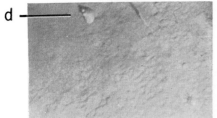

Fig. 2. Cruise 5, Sta. 21, Camera Sta. 21, Frame 17. Taken in the Drake Passage (west end), at 65°57′S, 70°15′W; depth, 371 meters.

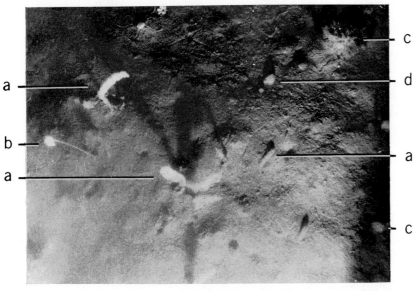

Fig. 3. Cruise 32, Sta. 24, Camera Sta. 14, Frame 3/0½–7. Taken in the Ross Sea, at 77°03′S, between 178°06′W and 178°08′W; depth between 581 and 858 meters.

Plate I. These photographs, taken from aboard the USNS *Eltanin*, reveal that the distribution of ascidians on the bottom in antarctic seas is surprisingly sparse. The identified species are: (a) *Distaplia cylindrica*, (b) *Pyura georgiana*, (c) *Pyura setosa*, and (d) *Styela nordenskjoldi*.

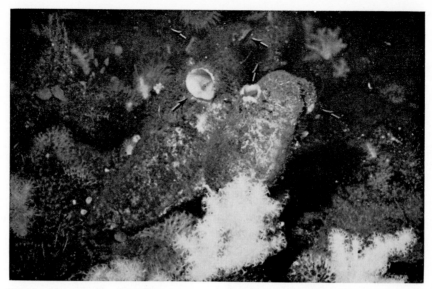

Fig. 1. Three mature individuals and several juveniles (in top left corner). The atrial siphon of the individual in the center of the field is obscured.

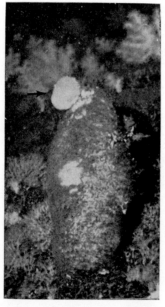

Fig. 2. An individual viewed below, branchial aperture widely extended.

Fig. 3. Profile of a single individual.

Plate II. Living specimens of *Cnemidocarpa verrucosa* (Lesson). Photographed at 23–28 meters, off Hut Point, Ross Island, by Paul Dayton, University of Washington, Seattle (NSF grant GA-1187). Apertures are shown in the open (feeding) position. The branchial siphon, from the anterior end of the body, is curved over so that the widely flared opening is directed downward. Branchial tentacles, supported by a basal velum, project into the branchial cavity to form a protective net across the base of the siphon. The smaller, atrial, aperture is directed upward from the antero-dorsal aspect of the body. (Arrows show direction of ciliary current.)

210

10 . REFERENCES

REPORTS ON ASCIDIAN COLLECTIONS previously made in the Antarctic by various expeditions are indicated in chapter 2, Previous Expeditions.

With the exception of six titles, each of the References has been checked against the original publication. The original was unobtainable for the following: Beneden, P. J. van, 1846 (however, the reprint of 1847 was seen); Della Valle, 1877; Lesson, 1830; Milne Edwards, 1841 (however, a reprint of 1842 was seen); Moeller, 1842; Oka, 1927 (which seems not to be available in libraries consulted to date); and Sars, 1851.

Adams, H., and A. Adams

[1853-] 1858 The genera of recent mollusks arranged according to their organization. London, 3 vols. [*I, II* & pls.]. [Tunicates, *II:* 587-609 (1858), pls. 123-126.] [Dates for all vols. printed in *vol. II*, p. 661.]

Alder, J., and A. Hancock

1870 *In* Hancock, A. On the larval state of *Molgula;* with descriptions of several new species of simple ascidians. Ann. Mag. Nat. Hist., (4)*6:* 353-368.

Andriashev, A. P.

1965 A general review of the antarctic fish fauna. *In* Biogeography and Ecology in Antarctica. Ed. J. van Mieghem and P. van Oye. Monographiae Biologicae, *15:* 491-550, figs. 1-18. The Hague.

Ärnbäck-Christie-Linde, Augusta

1922 Northern and arctic vertebrates in the collection of the Swedish State Museum (Riksmuseum). 8. Tunicata. 1. Styelidae, Polyzoidae. K. Syenska Vetensk. Handl., *63*(2): 1-62, figs. 1-6, pls. 1-3.

1923 Northern and arctic vertebrates in the collection of the Swedish State Museum (Riksmuseum). 9. Tunicata. 2. Botryllidae. K. Svenska Vetensk. Handl., *63*(9): 1-25, figs. 1-8, pl. 1.

1924 A remarkable Pyurid tunicate from Novaya Zemlya. Arkiv. f. Zool., *16*(15): 1-7, figs. 1-6.

1927 The genus *Tylobranchion* Herd. with supplementary notes on *Rhopaloea norvegica* Ärn. Arkiv. f. Zool., *18*(35): 1-20, pl. 1.

1928 Northern and arctic invertebrates in the collection of the Swedish State Museum (Riksmuseum). 9. Tunicata. 3. Molgulidae and Pyuridae. K. Svenska Vetensk. Handl., (3)*4*(9): 1-101, figs. 1-14, pls. 1-3.

1929 Chilean tunicates. Ascidians from the Guaitecas Islands. Arkiv. f. Zool., *21*(6): 1-27, pls. 1, 2.

1934 Northern and arctic invertebrates in the collection of the Swedish State Museum (Riksmuseum). 12. Tunicata. 4. Cionidae, Ascidiidae, Agnesiidae, Rhodosomatidae. K. Svenska Vetensk. Handl., (3)*13*(3): 1-91, figs. 1-21, pls. 1-6.

1938 Ascidiacea Part 1. *In* Further Zool. Results Swedish Antarctic Exped. 1901-1903, *3*(4): 1-54, figs. 1-11, pls. 1-4.

1950 Ascidiacea Part 2. *In* Further Zool. Results Swedish Antarctic Exped. 1901-1903, *4*(4): 1-41, text figs. 1-10, pls. 1-6.

Beneden, E. van, and M. de Selys-Longchamps

1913 Tuniciers. Caducichordata (Ascidiacés et Thaliacés). Rés. Voyage S. Y. *Belgica* 1897-1898-1899. Zool.: 1-122, figs. A-L, pls. 1-17.

Beneden, P. J. van

1846 Recherches sur l'embriogénie, l'anatomie et la physiologie des ascidies simples. Brussels, 66 pp., 4 pls.. 4° [see Hopkinson, 1913].

1847 Recherches sur l'embriogénie, l'anatomie et la physiologie des ascidies simples. Mém. Acad. Roy. Belge, *20:* 1-66, pls. 1-4. [This is a duplication of the 1846 text.—Ed.]

Berrill, N. J.

1929 Studies in tunicate development. Part 1. General physiology of development of simple ascidians. Phil. Trans. Roy. Soc. London, (B)*218:* 37-78, figs. 1-19.

1935 Studies in tunicate development. Part III. Differential retardation and acceleration. Part IV. Asexual reproduction. Phil. Trans. Roy. Soc. London, (B)*225*(525, 526): 255-326, figs. 1-31; 327-379, figs. 1-21.

1936 Studies in tunicate development. Part V. The evolution and classification of ascidians. Phil. Trans. Roy. Soc. London, (B)*226*(530): 43-70, figs. 1-14.

1947 The structure, development and budding of the ascidian, *Eudistoma.* J. Morph. *81*(2): 269-281, figs. 1-3.

1947a The structure, tadpole and budding of the ascidian *Pycnoclavella aurilucens* Garstang. J. Mar. Biol. Assoc. U. K., *27*(1): 245-251, figs. 1-3.

1948 Structure, tadpole and bud formation in the ascidian *Archidistoma.* J. Mar. Biol. Assoc. U. K., *27*(2): 380-388, figs. 1-6.

1948a Budding and the reproduction cycle of *Distaplia.* Quart. J. Micr. Sci., *89*(3): 253-289, figs. 1-19.

1948b The nature of the ascidian tadpole with reference to *Boltenia echinata.* J. Morph. *82*(3): 269-285, figs. 1-4.

1948c Tadpole larvae of the ascidians *Polycitor, Euherdmania* and *Polysyncraton.* J. Morph., *82*(3): 355-363, figs. 1-4.

1949 The structure of the ascidian *Pycnoclavella stanleyi* n. sp., and the nature of its tadpole larva. Canadian J. Res., *27*(2): 43-49, figs. 1, 2.

1950 The Tunicata with an account of the British species. Ray Soc., London, *133:* i–iv, 1–354, figs. 1–120.

1955 The origin of vertebrates. Oxford, viii + 257 pp., 31 text figs.

Bertrand, D.

1950 Survey of contemporary knowledge of biogeochemistry. 2. The biogeochemistry of vanadium. Bull. Amer. Mus. Nat. Hist., *94*(7): 403–455.

Bjerkan, P.

1905 Ascidien von dem norvegischen Fishereidampfer *Michael Sars* in den Jahren 1900–1904 gesammelt. Bergens Mus. Aarb., 1905 (2)*5:* 1–29, pls. 1–3.

Bourne, G. C.

1903 *Oligotrema psammites;* a new ascidian belonging to the family Molgulidae. Quart. J. Micr. Sci., N.S., *47*(1): 233–272, figs. 1–3, pls. 19–23.

Bovien, P.

1922 Ascidiae from the Auckland and Campbell Islands (Holosomatous forms). Papers from Dr. Th. Mortensen's Pacific Expedition 1914–1916, IV. Vidensk. Meddel. Dansk. Naturhist. Foren., *73:*33–47, figs. 1–5.

Brewin, B. I.

1946 Ascidians in the vicinity of the Portobello Marine Biological Station, Otago Harbour. Trans. Roy. Soc. New Zealand, *76*(2): 87–131, figs. 1–19, pls. 2–5.

1948 Ascidians of the Hauraki Gulf. Part I. Trans. Roy. Soc. New Zealand, *77*(1): 115–138, figs. 1–9, pl. 9.

1950 Ascidians from Otago coastal waters. Trans. Roy. Soc. New Zealand, *78*(1): 54–63, figs. 1–5.

1950a Ascidians of New Zealand. Part IV. Ascidians in the vicinity of Christchurch. Trans. Roy. Soc. New Zealand, *78*(2–3): 344–353, figs. 1–5.

1950b Ascidians of New Zealand. Part V. Ascidians from the east coast of Great Barrier Island. Trans. Roy. Soc. New Zealand, *78*(2–3): 354–362, figs. 1–7.

1951 Ascidians of New Zealand. Part VI. Ascidians of the Hauraki Gulf. Part II. Trans. Roy. Soc. New Zealand, *79*(1): 104–113, figs. 1–7.

1952 Ascidians of New Zealand. Part VII. Ascidians from Otago coastal waters. Part II. Trans. Roy. Soc. New Zealand, *79*(3–4): 452–458, figs. 1–5.

1952a Ascidians of New Zealand. Part VIII. Ascidians of the East Cape region. Trans. Roy. Soc. New Zealand, *80*(2): 187–195, figs. 1–3, pl. 37.

1953 Australian ascidians of the sub-family Holozoinae and a review of the sub-family. Trans. Roy. Soc. New Zealand, *81*(1): 53–64, figs. 1–4.

1956 *Atapozoa marshi,* a compound ascidian from Western Australia. J. Roy. Soc. Western Australia, *40*(1): 31–32, fig. 1.

1956a Ascidians from the Chatham Islands and the Chatham Rise. Trans. Roy. Soc. New Zealand, *84*(1): 121–137, figs. 1–4.

1956b The growth and development of a viviparous compound ascidian, *Hypsistozoa fasmeriana.* Quart. J. Micr. Sci., *97*(3): 435–454, figs. 1–9.

1957 Ascidians of New Zealand. Part X. Ascidians from North Auckland. Trans. Roy. Soc. New Zealand, *84*(3): 577–580, figs. 1–3.

1958 Ascidians of New Zealand. Part XI. Ascidians of the Stewart Island region. Trans. Roy. Soc. New Zealand, *85*(3): 439–453, figs. 1–3.

1959 An account of larval budding in the compound ascidian *Hypsistozoa fasmeriana.* Quart. J. Micr. Sci., *100*(4): 575–589, figs. 1–6.

1960 Ascidians of New Zealand. Part XIII. Ascidians of the Cook Strait region. Trans. Roy. Soc. New Zealand, *88*(1): 119–120.

Broch, H.

1961 Benthonic problems in antarctic and arctic waters. Sci. Results Norwegian Antarctic Exped., *3*(38): 1–32, figs. 1–5.

Broderip, W. J., and B. G. Sowerby

1830 Observations on new or interesting Mollusca, contained, for the most part, in the Museum of the Zoological Society. Zool. J. London, *5:* 46–50, pl. 3, figs. 4, 5, 6, (Jan.–May 1829). [see Hartmeyer, 1909–1911.]

Bruun, A.

1956 The abyssal fauna, its ecology, distribution and origin. Nature, London, *177*(4520): 1105–1108, figs. 1, 2.

Calman, W. T.

1894 On *Julinia,* a new genus of compound ascidians from the Antarctic Ocean. Quart. J. Micr. Sci., N.S., *37:* 1–17, pls. 1–3.

Carlisle, D. B.

1950 Alcune osservazioni sulla meccanica dell'alimentazione della Salpa. Pubbl. Staz. Zool. Napoli, *22*(2): 146–154, figs. 1–3.

1951 On the hormonal and neural control of the release of gametes in ascidians. J. Exp. Biol., *28*(4): 463–471, 1 fig.

1952 On ampullary tissue in the larva of *Polyclinum aurantium* Milne Edwards. J. Mar. Biol. Assoc. U. K., *31*(1): 63–64, fig. 1.

1953 The larva and adult of *Polycitor crystallinus* Renier (Ascidiacea, Polycitoridae). Proc. Zool. Soc. London, *123*(2): 259–265, figs. 1, 2.

1958 Niobium in ascidians. Nature, London, *181*(4613): 933.

Carlisle, D. B., and A. I. Carlisle

1954 Notes on the Didemnidae (Ascidiacea). 1. The presence of *Didemnum* (*Leptoclinides*) *faeröense* (Bjerkan) in the Plymouth area. J. Mar. Biol. Assoc. U. K., *33:* 21–25, figs. 1, 2.

Caullery, M.

1909 Recherches sur les Synascidies du genre *Colella* et considérations sur la famille des Distomidae. Bull. Sci. France et Belgique, *42:* 1–59, figs. 1–16, pl. 1.

Ciereszko, L. S., Esther M. Ciereszko, E. R. Harris, and C. A. Lane

1963 Vanadium content of some ascidians. Comp. Biochem. Physiol. *8*(2): 137–140.

Coifmann, I.

1933 Ascidiacei raccolti dalla R. Corvetta *Vettor Pisani*

negli anni 1882–1885. Ann. Mus. Zool. R. Univ. Napoli, N.S., *6*(9) : 1–7, figs. 1–4.

Crisp, D. J., and A. J. Southward

1953 Isolation of intertidal animals by sea barriers. Nature, London, *172*(4370) : 208–209.

Cunningham, R. O.

1871 Notes on the natural history of the Strait of Magellan and west coast of Patagonia made during the voyage of H.M.S. *Nassau* in the years 1866, 67, 68, & 69. Edinburgh: xvi + 517 pp., 21 pls. (col.), 1 map.

1871a Tunicata. *In* Notes on the Reptiles, Amphibia, Fishes, Mollusca and Crustacea obtained during the voyage of H. M. S. *Nassau* in the years 1866–1869. Trans. Linn. Soc. London, *27:* 465–502, pls. 58, 59. [Tunicata, pp. 488–490.]

Deacon, G. E. R.

1937 The hydrology of the Southern Ocean. *Discovery* Rept., *15:* 1–124, pls. 1–44.

Della Valle, A.

1877 Contribuzioni alla storia naturale delle Ascidie composte del golfo di Napoli con la descrizione di alcune specie e varietà nuove e di altre poco note. Napoli.

1881 Nuove contribuzioni alla storia naturale delle Ascidie composte del Golfo di Napoli. Atti R. Accad. Lincei, (3)*10:* 431–498, pls. 1–10.

Discovery Reports

1932 Station List, 1929–1931. *Discovery* Rept., *4:* 3–142.

Drasche, R. von

1882 *Oxycorinia*, eine neue Synascidien-Gattung. Verhandl. Zool.-Bot. Gesell., *32:* 175–178, pl. 13. Wien.

1883 Die Synascidien der Bucht von Rovigno (Istrien). Ein Beitrag zur Fauna der Adria. Wien: 41 pp., 11 pls.

1884 Über einige neue und weniger gekannte aussereuropäische einfache Ascidien. Denkschr. Kaiserl. Akad. Wiss., *48:* 369–387, pls. 1–8. Wien.

Dujardin, F.

1840 Les Tuniciens (Tunicata). *In* Lamarck, J. B. de. Histoire naturelle des Animaux sans Vertèbres, Ed. 2(3) : 473–541. Paris.

Ehrenberg, C. G.

1828 Praefatio, *in* Symbolae Physicae I, Zoologica I: 1–4. [*Rhodosoma* is on page facing author's p. 4, actually p. 6 of the Praefatio.]

Ekman, S.

1953 Zoogeography of the sea. London, xiv + 417 pp., 121 figs.

Endean, R. E.

1955 Studies on the blood and tests of some Australian ascidians. 1. The blood of *Pyura stolonifera*. Australian J. Mar. & Freshwater Res., *6*(1) : 35–59, figs. 1–6.

Fleming, J.

1822 The philosophy of zoology, *2:* 1–618. Edinburgh & London. [Section II, Acephala Tunicata, pp. 508–518.]

Forbes, E., and S. C. T. Hanley

1848–1853 A History of British Mollusca and Their Shells, vols. 1–4. [Tunicates are in vol. 1, 1848, under 'Acephala Tunicata,' pp. 1–54, pls. A–E (I, Botryllidae, pp. 1–41; II, Clavelinidae, pp. 25–28; III, Ascidiadae, pp. 29–41; IV, Pelonaiadae, pp. 42–46; V. Salpidae, pp. 47–54) ; in vol. 2, 1849, under 'Supplementary Notes on Acephala,' pp. 369–374; and in vol. 4, 1852, in an 'Appendix,' pp. 244–246.] The dates are those given on p. 592 of the 'Catalogue of the Books, Manuscripts, Maps, and Drawings in the British Museum (Natural History)' in which the date 1853 is also assigned to certain parts of vol. 1, viz.: pp. i–lxxx, 478–486, as well as to the title pages of all volumes.

    In the Archiv f. Naturg. (Wiegmann), 1849, XV(2), p. 106, F. H. Troschel lists the new species published in vol. 1 of the Forbes and Hanley, 'A History . . .'

Gaertner, J.

1774 Zoophyta quaedam minuta. *In* Pallas, P. S., Spicilegia Zoologica quibus novae imprimis et obscurae. Animalium species iconibus, descriptionibus atque commentariis illustrantur. T. *1*, Fasc. 10: 34–41. Berolini.

Garstang, W.

1891 Note on a new and primitive type of compound ascidian. Ann. Mag. Nat. Hist., (6)*8:* 265–268, figs. 1, 2. Also, Zool. Anz., *14*(378) : 422–424, figs. 1, 2.

1891a Report on the Tunicata of Plymouth. J. Mar. Biol. Assoc. U. K., N. S., *2:* 47–66, pl. 2.

1895 Outlines of a new classification of the Tunicata. Rept. British Assoc. Adv. Sci., 1895: 718–719.

1928 The morphology of the Tunicata, and its bearing on the phylogeny of the Chordata. Quart. J. Micr. Sci., *72:* 51–187, figs. 1–13.

Giard, A.

1872 Récherches sur les Ascidies Composées, ou Synascidies. Arch. Zool. Exp. et Gén., *1:* 501–704, pls. 21–30.

Goldberg, E. D., W. McBlair, and K. M. Taylor

1951 Uptake of vanadium by tunicates. Biol. Bull., *101*(1) : 84–94, figs. 1–5, tables 1–4.

Goodsir, J., and E. Forbes

1841 On *Pelonaia*, a new genus of ascidian Mollusca. Rept. British Assoc. Adv. Sci., *10:* 137–139.

Gould, A. A.

1852–1856 Mollusca and shells. *In* United States Exploring Expedition during the years 1838–1842 under the command of Charles Wilkes. *12:* i–xv, 1–510, 1852; atlas to same, 1856, pp. 1–16, pls. 1–52. Boston.

Gray, J. E.

1868 Note on *Oculinaria*, a new genus of social Ascidia. Proc. Zool. Soc. London, 1868: 564–565, 1 fig.

Hancock, Albany

1870 See Alder, J., and A. Hancock

Harant, H.

1927 Sur un genre nouveau d'Ascidies simples: *Bolteniopsis prenanti* n. gen., n. sp. Bull. Inst. Océanogr. Monaco, 487: 1–7, figs. 1–4.

1931 Contribution à l'histoire naturelle des ascidies et leurs parasites. Ann. Inst. Océanogr. Monaco, 8(4): 229–389, figs. 1–61.

Harant, H., and P. Vernières

1933 Une remarquable Ascidie des croisières de l'*Endeavour*, *Podostyela grynfeltii* n. gen., n. sp. Bull. Inst. Océanogr. Monaco 630: 1–4, figs. 1–3.

1938 Ascidiae compositae. Australasian Antarctic Exped. 1911–1914. Sci. Rept., Ser. C.—Zool. and Bot., 3(5): 1–13, pl. 14.

Harrington, J. H.

1965 Geology and morphology of Antarctica. *In* Biogeography and Ecology in Antarctica. Ed. J. van Mieghem and P. van Oye. Monographiae Biologicae, 15: 1–71. The Hague.

Hartmeyer, R.

1901 Zur Kenntnis des Genus *Rhodosoma* Ehrbg. Arch. Naturgesch., 1901, Suppl.: 151–168, pl. 4.

1903 Die Ascidien der Arktis. *In* Römer, F., and F. Schaudinn, Fauna Arctica, 3(2): 91–412, figs. 1–52, pls. 4–14. Jena.

1905 Ascidien von Mauritius. Zool. Jahrb., Suppl., 8: 383–406, pl. 13.

1908 Zur Terminologie der Familien und Gattungen der Ascidien. Zool. Annalen 3(1): 1–63. Würzburg.

1909 Zur Terminologie der Didemnidae. Sitzber. Gesell. Naturf. Freunde Berlin, 1909: 575–581.

1909–1911 Ascidien [continuation of work by O. Seeliger]. *In* Bronn, H. G., Klassen und Ordnungen des Tier-Reichs, Leipzig, vol. 3, Suppl., pts. 81–98: 1281–1773, figs. 1–43 [of which figs. 6–43 are maps]. [The species included are noticed in Arch. Naturgesch. 6(1): 3–27, 1911 (1912), under 'Tunikata für 1910,' grouped both systematically and faunistically, by A. Schepotieff.]

1911 Die Ascidien der deutschen Südpolar-Expedition 1901–1903. Deutsche Südpolar-Exped. (1901–1903), 12(4, Zool.): 403–606, figs. 1–14, pls. 45–57.

1912 Die Ascidien der Deutschen Tiefsee Expedition. Wiss. Ergeb. Deutsch. Tiefsee-Exped. *Valdivia*, 1898–1899, 16(3): 225–392, figs. 1–10, pls. 37–46.

1914 Diagnosen einiger Molgulidae aus der Sammlung des Berliner Museums nebst Bemerkungen über die Systematik und Nomenklatur dieser Familie. Sitzber. Gesell. Naturf. Freunde Berlin, 1914 (1): 1–27, figs. 1–9.

1919 Ascidien. *In* Results of Dr. E. Mjöberg's Swedish scientific expeditions to Australia 1910–13. K. Svenska Vetensk. Handl., 60(4): 1–150, figs. 1–25, pls. 1, 2.

1920 Ascidien von Juan Fernandez. *In* Skottsberg, C., Natural history of Juan Fernandez, 3: 131–136, fig. 1. Uppsala.

1921 Die Gattung *Atopogaster* Herdman (Ascidiacea). Zool. Anz., 53(11/13): 273–281.

1922 Miscellanea Ascidiologica. Mitt. Zool. Mus. Berlin, 10(2): 299–323, figs. 1–17.

1923 Ascidiacea, Part I. Zugleich eine Übersicht über die Arktische und boreale Ascidienfauna auf tiergeographischer Grundlage. Danish Ingolf-Exped., 2(6): 1–365, figs. 1–35, 1 pl.

1924 Ascidiacea. Part II. Zugleich eine Übersicht über die Arktische und boreale Ascidienfauna auf tiergeographischer Grundlage. Danish Ingolf-Exped., 2(7): 1–275, figs. 36–45.

1927 Zur Kenntnis phlebobranchiater und dictyobranchiater Ascidien. Mitt. Zool. Mus. Berlin, 13(1): 157–196, figs. 1–18.

Hecht, S.

1916 The water current caused by *Ascidia atra* Lesueur. J. Exp. Zool., 20(3): 429–434, 1 fig.

Heller, C.

1878 Beiträge zur nähern Kenntniss der Tunicaten. Sitzber. Akad. Wiss. Wien, 77(1): 83–110, pls. 1–6.

Herdman, W. A.

1880 Preliminary report on the Tunicata of the *Challenger* Expedition. Proc. Roy. Soc. Edinburgh, 10(Pt. 1, Ascidiadae): 458–472; (Ascidiadae and Pt. 2, Clavelinidae): 714–726.

1881 Preliminary report on the Tunicata of the *Challenger* Expedition. Proc. Roy. Soc. Edinburgh, 11 (Pt. 3, Cynthiadae): 52–88, 1 fig.; (Pt. 4, Molgulidae): 233–240.

1882 Report on the Tunicata collected during the voyage of H.M.S. *Challenger* during the years 1873–1876. Part I, Ascidiae simplices. *In* Thompson, C. W., and J. Murray, Rept. Sci. Res. Voy. H.M.S. *Challenger* during the years 1873–76. Zool., 6(17): 1–296, figs. 1–23, pls. 1–37.

1886 Report on the Tunicata collected during the voyage of H.M.S. *Challenger* during the years 1873–76. Part II, Ascidiae compositae. *In* Thompson, C. W., and J. Murray, Rept. Sci. Res. Voy. H.M.S. *Challenger* during the years 1873–76. Zool., 14(38): 1–432, figs. 1–15, pls. 1–49, 1 chart. Has two appendices: A. Supplementary report upon the Ascidiae simplices; B. Description of a new species of *Psammaplidium*.

1888 Report upon the Tunicata collected during the voyage of H.M.S. *Challenger* during the years 1873–76. Part III, The Ascidiae Salpiformes. The Thaliacea. The Larvacea. *In* Thompson, C. W., and J. Murray, Rept. Sci. Res. Voy. H.M.S. *Challenger* during the years 1873–76. Zool., 27(76): 1–166, figs. 1–28, pls. 1–11. Has two appendices: A. Descriptions of two new species of simple ascidians. B. Descriptions of the dorsal tubercle of a large species of Ascidia from Kerguelen Island.

1891 On the genus *Ecteinascidia* and its relations, with descriptions of two new species and a classification of the family Clavelinidae. Proc. Trans. Liverpool Biol. Soc., 5: 144–163, pls. 6, 7.

1891a A revised classification of the Tunicata, with definitions of the orders, suborders, families, subfamilies, and genera, and analytical keys to the species. J. Linn. Soc. London, 23: 558–652.

1898 Note on the tunicate fauna of Australian Seas. Ann. Mag. Nat. Hist., (7)1: 443–450.

1898a Description of some simple ascidians collected in Puget Sound, Pacific Coast. Trans. Liverpool Biol. Soc., 12: 248–267, pls. 11–14.

1899 Descriptive catalogue of the Tunicata in the Australian Museum, Sydney, N.S.W. Catalogue 17: 1–139, 45 pls. Liverpool.

1902 Tunicata. *In* Report on the collections of natural history made in the Antarctic regions during the voyage of the *Southern Cross*. London: 190–200, pls. 19–23.

1910 Tunicata. *In* National Antarctic Expedition [S. S. *Discovery*] 1901–1904, Nat. Hist., *5:* 1–26, figs. 1, 2, pls. 1–7. London.

1912 The Tunicata of the Scottish National Antarctic Expedition, 1902–1904. Trans. Roy. Soc. Edinburgh, *48*(2): 305–320, 1 pl. [Reprinted, under same title, 1915, *in* Bruce, W. S., Rept. Sci. Results Voyage S. Y. *Scotia*, 1902–1904, *4*(7): 83–102, 1 pl.]

1915 See Herdman 1912.

1923 Ascidiae simplices. Australasian Antarctic Exped. 1911–1914. Sci. Rept., Ser. C.—Zool. and Bot., *3*(3): 1–35, pls. 8–13.

Hopkinson, John
1913 A bibliography cf the Tunicata 1469–1910. Ray Soc. London, viii + 288 pp.

Huntsman, A. G.
1912 Ascidians from the coasts of Canada. Trans. Canadian Inst., *9*(2): 111–148.

1912a Holosomatous ascidians from the coast of western Canada. Contrib. Canadian Biol. 1906–1910: 103–185, pls. 10–21. Ottawa.

1913 The classification of the Styelidae. Zool. Anz., *41:* 482–501, figs. 1–13.

1922 The ascidian family Caesiridae. Proc. & Trans. Roy. Soc. Canada, (3)*16*(5): 211–234.

Huus, J.
1937 Zweite und letzte Unterklasse der Acopa: Ascidiaceae —Tethyodea—Seescheiden. *In* Kükenthal u. Krumbach, Handb. Zool., *5*(2): 545–692, figs. 454–581.

Ihle, J. E. W.
1935 *Octacnemus. In* Kükenthal u. Krumbach, Handb. Zool. *5*(2): 533–544, figs. 440–453.

Jaekel, O.
1915 Über fragliche Tunicaten aus dem Perm Siciliens. Palaont. Zeitschr., *2*(1): 66–74, figs. 1, 2, pl. 1.

Julin, C.
1904 Recherches sur la phylogenèse des Tuniciers. *Archiascidia neapolitana* nov. gen., nov. sp. Mitt. Zool. Sta. Neapel, *16:* 489–552, pl. 20.

Kesteven, H. Leighton
1909 Studies on Tunicata No. 1. Proc. Linn. Soc. New South Wales, *34:* 276–295, pls. 25–27.

Knox, G. A.
1960 Littoral ecology and biogeography of the Southern Oceans. Proc. Roy. Soc. London, (B)*152:* 577–624, figs. 54–73.

Kobayashi, S.
1949 On the presence of vanadium in certain Pacific ascidians. Sci. Rept. Tôhoku Univ., (4)*18*(2): 184–193.

Kott, Patricia
1952 The ascidians of Australia. I. Stolidobranchiata Lahille and Phlebobranchiata Lahille. Australian J. Mar. & Freshwater Res. *3*(3): 205–333, figs. 1–183.

1952a Observations on compound ascidians of the Plymouth area, with descriptions of two new species. J. Mar. Biol. Assoc. U. K., N. S., *31*(1): 65–83, figs. 1–3.

1954 Tunicata. Ascidians. B.A.N.Z. Antarctic Research Exped. 1929–1931. Reports, Ser. B. (Zool. and Bot.), *1*(4): 121–182, figs. 1–68.

1956 A new species of ascidian (Genus *Culeolus* Herdman, Family Pyuridae) from the west coast of Tasmania. Records Australian Mus., *24*(6): 59–60, figs. 1–4.

1957 The ascidians of Australia II. Aplousobranchiata Lahille: Clavelinidae Forbes and Hanley and Polyclinidae Verrill. Australian J. Mar. & Freshwater Res., *8*(1): 64–110, figs. 1–35.

1957a Some tunicates from Macquarie Island and Heard Island. A.N.A.R.E. Rept. (B)*1:* 4 pp. [unnumbered].

1957b The sessile Tunicata. Sci. Rept. John Murray Exped., *10*(4): 129–149, figs. 1–17.

1962 The Ascidians of Australia III. Aplousobranchiata Lahille: Didemnidae Giard. Australian J. Mar. & Freshwater Res., *13*(3): 265–334, figs. 1–50.

1963 The ascidians of Australia IV. Aplousobranchiata Lahille: Polyclinidae Verrill (continued). Australian J. Mar. & Freshwater Res., *14*(1): 70–118, figs. 1–26.

1963a *Adagnesia opaca* gen. nov., sp. nov., a remarkable ascidian of the Family Agnesiidae from Moreton Bay, Queensland. Univ. Qd. Papers, Dept. Zool., *2*(3): 75–79, figs. 1–4.

1964 Stolidobranch and Phlebobranch ascidians of the Queensland Coast. Univ. Qd. Papers, Dept. Zool., *2*(7): 127–152, figs. 1–10, tables 1, 2.

1966 Ascidians from Northern Australia. Univ. Qd. Papers, Dept. Zool., *2*(15): 279–304, figs. 1, 2, tables 1–3.

1967 *Atopozoa* [*sic*] *deerata* (Sluiter): a discussion of the relationships of the genus and species. Proc. Linn. Soc. New South Wales, *91*(3): 185–188, figs. 1–4.

Lacaze-Duthiers, H. de
1877 Histoire des ascidies simples des côtes de France. 2ième partie. Arch. Zool. Exp. et Gén., *6:* 457–673, figs. 1–3, pls. 14–27.

Lacaze-Duthiers, H. de, and V. Delage
1892 Faune des Cynthiadées de Roscoff et côtes de Bretagne. Mém. Acad. Sci. Inst. France, (2)*45:* 1–323, figs. 1–4, pls. 1–20.

Lahille, F.
1886 Systéme musculaire du *Glossoforum sabulosum* (G.). (*Polyclinum sabulosum* Giard). Soc. Hist. Nat. Toulouse, *20:* 107–116.

1887 Sur la classification des tuniciers. Compt. Rend. Assoc. Franç. Av. Sci. (16)*1:* 273, 274.

1888 Étude systématique des tuniciers. Compt. Rend. Assoc. Franç. Av. Sci., Toulouse, 1887, (16)*2:* 667–677.

1890 Recherches sur les tuniciers des côtes de France. Toulouse, 330 pp., 176 figs.

Lesson, R. P.
1830 Zoologie. *In* Voyage autour du monde sur la cor-

vette *La Coquille* pendant 1882–1825. Paris, *2*(1):
1–471, pls. 1–16. [Tunicates, pp. 256–279, 433–440,
pls. 4–9, 13; see Hopkinson.]

1830a Centurie zoologique, ou choix d'animaux rares, nou-
veaux ou imparfaitement connus. Paris, 244 pp., 80
pls.

Levine, E. P.

1961 Occurrence of titanium, vanadium, chromium, and
sulfuric acid in the ascidian *Eudistoma ritteri.* Science, N.Y., *133*(3461): 1352–1353.

Linnaeus, C.

1767 Systema naturae. Stockholm, 3 vols. [Ascidians in
1(2): 1087, 1089, 1294, 1295, 1319.]

Macdonald, J. D.

1858 Anatomical observations on a new form of compound
Tunicata. Ann. Mag. Nat. Hist. (3)*1*: 401–406, figs.
A–D.

1859 On the anatomical characters of a remarkable form
of compound Tunicata. Trans. Linn. Soc. London,
22(4): 373–375, pl. 65, Div. I.

MacGinitie, G. E.

1939 The method of feeding of tunicates. Biol. Bull.,
77(3): 443–447.

Mackintosh, N. A.

1946 The antarctic convergence and the distribution of
surface temperatures in antarctic waters. *Discovery*
Rept. *23:* 177–211, pls. 1–14.

MacLeay, W. S.

1825 Anatomical observations on the natural group of the
Tunicata, with the description of three species collected in Fox Channel during the late Northern Expedition. Trans. Linn. Soc. London *14*(3): 527–555,
pls. 18–20.

Markham, C. R.

1912 Review of the results of twenty years of antarctic
work originated by the Royal Geographical Society.
Geograph. J., *39:* 575–580, 1 map.

Michaelsen, W.

1898 Vorläufige Mitteilung über einige Tunicaten aus dem
Magalhaensischen Gebiet, sowie von Süd-Georgien.
Zool. Anz. *21:* 363–371.

1900 Die holosomen Ascidien des magalhaensisch-süd-
georgischen Gebietes. Zoologica, Stuttgart, *12*(31):
1–148, 1 fig., pls. 1–3.

1904 Die stolidobranchiaten Ascidien der deutschen Tiefsee-
Expedition. Wiss. Ergeb. deutschen Tiefsee-Exped.
auf dem Dampfer *Valdivia*, 1898–1899, *7*(2): 181–260,
pls. 10–13.

1904a Revision der compositen Styeliden oder Polyzoinen.
Mitt. Naturhist. Mus. Hamburg, *21*(2): 1–124, 1 fig.,
1 map, pls. 1, 2.

1907 Tunicaten. *In* Ergeb. der Hamburger magalhaensischen Sammelreise 1892/93. Hamburg, 1: 1–84, pls.
1–3.

1908 Die Pyuriden [Halocynthiiden] des Naturhistorischen
Museums zu Hamburg. Jahrb. Wiss. Anst. Hamburg,
25(2): 227–287, pls. 1, 2.

1912 Die Tethyiden (Styeliden) des Naturhistorischen Museums zu Hamburg, nebst Nachtrag und Anhang,
einige andere Familien betreffend. Mitt. Naturhist.
Mus., Hamburg, *28:* 109–186, figs. 1–25.

1915 Tunicata. *In* Beiträge zur Kenntnis der Meeresfauna
Westafrikas. Hamburg. *1*(3): 319–518, figs. 1–4, pls.
16–19.

1918 Die ptychobranchen und diktyobranchen Ascidien des
westlichen Indischen Ozeans. Jahrb. Wiss. Anst. Hamburg, *35*(2): 1–73, figs. 1–9, 1 pl.

1919 Zur Kenntniss der Didemniden. Abh. naturwiss. Ver.
Hamburg, *21*(1): 1–44, figs. 1–3.

1920 Die Krikobranchen Ascidien des westlichen Indischen
Ozeans: Didemniden. Jahrb. Wiss. Anst., Hamburg,
37: 1–74, figs. 1–6, pls. 1, 2.

1921 [often cited as 1920—Ed.]
Ascidiae Krikobranchiae des Roten Meeres: Clavelini-
dae und Synoicidae. *In* Exped. S. M. Schiff *Pola*,
Rote Meer, nördl. u. südl. Hälfte 1895/96–1897/98,
Zool. Ergeb. 33. Denkschr. Akad. Wiss. Wien, math.-
nat. Kl., *97:* 1–38, figs. a–c, 1 pl.

1922 Ascidiae Ptychobranchiae und Diktyobranchiae von
Neuseeland und den Chatham-Inseln. (Papers from
Dr. Th. Mortensen's Pacific Expedition 1914–16. No.
11.) Vidensk. Meddel. Dansk. Naturhist. Foren., *73:*
359–498, figs. 1–35.

1924 Ascidiae Krikobranchiae von Neuseeland, den Chat-
ham- und den Auckland-Inseln. Vidensk. Meddel.
Dansk. Naturhist. Foren., *77:* 263–434, figs. 1–30.

1930 Ascidiae Krikobranchiae. Fauna Südwest-Australiens,
5(7): 461–558, figs. 1–12.

Mieghem, J. van, and P. van Oye [Editors]

1965 Biogeography and ecology in Antarctica. Monographiae Biologicae, *15:* I–XXVII, 1–762; illustrated.
The Hague.

Millar, R. H.

1953 On a collection of ascidians from the Gold Coast.
Proc. Zool. Soc. London, *123*(2): 277–325, figs. 1–26,
1 table.

1954 The annual growth and reproductive cycle of the
ascidian *Dendrodoa grossularia* (Van Beneden). J.
Mar. Biol. Assoc. U. K., *33*(1): 33–48, figs. 1–11.

1954a *Protostyela heterobranchia* n. g., n. sp., a styelid
ascidian from the Scottish West Coast. J. Mar. Biol.
Assoc. U. K., *33*(1): 677–679, fig. 1.

1954b The breeding and development of the ascidian *Pelonaia corrugata* Forbes and Goodsir. J. Mar. Biol.
Assoc. U. K., *33*(3): 681–687, figs. 1–3.

1954c *Pseudodistoma africanum* sp. n., a new compound
ascidian from South Africa. Ann. Mag. Nat. Hist.,
(12)*7:* 128–132, fig. 1, table 1.

1955 On a collection of ascidians from South Africa. Proc.
Zool. Soc. London, *125*(1): 169–221, figs. 1–40.

1955a Ascidiacea. Rept. Swedish Deep Sea Exped., Zool.,
2(18): 223–236, figs. 2–7.

1956 Structure of the ascidian *Octacnemus* Moseley. Nature, London, *178*(4535): 703–704.

1959 Ascidiacea. *Galathea* Rept., *1:* 189–209, pl. 1.

1960 Ascidiacea. Discovery Rept., *30:* 1–160, figs. 1–67,
pls. 1–6.

1960a The identity of the ascidians *Styela mammiculata* Carlisle and *S. clava* Herdman. J. Mar. Biol. Assoc. U. K. *39*(3) : 509–511, figs. 1a–d.

1961 *Euherdmania vitrea*, a new species of ascidian from Brazil. Ann. Mag. Nat. Hist., (13)*4:* 143–147, 1 fig., 1 table.

1962 Further descriptions of South African ascidians. Ann. South African Mus. *46*(7) : 113–221, figs. 1–45, tables 2, 3.

1962a Budding in the ascidian *Aplidium petrense* Michaelsen. Ann. Mag. Nat. Hist., (13)*5:* 338–340, figs. 1, 2.

1962b The breeding and development of the ascidian *Polycarpa tinctor*. Quart. J. Micr. Sci., *103*(3) : 399–403, figs. 1–4.

1963 The structure and relationships of the ascidian *Ciallusia longa* Van Name. Proc. Zool. Soc. London, *141*(3) : 623–628, figs. 1–3.

1963a Australian ascidians in the British Museum (Natural History). Proc. Zool. Soc. London, *141*(4) : 689–746, figs. 1–47.

1963b The development and larva of *Styela coriacea*. J. Mar. Biol. Assoc. U. K., *43*(1) : 71–74, figs. 1, 2.

1964 Ascidiacea: Additional material. Sci. Results Danish Deep-sea Exped. round the world 1950–52. *Galathea* Rept., 7: 59–62, figs. 1–4, pl. 1.

1966 Evolution in Ascidians. *In* Some contemporary studies in marine science. Ed. H. Barnes, London, New York: 519–534, figs. 1–5.

1966a Tunicata. Ascidiacea. Marine invertebrates of Scandinavia. 1: 1–123, figs. 1–86.

1966b Port Phillip Survey 1957–1963. Ascidiacea. Mem. Nat. Mus. Victoria, Melbourne. No. 27: 357–375, figs. 1–11.

Milne Edwards, H.

1841 Observations sur les Ascidies composées des côtes de la Manche. 110 pp., 8 pls. 4°. Paris [see Hopkinson 1913].

1842 Observations sur les Ascidies composées des côtes de la Manche. Mém. Acad. Sci. Inst. France, *18:* 271–326, pls. 1–8. [This is a duplication of the 1841 text.—Ed.]

Moeller, H. P. C.

1842 Index molluscorum Groenlandiae. Naturhist. Tidsskr., Copenhagen, 4: 76–97.

Molina, G. I.

1782 Saggio sulla storia naturale de Chili. IV Animali del Chili. Bologna, 2nd Ed. 1810: v + 308 pp.

Moseley, H. N.

1876 On two new forms of deep-sea ascidians, obtained during the voyage of H.M.S. *Challenger*. Trans. Linn. Soc. London, (2)*1:* 287–294, pl. 44.

Mueller, O. F.

1776 Zoologiae Danicae prodromus, seu Animalium Daniae et Norvegiae indigenarum characteres, nomina, et synonyma imprimis popularium. Copenhagen. [Ascidians, pp. 224–226.]

Nakauchi, M.

1966 Budding and colony formation in the ascidian, *Amaroucium multiplicatum*. Jap. J. Zool., *15*(2) : 151–172, figs. 1–17.

1966a Regeneration in the zooid of *Polycitor mutabilis*. Sci. Rept. Tokyo Daig. B *12*(184) : 151–189, figs. 1–72.

1966b Budding and growth in the ascidian *Archidistoma aggregatum*. Rept. Usa Mar. Biol. Sta., Kochi Univ., *13*(1) : 1–10, figs. 1–6.

Nott, J. T.

1892 On the composite ascidians of the North Shore Reef. Trans. New Zealand Inst., *24:* 305–334, pls. 24–30.

Oka, A.

1913 On *Cyathocormus mirabilis* n. gen., n. sp., the type of a new family of compound ascidians from Japan. J. College Sci. Imp. Univ. Tokyo *32*(12) : 1–30, figs. 1–6, pls. 1–3.

1913a Zur Kenntnis der zwei aberranten Ascidiengattungen *Dicopia* Sluit. und *Hexacrobylus* Sluit. Zool. Anz. *43*(1) : 1–10, figs. 1–6.

1915 Report upon the Tunicata in the collection of the Indian Museum. Mem. Indian Mus., *6:* 1–33, pls. 1–5.

1915a Eine neue Ascidienart aus der Gattung *Agnesia* Michaelsen. Annot. Zoologicae Japonenses, *9*(1) : 1–6, figs. 1–3.

1918 *Megalodicopia hians* n.g. n.sp., eine sehr merkwürdige Ascidie aus dem japanischen Meere. Annot. Zoologicae Japonenses, *9*(4) : 399–406, figs. 1, 2.

1926 On a new genus of compound ascidians (*Syndiazona* nov. gen.). Proc. Imp. Acad. Japan, *2*(3) : 133–135, figs. a, b.

1926a On the mode of gemmation in *Dictyostyela depressa* n.g. n.sp. (Ascidiae Sociales). Proc. Imp. Acad. Japan, *2*(7) : 348–351, figs. 1, 2.

1927 Ascidians. *In* Figuraro de Japonaj Bestoj: 494.

1927a Zur Kenntnis der japanischen Botryllidae. (Vorläufige Mitteilung). Proc. Imp. Acad. Japan, *3*(9) : 607–609.

1929 Ueber eine neue gestielte Monascidie *Podocynthia turboja* n.g. n.sp. Proc. Imp. Acad. Japan, *5*(2) : 94–96, figs. A, B.

1929a Eine zweite japanische Art der Gattung *Agnesia*. Proc. Imp. Acad. Japan, *5*(3) : 152–154, figs. A, B.

1930 Über eine merkwürdige Cynthiide aus der Bucht von Sagami. Proc. Imp. Acad. Japan, *6*(8) : 317–320, figs. A–D.

1931 Ueber *Myxobotrus*, eine neue Synascidien-Gattung. Proc. Imp. Acad. Japan, *7*(6) : 238–240, figs. A, B.

1932 Ueber *Psammobotrus purpureus* n. g. n. sp., eine mit Sand bedeckte Botryllide. Proc. Imp. Acad. Japan, *8*(3) : 102–104, figs. A. B.

1932a Ueber *Vannamea*, eine neue Styeliden-Gattung. Proc. Imp. Acad. Japan, *8*(7) : 321–323, figs. A, B.

1932b Ueber *Azygocarpa*, eine neue Styeliden-Gattung. Proc. Imp. Acad. Japan, *8*(8) : 391–393, 1 fig.

1933 Ueber *Sigillinaria*, eine neue Synascidiengattung aus Nordpazifik. Proc. Imp. Acad. Japan, *9*(2) : 78–81, figs. A–C.

1935 Report of the Biological Survey of Mutsu Bay. 28. Ascidiae simplices. Sci. Rept. Tôhoku Imp. Univ., (4)*10*(3) : 427–466, figs. 1–35.

Ostapoff, F.

1965 Antarctic oceanography. *In* Biogeography and ecology
      in Antarctica. Ed. J. van Mieghem and P. van Oye.
      Monographiae Biologicae, *15:* 97–126, figs. 1–15, 1
      table. The Hague.

Pérès, J. M.

1949 Contribution à l'étude des ascidies de la côte occiden-
      tale d'Afrique. Bull. Inst. Franç. d'Afrique noire,
      11(1–2) : 159–207, figs. 1–27.

1952 Sur quelques ascidies récoltées aux Iles Kerguelen par
      le Dr. Arétas. Bull. Mus. Hist. Nat., Paris, (2)*24:*
      213–219, 2 figs.

Perrier, J. O. E.

1898 Note sur la classification des Tuniciers. Compt. Rend.
      Acad. Sci., Paris, *126:* 1758–1762.

Pfeffer, G.

1889 Zur Fauna von Süd-Georgien. Mitt. Naturhist. Mus.,
      Hamburg, *6*(5) : 1–19 (37–55). [Tunicates, pp. 3, 4
      (39, 40).]

1890 Die niedere Thierwelt des antarktischen Ufergebietes.
      In Neumayer, G., Die deutschen Expeditionen und
      ihre Ergebnisse. Berlin, *2*(17) : 455–572.

Philippi, R. A.

1843 *Rhopalaea* ein neues Genus der einfachen Ascidien.
      Arch. Anat. Physiol., Jahrg. 1843: 45–57, pl. 4.

Phipps, C. J.

1774 A voyage towards the North Pole undertaken by His
      Majesty's command 1773. London, 253 (+ 1) pp.,
      illus. [French translation, 1775, 'Voyage au pole
      boreale.' Paris, xii + 259 (+ 3) pp.]

Pizon, A.

1896 Description d'un nouveau genre d'ascidie simple de la
      famille des Molgulidées, *Gamaster dakarensis.* Compt.
      Rend. Acad. Sci., Paris, *122:* 1345–1347.

1898 Étude anatomique et systématique des Molgulidées
      appartenant aux collections du Muséum de Paris.
      Ann. Sci. Nat., Zool., (8)*7:* 305–391, pls. 11–15.

1898a Classification des Molgulidées. Formes nouvelles des
      collections du Muséum. Compt. Rend. Acad. Sci.,
      Paris, 126: 1814–1817.

1898b Révision des tuniciers du Muséum (Famille des Mol-
      gulidées). Bull. Mus. Hist. Nat., Paris, *4:* 272–274.

Porro, Carlo

1840 Note per una Bibliografia Malacologica. Series III.
      Geografica. No. 1–4, pp. i–iii and numbered columns,
      two on a page, 27–130 [*Polycitor crystallinus* is in
      column 102] + index of 4 unnumbered pages. [Various
      dates have been cited for this paper; the one used
      here is that given in 'Catalogue of the Books, Manu-
      scripts, Maps, and Drawings in the British Museum
      (Natural History),' vol. 4.]

Powell, A. W. B.

1965 Mollusca of antarctic and subantarctic seas. *In* Bio-
      geography and ecology in Antarctica. Ed. J. van
      Mieghem and P. van Oye. Monographiae Biologicae,
      15: 333–380, figs. 1–6. The Hague.

Quoy, J. R. C., and J. P. Gaimard

1834–1835 Voyage de découvertes de l'*Astrolabe* pendant
           les années 1826–1829. Zool. *3:* 1–952. [Ascidia,
           3(2) : 603–626, pls. 87–92, 1835.]

Redikorzev, V.

1913 Neue Ascidien. Zool. Anz., *43:* 204–213, figs. 1–6.

1927 Zehn neue Ascidien aus dem fernen Osten. Zool.
      Jahrb., Syst., *53*(4/5) : 373–404, figs. 1–20.

Renier, Stefano Andrea

1804 Prospetto della Classe dei Vermi, pp. xv–xxvii [*Poly-
      citor* is genus XIII, p. xvii, spp. *botrillo, dipartimen-
      tato, cristallino, mollissimo*]. [Issued, together with
      'Tavola alfabetica delle Conchiglie Adriatiche,' pp.
      x–xiii, by the same author, in 1804 (Meneghini's in-
      troduction to Renier's 'Osservazioni postume,' etc.).
      See Porro, 1840, column 102; also Hopkinson, 1913,
      p. 178.]

Ritter, W. E.

1901 The ascidians. *In* Papers from the Harriman Alaska
      Expedition. Proc. Wash. Acad. Sci., *3:* 225–266, pls.
      27–30.

1904 *Euherdmania* vs. *Herdmania* preoccupied. Zool. Anz.,
      27: 650–651.

1907 The ascidians collected by United States Fisheries
      Bureau Str. *Albatross* on the coast of California dur-
      ing the summer of 1904. Univ. Calif. Publ. Zool.
      4(1) : 1–52, pls. 1–3.

1912 Quantity and adaptation of the deep-sea ascidian
      fauna. Proc. 7th Internat. Zool. Congress, Boston,
      19–24 August, 1907: 949–955.

1913 The simple ascidians from the north-eastern Pacific
      in the collection of the United States National Mu-
      seum. Proc. U. S. Nat. Mus., *45:* 427–505, pls. 33–36.

Rodrigues, S. de A.

1966 Notes on Brazilian ascidians. I. Papéis Dept. Zool.,
      São Paulo, *19*(8) : 95–115, figs. 1–42.

Roule, L.

1884 Recherches sur les ascidies simples des côtes de
      Provence. 1. Phallusiadées. Ann. Mus. Hist. Nat.,
      Marseille, *2*(1) : 1–270, figs. 1–14, pls. 1–13.

1886 Recherches sur les ascidies simples des côtes de
      Provence. [3ème partie] Ann. Sci. Nat. (Zool.),
      (6)*20:* 1–229, pls. 1–10.

Rowe, F. W. E.

1966 A review of the genus *Diplosoma* Macdonald, 1859,
      (Ascidiacea: Didemnidae) with a description of the
      proposed neotype of *Diplosoma listerianum* (Milne
      Edwards), 1841. Ann. Mag. Nat. Hist., (13)*9:* 457–
      467, figs. 1–5.

Salfi, M.

1925 Le Sinascidie del Gen. *Sycozoa* Less. raccolte dal Cap.
      G. Chierchia durante il viaggio di circumnavigazione
      della R. Corvetta *Vettor Pisani* negli anni 1882–1885.
      Ann. Mus. Zool. R. Univ. Napoli (N.S.), *5*(11) : 1–9,
      figs. 1, 2.

Sars, M.

1851 Beretning om en i Sommeren 1849 foretagen zoolo-

gisk Reise i Lofoten og Finmarken. Nyt. Mag.
Naturvid., *6:* 121–211.

Savigny, J. C.

1816 Mémoires sur les animaux sans vertèbres. Paris, part
2: i–iv, 1–239, pls. 1–24.

Schell, J.

1965 Introductory remarks. *In* Biogeography and ecology
in Antarctica. Ed. J. van Mieghem and P. van Oye.
Monographiae Biologicae, *15:* IX–XXVII. The Hague.

Schepotieff, A.

1911 (1912) See Hartmeyer, R., 1909–1911.

Seeliger, O.

1893–1907 Tunicata (Manteltiere). *In* Bronn, H. G., Klassen und Ordnungen des Tier-Reichs, Leipzig, vol. 3,
Suppl., Abt. 1 (Die Appendicularien und Ascidien),
pts. 1–80: i–xi, 1–1040, figs. 1–241, pls. 1–41. [Con-
tinued by Hartmeyer, 1909–1911.]

Shipley, A. E.

1901 On the abysmal fauna of the antarctic region. *In* The
antarctic manual for the use of the expedition of 1901.
Ed. George Murray. Roy. Geogr. Soc. London: 241–
275 [Tunicata: 271, 272].

Skottsberg, C.

1960 Remarks on the plant geography of the southern cold
temperate zone. Proc. Roy. Soc. London, (B) *152:*
447–457.

Sluiter, C. P.

1890 Die Evertebraten aus der Sammlung des königlichen
naturwissenschaftlichen Vereins in niederländisch In-
dien in Batavia. Natuurk. Tijdschr. Nederl.-Indië, *50:*
329–348, pls. 1, 2.

1895 Tunicaten. *In* Semon, R., Zoologische Forschungs-
reisen in Australien und den malayischen Archipel.
Denkschr. med.-naturw. Gesell., Jena, *8:* 163–186, pls.
6–10.

1898 Beiträge zur Kenntniss der Fauna von Süd-Afrika.
Ergebnisse einer Reise von Prof. Max Weber im
Jahre 1894. II. Tunicaten von Süd-Afrika. Zool.
Jahrb., Syst., *11*(1): 1–64, pls. 1–7.

1898a Tuniciers recueillis en 1896 par la *Chazalie* dans la
Mer des Antilles. Mém. Soc. Zool. France, *11:* 5–34,
pls. 1–3.

1900 Tunicaten aus dem Stillen Ocean. Ergebnisse einer
Reise nach dem Pacific. (Schauinsland 1896–1897.)
Zool. Jahrb., Syst., *13:* 1–35, pls. 1–6.

1904 Die Tunicaten der Siboga Expedition. Abt. 1. Die
socialen und holosomen Ascidien. Siboga Exped.,
Monogr. *56a:* 1–126, pls. 1–15.

1905 Zwei merkwürdige Ascidien von der Siboga Expedition. Tijdschr. ned. dierk. Vereen. (2)*9:* 325–327,
figs. 1, 2.

1905a Die Tunicaten der Siboga Expedition. Supplement to
Abt. I. Die socialen und holosomen Ascidien. Siboga
Exped., Monogr. *56a:* 129–139, pl. 16.

1905b Note préliminaire sur les Ascidiens holosomates de
l'Expédition antarctic française commandée par le Dr.

Charcot. Bull. Mus. Hist. Nat., Paris, *11*(6): 470–
475.

1906 Tuniciers. *In* Expédition antarctique française (1903–
1905). Paris (Masson): 1–48, figs. 1–10, pls. 1–5.

1906a Seconde note sur les Tuniciers recuèllis dans l'Antarctique par l'Expédition du Dr. Charcot. Bull. Mus.
Hist. Nat., Paris, *12:* 551–555.

1909 Die Tunicaten der Siboga-Expedition. Abt. 2. Die
merosomen Ascidien (Krikobranchia excl. Clavelinidae). Siboga-Exped., Monogr. *56b:* 1–112, 2 figs.,
pls. 1–8.

1911 Une nouvelle espèce de *Tethyum* (*Styela*) provenant
de l'Expédition antarctique française (1903–1905).
Commandée par le Dr. J. Charcot. Bull. Mus. Hist.
Nat., Paris, *17*(1): 37–38.

1912 Les Ascidiens de l'Expédition antarctique française
du *Pourquoi-Pas?* commandée par le Dr. Charcot,
1908–1909. Bull. Mus. Hist. Nat., Paris, *18*(7): 452–
460.

1913 Ascidien von den Aru-Inseln. Abh. Senckenb. Natur-
forsch. Gesell., *35*(1): 65–78, pls. 5, 6.

1914 Les Tuniciers. *In* Deuxième Expédition antarctique
française (1908–1910) commandée par le Dr. Jean
Charcot. Sciences Naturelles: Documents Scientifiques.
Paris (Masson): 1–39, pls. 1–4.

1919 Über einige alte und neue Ascidien aus dem Zoolo-
gischen Museum von Amsterdam. Bijdr. Dierk. Amsterdam, Feest-nummer 21: 1–12, pl. 1.

1927 Les ascidies de la côte atlantique du Maroc. Bull.
Soc. Sci. Nat. Maroc, *7*(1–3): 50–99, figs. 1–11,
pls. 6, 7.

1932 Die von Dr. L. Kohl-Larsen gesammelten Ascidien
von Süd-Georgien und der Stewart-Insel. Sencken-
bergiana, *14*(1/2): 1–19, figs. 1–12.

Stimpson, W.

1852 Several new ascidians from the coast of the United
States. Proc. Boston Soc. Nat. Hist., *4:* 228–232.

Studer, T.

1879 Die Fauna von Kerguelensland. Arch. Naturgesch.,
(45)*1:* 104–141 [Tunicates, p. 130].

1889 Thl. III. Zoologie und Geologie. *In* Die Forschungs-
reise S.M.S. *Gazelle* 1874–1876. Berlin, *3:* i–vi, 1–322,
figs. 1–18, pls. 1–33.

Sverdrup, H. V., M. S. Johnson, and R. V. Fleming

1942 The Oceans. New York (Prentice Hall), x + 1087
pp., 265 text figs., tables 1–21 + I–III, IV, a, b, V, a,
b, charts I–VIII.

Tokioka, T.

1949 Contributions to the Japanese ascidian fauna. I. Ascidians collected by Prof. Miyadi and Mr. Masui during the bottom survey 1939–40. Publ. Seto Mar. Biol.
Lab., *1*(1): 1–17, pls. 1–7.

1949a Contribution to Japanese ascidian fauna. II. Notes on
some ascidians collected chiefly along the coast of Kii
Peninsula. Publ. Seto Mar. Biol. Lab., *1*(2): 39–64,
figs. 1–16, 1 pl.

1950 Ascidians from the Palao Islands. I. Publ. Seto Mar.
Biol. Lab., *1*(3): 115–150, figs. 1–23, pls. 9, 10.

1952 Ascidians collected by Messrs. Renzi Wada and Seizi

Wada from the pearl-oyster bed in the Arafura Sea in 1940. Publ. Seto Mar. Biol. Lab., *2*(2) : 91–142, figs. 1–29.

1953   Ascidians of Sagami Bay. Iwanami Shoten, Tokyo, 315 pp., 25 figs., 79 pls., 1 map.

1953a Contributions to Japanese ascidian fauna. V. Ascidians collected near the Marine Biological Laboratory of Hiroshima University in the Inland Sea. Publ. Seto Mar. Biol. Lab., *3*(1) : 1–25, figs. 1–16.

1953b Contributions to Japanese ascidian fauna. VI. Simple ascidians of the Museum of Hukui. Publ. Seto Mar. Biol. Lab., *3*(1) : 27–32, figs. 1–3, 1 pl.

1954   Contributions to Japanese ascidian fauna. X. Notes on some ascidians collected in Osaka Bay. Publ. Seto Mar. Biol. Lab., *4*(1) : 75–98, figs. 1–7, pls. 5–8.

1958   Contributions to Japanese ascidian fauna. XII. Sporadic memoranda. Publ. Seto Mar. Biol. Lab., *6*(3) : 313–325, figs. 1–6.

1959   Contributions to Japanese ascidian fauna. XIII. Sporadic memoranda. Publ. Seto Mar. Biol. Lab., *7*(2) : 223–236, 1 fig., pls. 13–18.

1960   Contributions to Japanese ascidian fauna. XVII. Ascidians found in the benthonic samples dredged in the Ariake Sea 1957–58. Publ. Seto Mar. Biol. Lab., *8*(1) : 205–221, figs. 1, 2, pls. 26–30.

1962   Contributions to Japanese ascidian fauna. XVIII. Ascidians from Sado Island and some records from Sagami Bay. Publ. Seto Mar. Biol. Lab., *10*(1) : 1–20, figs. 1–4, pls. 1–3.

1967   Pacific Tunicata of the United States National Museum. Bull. U. S. Nat. Mus., *251:* 1–247, figs. 1–105.

Trason, W. B.

1957   Larval structure and development of the zooid in the ascidian *Euherdmania claviformis*. J. Morph., *100*(3) : 510–526, pls. 1–9.

1963   The life cycle and affinities of the colonial ascidian *Pycnoclavella stanleyi*. Univ. Calif. Publ. Zool., *65*(4) : 283–326, figs. 1–125.

Traustedt, M. P. A.

1882   Vestindiske Ascidiae simplices. Først Afd. (Phallusiadae). Vidensk. Meddel. Naturhist. Foren., Kjöbenhavn, ann. 1881: 257–288, 1 fig., pls. 4, 5.

1883   Vestindiske Ascidiae simples. Anden Afd. (Molgulidae og Cynthiadae). Vidensk. Meddel. Naturhist. Foren., Kjöbenhavn, ann. 1882: 108–136, pls. 5, 6.

1885   Ascidiae simplices fra det stille Ocean. Vidensk. Meddel. Naturhist. Foren., Kjöbenhavn, ann. 1884: 1–60, figs. 1–4, pls. 1–4.

van Beneden, E., and M. de Selys-Longchamps

See Beneden, E. van, and M. de Selys-Longchamps

van Beneden, P. J.

See Beneden, P. J. van

Van Name, W. G.

1902   The ascidians of the Bermuda Islands. Trans. Conn. Acad. Arts. Sci., *11:* 325–412, pls. 46–64.

1912   Simple ascidians of the coasts of New England and neighboring British provinces. Proc. Boston Soc. Nat. Hist., *34*(13) : 439–619, text figs. 1–43, pls. 43–73.

1918   Ascidians from the Philippines and adjacent waters. Bull. U. S. Nat. Mus., *100*(1) : i–iii, 49–174, figs. 1–115, pls. 23–33.

1921   Ascidians of the West Indian region and southeastern United States. Bull. Amer. Mus. Nat. Hist. *44:* 283–494, figs. 1–159.

1945   The North and South American ascidians. Bull. Amer. Mus. Nat. Hist., *84:* i–vii, 1–476, figs. 1–327, pls. 1–31.

1945a *In* Schmitt, W. L., Miscellaneous zoological material collected by the United States Antarctic Service Expedition 1939–1941. Proc. Amer. Phil. Soc., *89*(1) : 297.

Verrill, A. E.

1871   Descriptions of some imperfectly known and new ascidians from New England. Amer. Jour. Sci. Arts, (3)*1:* 54–58; 93–100; 211, 212; 288–294; 443–446, 26 figs.

1885   Results of the explorations made by the Str. *Albatross* off the northern coast of the United States, in 1883. Rept. U. S. Com. Fish and Fisheries, 1883: 503–699, pls. 1–44.

1885a Notice of recent additions to the Marine Invertebrata of the northeastern coast of America, with descriptions of new genera and species and critical remarks on others. 5. Annelida, Echinodermata, Hydroida, Tunicata. Proc. U. S. Nat. Mus., *8:* 424–448.

Verrill A. E., and R. Rathbun

1879   List of Marine Invertebrata from the New England coast, distributed by the U. S. Commission of Fish and Fisheries. Proc. U. S. Nat. Mus., *2:* 227–232.

Vinogradov, A. P.

1953   The elementary chemical composition of marine organisms. Memoir II, Sears Foundation for Marine Research. Yale Univ. Press, New Haven, xii + 647 pp.

Vinogradova, N. G.

1958   On the finding of a new ascidian species—*Cnemidocarpa zenkevitchi* in the fiord of the Banger 'oasis' (Antarctic). Zool. J. [Moscow], *37*(9) : 1375–1379, figs. 1–3.

1962   Ascidiae simplices of the Indian part of the Antarctic. Biol. Results Soviet Antarctic Exped. (1955–1958), 1. Explorations of the fauna of the seas. Acad. Sci. USSR, Zoological Institute, *1*(9) : 195–215, figs. 1–5.

von Drasche, R.

See Drasche, R. von

Wace, N. M.

1965   Vascular plants. *In* Biogeography and ecology in Antarctica. Ed. J. van Mieghem and P. van Oye. Monographiae Biologicae, *15:* 201–266, figs. 1–13, tables I–VIII. The Hague.

Waite, E. R.

1916   Fishes. Sci. Rept. Australasian Antarctic Exped. 1911–1914. Sci. Rept., Ser. C—Zool. and Bot., *3*(1) : 1–92, pls. 1–5, maps 1, 2.

Wallace, H.
  1961 The breeding and development of *Styela mammiculata*
        Carlisle. J. Mar. Biol. Assoc. U. K., *41*(1) : 187–190,
        figs. 1A–D.

Webb, D. A.
  1939 Observations on the blood of certain ascidians, with
        special reference to the biochemistry of vanadium.
        J. Exp. Biol., *16*(4) : 499–523, figs. 1–4, pls. 1, 2.

Weel, P. B. v.
  1940 Beiträge zur Ernährungsbiologie der Ascidien. Pubbl.
        Staz. Zool. Napoli, *18*(1) : 50–79, figs. 1–13.

Wiegmann, A. F. A.
  1835 Bericht über die Fortschritte der Zoologie im Jahre
        1834. [*Acephala nuda s. Tunicata,* p. 309.] Arch.
        Naturgesch., *1*(1) : 301–361.

Wyrtki, K.
  1962 Upwelling in the region between Java and Australia
        during the south-east monsoon. Australian J. Mar. &
        Freshwater Res., *13*(3) : 217–225, figs. 1–9.

Zenkovitch, L. A., and J. A. Birnstein
  1960 The problem of the antiquity of the deep sea fauna.
        Deep-Sea Res., *7*(1) : 10–23, 1 fig.

ACKNOWLEDGMENTS

SINCE HIS INITIATION of this work, Dr. Waldo L. Schmitt of the U. S. National Museum has been of continuing assistance. I am especially grateful to him for his enthusiastic support and encouragement.

The work was done under contract with the Smithsonian Institution using funds from the U. S. National Science Foundation and from the University of Queensland Research Grants. For this support I am indebted to Dr. I. E. Wallen, Smithsonian Institution, Professor W. Stephenson, Zoology Department of the University of Queensland, and Professor Sir Fred Schonell, the Vice Chancellor of the University of Queensland.

The examination of types and other specimens from the Australian Museum, Sydney, has been possible only through the cooperation of Miss Elizabeth Pope, who has very generously responded to my continuing requests for specimens over the past two years. For permission to release the material, I am grateful to Dr. F. Talbot, Director, Australian Museum, Sydney.

The reference list is long and comprehensive, and I am greatly indebted to Miss Lucile McCain, Smithsonian Institution, who, in addition to the tedious and time-consuming job of checking all the entries for both accuracy and relevance, has provided the annotations clarifying some of the more obscure and earlier works. Because of her efforts this reference list will prove to be an invaluable section of the present volume and will also be of inestimable assistance to others interested in the systematics of the Ascidiacea.

Miss Joan Veitch, of the Zoology Department, University of Queensland, has typed the manuscript with enthusiasm and understanding.

Finally, I would like to express my deep appreciation to all those who have taken some part in the collection and preparation of the new American material that it has been my privilege to examine and report on in this volume. I would like to mention particularly, in this regard, the scientists and mariners on board those ships of the United States of America from which the collections have been made; and those members of the Smithsonian Oceanographic Sorting Center who have dispatched many shipments of ascidian specimens to me without the loss of even a single individual.

PATRICIA KOTT
Zoology Department
University of Queensland
Brisbane, Australia

SYSTEMATIC INDEX

Names of new genera and species appear in **boldface**; page numbers of principal accounts, in *italics*; other page references, in roman.

223

232

Paramolgula (*continued*)

patagonica, 164
schultzei, 164
schultzii, 164
villosa, 164
Parascidia, 7
Paratcna, 8
Pareugyrioides, 9, 145, *160* (key), 164, 166, 203
    arnbackae, 12, 13, 14, 15, 17, 21, 160, *161*, 162 (fig.), 164, 177, 199, 200
    filholi, 12, 16, 160, 162 (fig.), *163*, 164, 201
    galatheae, 12, 19, 160, *161*, 162 (fig.), 204
    japonica, 160
    macquariensis, 163
partita, Styela, 174, 175
patagonica, Paramolgula, 164
    Polyzoa opuntia, 100
    Polyzoa pictonis var., 100
pediculata, Abyssascidia, 84, 206
pedunculata, Ascopera, 155
    Caesira, 145
    Colella, 26
    Goodsiria, 100
    Molgula, 12, 15, 18, 19, 21, *145*, 146 (fig.), 148, 199
pedunculata, Protoholozoa, 11, 16, 17, 18, 19, 34 (fig.), *35*, 176, 177, 203, 204, 205
pedunculata, Ritterella, 188
pedunculatum, Aplidium, 26
    Protopolyclinum, 187
pellucidum, Synoicium, 70
Pelonaia, 8, 106
    corrugata, 175
pererratum, Macroclinum, 71
    Synoicium, 11, 14, 58, 64, *71*, 200, 207
perlatus, Culeolus, 142, 144
perlucidum, Culeolus, 142
perlucidus, Culeolus, 143, 144
Perophora, 7, 180, 182 (fig.)
Perophoridae, 5, *7*, 10, 179, 190, 192
perrieri, Colella, 26
    Sycozoa, 26
perspicuus, Cystodytes, 37
pfefferi, Cnemidocarpa, 120
    Styela, 12, 14, 110, 111, 118 (fig.), *120*, 121, 199
Phallusia, 7, 89, 180
    challengeri, 90
    charcoti, 90
    depressiuscula, 177
    mammillata, 173
    meridionalis, 92
    nigra, 176
    translucida, 93
Phallusiopsis, 7
Pharyngodictyon, 7, 40, *44* (key), 45, 203
    mirabile, 11, 18, 43 (fig.), *44*, 45, 204
    reductum, 11, 44, *45*, 204
Phlebobranchia, 2, 5, 7, 10, 11, *83*, 170, 174, 175, 179, 191, 192, 198
phortax, Aplidium, 53, 60
pictonis, Polyzoa, 100
    Polyzoa opuntia, 100

    f. patagonica, Polyzoa, 100
    var. georgiana, Polyzoa, 100
    var. waerni, Polyzoa, 100
pizoni, Diplosoma, 173
placenta, Goodsiria, 105
    var. fusca, Goodsiria, 105
    Goodsiria (Gynandrocarpa), 105
    Gyandrocarpa, 105
    Polyandrocarpa, 12, 101 (fig.), *105*, 201
Placentela, 7, 41, *42*, 44, 187, 192
    arenosa, 187, 188
    areolata, 187
    crystallina, 42
    longigona, 187
    michaelseni, 187
    translucida, 11, 16, *42*, 43 (fig.), 66, 185, 197, 198, 200
platana, Molgula, 148, 149
platybranchia, Cnemidocarpa, 122
Pleurogona, 5, 8, 10, 12, *99*
plicata, Ascidia, 93
Podoclavella, 1, 6, 25, 204
    cylindrica, 177
    dagysa, 177
    detorta, 177
    kottae, 177
    meridionalis, 25
    molucciensis, 177
Podoclavella, 11, *25*
    species, 11, 18, *25*, 203
Podocynthia, 8
Podostyela, 8, 107
Polyandrocarpa, 8, 100, *105*
    placenta, 12, 101 (fig.), *105*, 201
Polycarpa, 8, 99, *107*, 175, 179, 192
    clavata, 177
    fibrosa, 175
    minuta, 12, 99, *107*, 202
    pomaria, 175
    rustica, 175
    tinctor, 175
Polycitor, 6, 36, *37*, 181 (fig.), 182 (fig.), 189
    circes, 185
    clava, 11, 39
    crystallinus, 37, 186
    giganteum, 39
    glareosus, 11, *37*, 39, 200
    magalhaensis, 39
    (Eudistoma) magalhaensis, 39
    möbiusi, 40
    (Eudistoma) möbiusi, 40
    proliferus, 185, 188
    vitreus, 39, 176, 184
Polycitorella, 6, 36
Polycitoridae, 2, 6, 10, 11, *36* (key), 39, 42, 179, 180, 181, 183, 184, 185, 186, 188, 192
Polyclinidae, 2, 7, 10, 11, 25, 39, *40*, 46, 179, 181, 184, 186, 198
Polyclininae, 7, 10, 11, *45*, 46 (key), 176, 180, 186, 188, 189, 192
Polyclinum, 7, 46 (key), 181 (fig.), 189, 192
    adareanum, 65
    clava, 39
    minutum, 70

SUBJECT INDEX